HIDING:

What Fig Leaves and Chronic Pain Have in Common

EMILY STEWART ESMAILI

Printed in the United States of America
First Printing, 2019
Library of Congress Control Number: 2019918516
ISBN 978-1-7342871-0-3
Talim Publishing
P.O. Box 1842 Parker, CO 80134
www.TalimPublishing.com

www.EmilyStewartEsmaili.com

Cover Design by Carrie Knoles, CK Design

To my Mom.

CONTENTS

FOREWORD

By Patricia A. Stewart, R.N. (Mother of the Author)

By the first day of her life, little Emily had already been confronted with pain (when the obstetrician spanked her repeatedly to make her cry), and sickness (her Mommy, due to a bad cold, was required to wear a white hospital mask each time she came near). Did she wonder what kind of strange creature her mother was and what was she trying to hide? Her quizzical look conveyed that all was not well.

Pain, hers and mine, would affect her for many years as she herself suffered bouts of bladder infections until a well-known pediatric urologist in Denver diagnosed her problem — she required immediate surgery, he said, or she would lose the use of her kidneys! He said the nine-day recovery period was enough to drive adults, with the same procedure, insane! What would my tiny four-year-old have to go through? I was terrified. Even the belladonna and opium pain suppositories post-op were only partially effective. The staff had not counted on such bravery in such a young patient, but that fortitude would continue until today. She was soon healed and has experienced no further symptoms. We thank God often!

I, however, dealt with chronic issues her entire life; migraines, fibromyalgia, chronic fatigue, PMS, and depression were constants. Despite living in a fog of pain, and often depression as a result, I was determined to be a "good" — no, perfect! — mom! Meals were regularly prepared, kids were driven to school and back, school plays and sports events were attended,

1

clothes were sewn or bought, games were played, holidays were grandly celebrated, devotions were held, church programs were attended, hours of listening and talking were spent — I was completely immersed in their lives.

Yet there were days when the pain — physical or emotional — kept me distant as I surrendered to my bed, and more medications.

I felt misunderstood and judged, even accused by others of being manipulative and dishonest about my pain.

Years of doctors, therapies, medications and hospitals stole precious hours that could have been spent otherwise. Life was too stressful, and I longed for the day when I'd finally be "normal." God didn't seem to be answering my pleas for mercy and relief.

The greatest crisis I would ever face was about to occur years later. Tat, my husband, Emily and her three kids and I were happily headed towards Wal-Mart — I was holding 7-year-old Zak's hand, not paying much attention to the asphalt parking lot. Suddenly, my shoe caught on a raised crack in the asphalt, I "flew" for a second, and came down hard on my forehead and cheek. My nursing instinct kicked in, warning me not to move in case my neck had been broken — all I could see were the feet of my family, shoppers, and a kind nurse who stayed with me till the ambulance arrived. I was so afraid — too many scenarios raced through my mind of what might happen next. Tests at the ER showed no serious damage — mainly a black and blue face and a black eye — very little bleeding. At home, I felt better and gradually continued life as usual. About two weeks later, however, I felt so ill, I felt I might have caught some bug. Every part of my body felt beaten up, I couldn't sleep at night or during the day, the nausea was unbearable, and I developed anxiety such as I'd never thought possible! Terror constantly gripped my life. I quickly began to lose weight to the point that I'd cry whenever I stepped on the scales — 130 pounds melted down to 93. The only thing I could eat was some feta cheese on toast or scrambled eggs. My recliner became my world — I left it as little as possible, mostly to visit various doctors to be subjected to tests I'd never known existed; none of them (even radioactive isotopes) revealed any pathology.

Visiting nurses, physical therapists, praying friends and family tried valiantly to encourage me to build up strength, but I was so very ill, everything was too great an effort. I wanted to die. God was obviously finished with me, and the ministry I'd lived for had been removed. I contemplated suicide — the prospect of remaining in screaming terror and pain indefinitely was unthinkable, but I determined that would not be my legacy.

The final insult was when I visited a doctor who'd been highly recommended. His solution was antidepressants, but I reminded him none had ever been effective. In frustration, he said, "You look fine!" (I wanted to ask if he had developed x-ray vision?? Look fine?? What doctor ever said that??) "Just get on with your life—there's nothing wrong with you!!" And he hurried out of the room. Unbelievable! I was so angry with his condescending attitude, I vowed never to see him again.

For four years, I tried to hang on to any hope — Tat had become my caretaker and housekeeper — at least, when he wasn't traveling which was often. The terror of his leaving exacerbated all my existing symptoms. I blamed him for putting his work ahead of me — anger merged with anxiety and fear —there was no escape. Everything people suggested left out the fact that I couldn't get out of my own body — I felt totally trapped.

During this period, my parents, Dr. Thomas and Nancy Murray, needed more care — they were approaching their nineties and were moved from one facility to another, depending on their needs at the time. I tried desperately to be there for them, as often as Tat could drive me to see them — the guilt of not being able to help them added to my seemingly hopeless situation.

My wonderful brother Scott often spent the nights in our guest room when Tat was gone, and my dear friend Chris spent hours during the day, encouraging me and helping me to laugh again.

Emily visited and texted often and kept up with my latest complaints and therapies. Suddenly, one day, out of sheer frustration, she asked, "Mom, why do you keep going to all these doctors?? I can help you!!"

What? Had I missed something? I knew how well-studied she was in the fields of health, exercise, and spiritual matters, but we hadn't even discussed her possible role in my regaining my life! I was skeptical. (Hey, she was my daughter! Parents should be telling their kids what to do, right? What could she possibly accomplish that a host of specialists had failed to do?) "Mom, I'll be very professional. Just give me a chance. If there's no difference in three months, then I'll bow out." She was so sincere and confident — so loving! — I couldn't say no.

I then began a program she personally designed for me. She reviewed my dietary habits, she showed me some basic exercises to regain some of the strength I'd lost, she sent me important information on what I could be doing on a daily basis, and then — she began addressing my emotional train wreck, the lies and beliefs I'd held onto for years, the anger I thought I'd managed to suppress or deal with the right way (I thought). She explained how my brain was desperately trying to keep me from acknowledging my emotions (unacceptable, generally, in polite Christian circles). My body had created physical symptoms which were "easier" to deal with — pills, doctors, heating pads, therapies— things more socially acceptable, although annoying when you talk about them too much!

I'm thrilled to recommend this book to you, first, as her proud mother, but most of all, as a formerly hopeless patient, who now has hope, can travel again (even to Australia!), whose anxiety and fear is almost nonexistent, and whose headaches, fibromyalgia, chronic fatigue, frequent colds, deep depression, and a litany of other issues, are much improved if not entirely gone.

There are still areas to be dealt with (after all, it took me nearly 70 years to hone them!), but I praise God for a daughter who helped bring me out of my prison of figurative death, into the light of new possibilities of doing the "normal" things I was designed to do! I pray you will be as open as I was (eventually!) to the message of this book. It may go against what you've always believed was helpful, but the results will be so worth your being willing to hear what she has to say. I know I'm glad I listened!

I love you, Emily!

PREFACE

I was working with one particular client who had had pain most of her life. She had been in several car accidents, had chronic neck pain and headaches, fibromyalgia, chronic fatigue, food sensitivities, insomnia, anxiety, depression, and various other pains in her body. Most days she could barely get up out of her chair. She couldn't play with her grandkids the way she wanted to, becoming exhausted after only a few minutes. Pain ruled her days and nights, and there didn't appear to be any remedy. Doctors had her on various medications, but none seemed to take the pain away. She was miserable and turned to me for help. I advised the usual: plant-based diet for six weeks with no sugar, salt, oil, or processed foods, and after that time of cleansing, eating 80% plant-based and 20% animal foods, incorporating strength training and a general increase in physical activity. The week before we were to meet again, I felt the need to make a stop at the library. I don't remember what I was looking for, but I had a library basket in my hand and was browsing the new releases. Suddenly, a book toppled off the shelf and into my basket. It was *The Divided Mind* by Dr. John Sarno. [1] The summary on the back of the book intrigued me. I took it home and started reading. Two chapters in, I scrapped the program I had been working on and moved up our appointment so I could share with her the insights I had learned. I felt as if I had wandered into a whole new arena of understanding, and I began to research the MindBody concept in great detail.

After reading over ninety books and countless articles on the subject, I have come to better understand the great deception that is perpetuated in the United States surrounding chronic pain. The current understanding of pain

5

as being purely physical and requiring physical intervention alone is sadly in error and is robbing patients of their hope for a pain-free future.

If you have chronic pain or illness, you may find yourself uncomfortable with the information in this book. You may become upset, thinking I have lost my senses altogether. It contradicts everything you have heard or believed to be true. New ideas are seldom embraced at first hearing.

We *all* hide, a concept we will become well acquainted with in the pages to follow. Sometimes we hide with illness, sometimes with pain, sometimes with our pride in never being sick or in pain! It's laughable to think any of us would ever be immune to sinful hiding. So warm up your sense of humor, because you may find yourself laughing at yourself and at Satan's deceptions and how easily we fall for them.

Once you see the connection between emotions and pain, you will...

- ...be more aware of your own personal thoughts, emotions, and needs and how they relate to your health.
- ...be able to minister to others more intentionally and deeply, seeing beyond their physical needs to the emotional needs beneath.
- ...be free from the cycle of hiding; it will be out in the open and more easily dealt with.

There is hope. If you have tried all the traditional remedies (maybe even some not-so-traditional ones) with little success, what do you have to lose?

Remember the client I mentioned above? She has been working on these principles for almost two years now. She is free from chronic fatigue and fibromyalgia, is eating all her favorite foods again, has been working out at the gym lifting weights, has a music ministry online, and is back to being the mother and grandmother she always wanted to be. I have to attest to that last part because she happens to be my mom, and I'm so glad to have her back.

PART ONE: PAIN

CHAPTER ONE:
WHAT IS PAIN?

Stabbing, throbbing, burning, tingling, aching, pulsing. *Pain.* We've all experienced it, either personally or through the eyes of a loved one. Pain leaves us raw with despair and frustration, unable to free ourselves from the crippling prison that our body has become. Every person feels pain differently and to varying degrees. Some of our pain has been with us since we were born; other pain entered our lives through injury or accident or disease. Some of our pain has become a part of our lives from almost out of nowhere, with no explanation of why it even exists.

We were created to live forever. Think about what that must have been like — at the dawn of the world, having no pain and unlimited life spans. There would be no fear! If I knew I could feel no pain, I'd be the first in line to dive off a cliff into a pool of clear water or climb the tallest tree. I would run through fields with my eyes closed, dive deep into the ocean, and hug a tiger. Life would be full of adventure! Sadly, we don't hear the tales of what life was like before the Fall; maybe because it would break our hearts to hear all that we lost.

> "And the LORD God commanded the man, saying, 'Of every tree of the garden you may freely eat; but of the tree of the knowledge of good and evil you shall not eat, for **in the day that you eat of it** you shall surely die.'" (Genesis 2:17 NKJV emphasis mine)

9

We like to gloss over that part about immediate death, since Adam and Eve didn't drop dead right after they sinned. However, scientists in the 1800s identified a "cell death program" that is present in every single one of our cells called "apoptosis." [1] Our bodies literally started dying from the moment we sinned. Even though Adam and Eve didn't immediately die, they began to die that day on a cellular level. Suddenly, there were all kinds of new opportunities for pain and disease, as many as there are cells in our bodies. Anything that can go wrong, does go wrong. Babies are born with chromosomal defects, with failed senses or deformities. There is pain simply from being human in a fallen world.

Mercifully, much of our Edenic healing abilities remains as evidence of God's grace in upholding His creation. Imagine what would happen if you couldn't heal? One paper cut and you'd be through. Our life spans would be drastically reduced, and the population would die out rather quickly. God has not abandoned His "very good" creation to a slow, painful death. Living in a world where death is inevitable doesn't mean that you can't fully enjoy the life you have while you have it; Jesus came that we might have an *abundant* life (John 10:10), so we cannot succumb to fatalism or despair. We also cannot neglect the upkeep of our physical or emotional health under the pretense that any efforts on our part would be pointless; God still has a purpose for every living creature on this earth, and He always accomplishes His purposes, even using evil for good (Genesis 50:20).

Pain has its benefits in a fallen world. There are dangers we must guard against, and pain serves as a warning bell to alert us to things that could harm us. Without danger, there would be no pain. Feelings of security are often accompanied by coziness and comfort, both physical and emotional. In Eden, we were safe. Only with the arrival of sin was there a need for pain, not only in alerting us to danger to our bodies but to danger in our minds: our greatest enemy had become ourselves.

What is Pain?

Most believe that pain is a tool the body uses to alert you when something is wrong -- while that is one of its purposes, there is more to it than that:

Pain is an **emotion**.

Notice I didn't say pain is a feeling, because it's more than just a physical feeling. Pain involves your entire body and mind and heart. Why else do we say, "heartbreak"? Or "gut feeling"? It's impossible to have a thought without it showing up in your body — the science of body language is based on the fact that we can't help but show our emotions in our facial expressions and our arm positioning; even our breathing changes when we are upset or scared. Police detectives can tell if you're lying by where you glance as you speak. It's even been said that you can tell how interested a person is in what you are saying by the position of their feet! Our bodies and our minds affect each other in more ways than we can imagine. Pain is no exception.

Emotions are defined as physiological changes in your body based on a decision made by the brain — pain is produced using identical processes, even using the same neurological pathways. Feelings are simply the manner in which we describe these physiological sensations. [2]

You could say that an emotion is how you feel (in mind and body), whereas a feeling is how you *feel* about how you feel. You may experience sadness in your body before you even recognize it or identify it as sadness. On the flip side, it's almost impossible to feel sadness without its effects being present in your physical body. Even if you are not conscious of the emotion, *the body always knows*. This may sound like I'm splitting hairs, but this concept is critical to understand, as it is the very key to eliminating chronic pain once and for all.

Emotions reside in the body long before the mind is even aware of their existence. Before the conscious brain can evaluate and identify emotions intellectually, they tend to remain piled up in confusing jumbles. Have you ever had to turn down the car radio to find a street sign? Or thought you were hungry when you were just dehydrated? Or closed your eyes to better hear a lecture? Our senses are oddly connected to each other, and they often get mixed up. The same goes with our emotions, and since pain is also an emotion, it makes sense that there would be quite a bit of crossover and confusion there as well.

It's easy to see how being in pain can make you emotional. It's more difficult to see how emotions can bring about pain. We don't like to talk about emotions, really, at least not the painful ones — but they are a huge part of who we are.

Because pain itself is an emotion, the mind does not distinguish between emotional pain and physical pain. When you are waiting behind the curtain to go onstage for a performance, you feel afraid emotionally, and physically you may feel butterflies in your stomach, the urge to run to the bathroom, cold sweats, lightheadedness, and a dry mouth. Those sensations are the physical manifestations of the emotional turmoil you are experiencing. Mind and body are indistinguishable from each other when it comes to emotion. You simply cannot feel emotion without a physical sensation and vice versa; pain is the body's way of expressing emotion.[3]

Where Does Pain Come From?

Pain is not without its benefits. Acute pain is critical to our survival. People unable to feel physical pain are in grave danger; they are without the body's natural warning system that alerts them to move their hand from the flame or rush to a hospital if they've severed an artery.

If hunger were not painful, you would never eat. If you never felt exhausted, you would never sleep. Pain is a necessary part of human survival.

Because of the obvious benefits of and purpose behind acute pain, we assume that there is a physical reason behind *every* pain — a back spasm means we moved the wrong way, a shoulder ache means we lifted something with bad form, and a headache means we ate the wrong foods. We assume that a physical sensation always has a physical cause.

It may surprise you to hear that there are no pain receptors in the body. [4] When you get a paper cut, your finger is not sending pain messages to your brain. It's not that simple. What you have are nociceptors that alert the brain when there may be a threat to the body — broken skin, inflammation, or a broken bone. These nociceptors communicate the situation to the brain, which then filters this information through an amazing database filled with your life experiences, your feelings, your medical history, your current stress level, and your environment, and determines whether you feel pain. [5] The actual pain sensation begins in the brain. Pain is not as much a physical event as it is an emotional choice initiated by the mind.

The brain always attempts to work in your best interests. The database that the brain uses to make decisions includes memories you may have forgotten were there, fears inherited from your parents and stored in your DNA, experiences you were too young to understand, and environmental cues that have escaped your conscious awareness. The entire pain decision process can appear to work in a seemingly less than beneficial way. If you are allergic to bee stings, and your nociceptors detect a slight touch on your leg, your brain may send you intense pain signals to alert you just in case it was indeed a bee sting. Your brain weighs all possibilities, using data such as life experiences, social and cultural influences, current environment, stress level, and attitude, [6] and acts in a way that will benefit you most even if it doesn't always appear to be the case.

Pain can occur where there is no real injury, as I have just mentioned in the case of the suspected bee sting. As I am writing this, the local police department is performing a test of their emergency notification system. My land line is ringing, my email alert is pinging, and my cell phone is buzzing. There is no emergency, but the system is responding as if there were. The messages between the brain and the nociceptors are sometimes one way only.

You may have dismissed the article you read on the new deadly flu virus going around, and you may not have noticed that the person next to you in church was coughing, but your brain was paying attention. Even if you have never once in your life gotten the flu, you may start to feel chills and a headache as you leave the church service… just in case. That's been my experience more times than I can count. A friend texts me saying her son or daughter has caught a cold, and I start to sniffle! You can call it the power of suggestion, but I like to think of it as your brain alerting you to the possible danger so you pay better attention.

All of your senses work together to evaluate a given situation, and the more senses involved, the stronger the reaction.[7] If your senses repeatedly evaluate consecutive situations the same way, eliciting the same collaborative reaction, the pain pathway is strengthened further. Once a pain pathway has been established, it can become habitual.

A pain sensation does not always signify a physical cause for the pain. All pain begins in the brain, and the brain decides whether to emit a pain signal based on a large variety of factors. ***No brain, no pain.***

Many Types of Pain

As there are many types and combinations of emotions, there are also many types and degrees of pain. No two experiences of pain are alike — they vary from person to person, just as emotions do. To say that one person has more pain than another is too simplistic.

Just as we have favorite colors and food preferences, we have personal aversions unique to us that have most likely evolved out of our individual life experiences. Personally, I would rather be dirty than sticky, cold than hot, and tired than hungry. Each person has a different spectrum of what kinds of pain troubles them more than others. My husband can drive with a migraine, while I can clean the house with back pain, but not vice versa. Pain cannot be quantified by the cause, only by the experience of the sufferer. A pain scale is posted in every hospital room; otherwise, it would be assumed that every patient with a specific malady would require the same type of pain mitigation.

Different cultures experience pain differently, depending on what each culture believes about what should cause pain and what shouldn't. [8] One culture might view pain as natural or even a sign of honor when it is the result of hard work, while others might view pain as a medical crisis in need of treatment. Men and women have different responses to pain as well — it's been theorized that women can endure pain longer while men can endure more intense pain. Regardless of what we can prove scientifically, I think we can all agree that pain is personal.

Some pains appear to be strictly physical; however, on closer inspection, *all* pain is rooted in emotion. Pain is an emotion itself, and emotions travel in groups. Identifying the emotion instigating the pain can be more difficult the more buried the emotion has become. Both physical and psychological pain have the same root in emotion. For example, with addictions and compulsions, there is real pain involved when an urge is not satisfied or accommodated. A person suffering from Obsessive Compulsive Disorder (OCD) can experience severe physical discomfort if household items are not set in order.

Chronic Pain

If acute pain results from injury, what is chronic pain? We label pain "chronic" when it persists beyond six months after an injury, at which point the pain moves to the emotional center of your brain, taking on an entirely new identity, so to speak. Since pain is an emotion, chronic pain is at the extreme end of the emotional spectrum. Chronic pain wears you down, consumes your thoughts, and takes over your life. You seek answers and having a diagnosis can feel like closure and validation. But it can also feel like a dead-end if there is no effective solution or treatment for your diagnosis. Doctors may give you an elaborate maze of do's and don'ts, none of which completely take the pain away. You may resort to surgery, but find the pain reemerging elsewhere at a later date. While acute pain responds rather well to medication and other physical interventions, the solution for chronic pain has eluded us since the very beginning.

Chronic pain leaves us with more questions than answers:

1. Why is my pain getting worse?
2. If my chronic pain is from an old injury, why wouldn't my injury

      have healed correctly?
3.   Why do other people heal, and I don't?
4.   Why doesn't medication work 100%?
5.   Why do I have good days and bad days?
6.   Why ME?

The traditional approach to addressing chronic pain assumes the cause to be solely physical. If this were true, we would have noticed two things: First, we would see a definite correlation between treatment and result, a predictable outcome every time — which we do not. Second, we would be seeing a marked and steady decrease of pain in society at large as more medical advancements are made. There has in fact been an alarming surge in the incidence of pain despite all the medical advancements that have been made over the past few decades. [9] This chronic pain crisis is not going away any time soon. Chronic pain does not respond in ways that modern medicine can predict. The fact that pain sufferers respond differently to the same treatment should cause us to reconsider our current methods, as unreliable results indicate poor science.

The word "chronic" is misleading in all actuality. Patients claim to be in constant pain; however, research has proven this to be false. [10] When someone with chronic pain has a spasm or flare-up, the intensity of that pain infiltrates all former memories. For example, you may be watching your favorite television program, laughing along with the dialog, when a commercial comes on for a popular pain reliever. Your pain is triggered, agony ensues, and you assume you must have felt pain the entire time you were sitting there. This phenomenon occurs due to the nature of memory itself. Every time you remember something, the memory itself evolves [11] — where you are when you remember something, how you're feeling when you remember it, and what made you remember it in the first place all get tangled up and linked to that memory.

Chronic pain is not objective, and it cannot be trusted as an accurate reading of the physical state of the body. The more credibility we give chronic pain as a diagnostic tool, the more misled we become. The more subjective the data, the less scientific the result.

Chronic pain is modified by memory, experienced differently from person to person, ever-evolving and spreading, and does not respond consistently to treatment. Yet, we continue to assume that it is a reliable variable in our quest for answers.

What other assumptions have we been making?

PART TWO:
OUR TRADITIONAL
RESPONSE TO PAIN

CHAPTER TWO:
HOW DIAGNOSES ARE MADE

Symptoms

Symptoms are the primary reason we seek medical treatment, and if you present your doctor with a long list of them, he or she would be foolish to not even attempt to explain why you feel the way you do.

In the Descartian medical model where mind and body are considered separate entities with no overlap between them, every physical symptom has a physical cause — leading doctors to make diagnoses that would not even make sense if they considered more factors. Presented with a lineup of suspects, the human brain becomes desperate to implicate one of them, even if they are all innocent. Rather than say, "I don't know," doctors will find a way to provide the answers you are looking for.

What constitutes a legitimate symptom? How quickly do we assume that an ache or a rash or a pang *means* something when, most of the time, these sensations come and go with no lasting harm? Giving them undue attention can lead to unnecessary medical intervention that *can* cause harm.

Have you ever cleaned up your room only to find a pile of items left over that have no home? What do you do? Put them in a bin labeled "miscellaneous!" It's human nature to want to define and label and sort things, even if they medically "have no home." Treatment plans based on this forced labeling miss the mark and can have devastating effects; nowhere do we see this more than in the field of psychiatry.

Psychiatric Diagnoses

Psychiatric care will most often lead to a diagnosis, even if the reasons you sought it were temporary. Psychiatric professionals deal with abstract emotions almost exclusively; they cannot quantify emotions as they can heartbeats or brainwaves. So how can psychiatrists provide value to their patients? By mimicking the medical profession in applying reductionistic methods to emotional health by creating a system through which the complex — *you* — can be simplified.

Their reductionistic system involves the use of a manual that groups random symptoms into cohesive disorders: the *DSM*, or the *Diagnostic and Statistical Manual of Mental Disorders*. This manual provides a psychiatrist with the same diagnosing legitimacy as a cardiologist or an oncologist. Included are familiar disorders such as "Obsessive Compulsive Disorder," "ADHD," and "Bipolar Disorder," as well as more obscure disorders such as "Specific Learning Disorder," "Internet Gaming Disorder," and "Disruptive Mood Dysregulation Disorder." There is a disorder associated with just about any set of behaviors.

But hold on a minute. Just how are these disorders added to this manual? *They are simply voted in by a panel of professionals.* In medical literature, there is a burden to prove a biological basis or pathology for a disorder or disease before acknowledging or naming a disease. In the *DSM*, however, the disorder is named *before* there is any pathology identified. [1] And it may also surprise you that, aside from a handful of disorders (such as epilepsy and Huntington's), no biological markers have ever been found for the psychiatric disorders named in the manual. [2] Yet they are still being added, every new edition, and given professional recognition and validity — all based on little more than consensus.

Mental disorders are not being *discovered*, they are being manipulated and created by simply grouping emotions and behaviors into subjective categories. [3] This process is rife with errors, as disorders can change from year to year as the culture's beliefs evolve. Also, with no objective evidence for a disorder, there are plenty of opportunities for bias. These same professionals have been known to edit disorders and rule them out simply because they hit too close to home. [4]

Well, what's wrong with that? Don't these professionals know what they're doing? There are a few red flags I should point out with the entire diagnosing process:

Consensus does not follow the scientific method. There is no attempt to "prove" or "validate" a hypothesis; it's merely agreed upon as fact. The same data can lead to extremely different conclusions by different doctors. There is little motivation to provide evidence for a diagnosis other than a doctor's subjective opinion magnified by a patient's desperate desire for answers. Also, if a patient has been diagnosed with a disorder, and a year later a new and improved disorder is created, that patient may have that new disorder simply *added* to his diagnosis, rather than have the original diagnosis modified or even reevaluated. Because there was no concrete foundation for the diagnosis in the first place, there is no process by which a doctor can verify the results or even evaluate meaningful progress.

Grouping human emotions and behaviors into convenient "disorders" ignores context and leads to over-medicalization. Behaviors that may have been seen as personal quirks before are now part of a disorder that must be treated, most often with pharmaceuticals. Anything that appears to be contrary to the norm can be classified as a disorder, not taking into consideration that we all come from different backgrounds, cultures, and family belief systems. [5]

Even normal emotions "abnormally" experienced can be seen as illness. One edition of the *DSM* proposes to classify grief, if it extends past two weeks after losing a loved one, as a mental disorder. [6] However, since this creates problems for the drug companies, implying that there are normal and natural expressions of grief, not just chemically driven ones, the latest DSM has eliminated this "grief exception" — a person can be diagnosed with a mental illness the day after their spouse is murdered or their child dies from cancer. [7] Emotions are not deemed natural and must be addressed and eradicated. Normal human sadness, fear, and frustration are not problems to be solved; rather, they can motivate a person to make necessary changes in their life that, if medicated, would never be made. Not only are these diagnoses denying patients the freedom to express emotions free of labels, they also neglect to hold individuals accountable for their own emotions. Once labeled with a disorder, there is a built-in excuse for their actions, thus making it more difficult for them to take responsibility for any behaviors that result.

Medicalization is not effective and can even be dangerous. Placebos have been proven to work just as well as antidepressants, [8] and the whole basis for pharmacological treatments, "chemical imbalance," has been debunked as "last century thinking," "bio-babble," and "on the verge of collapse": [9]

First, there is no way to measure brain chemicals while a person is alive,[10] and even studies conducted postmortem are unable to prove lower levels of norepinephrine and serotonin in patients with depression. [11]

Second, drugs that decrease serotonin levels in the brain (e.g. *tianeptine*) result in a reduction of depression symptoms [12], quite the opposite of what we would expect were the theory correct. Headaches aren't caused by a pain reliever deficiency, but it is this same logic that is often used in the reductionist medical model. If lowered serotonin levels truly cause depression, then shouldn't lowering serotonin levels through medication induce depression symptoms? Yet they do not in actuality do so. [13]

Some medications given for psychiatric disorders destroy brain tissue and cause permanent damage. [14] Since antidepressants don't merely act upon one part of the brain but on the entire body — distinguishing only between receptor type and not location — there is much room for error. There are other cells in the immune system that have the same receptor type as is being targeted by the medication; therefore, the same drug that promises mental relief could be simultaneously damaging healthy cells — inhibiting their ability to fight off cancer or other diseases. [15]

These drugs sound so appealing and tempting in that they promise to ease the pain of life, but they cannot deliver. The research they use to prove efficacy is not the complete story, as it is standard practice to conveniently exclude data from failed trials [16] — by the time the "evidence" is published, it has been cleaned and tidied up to show only the shiny face of success and health to potential patients. They use testimonials more in the selling of these drugs than actual science; the power of suggestion along with the desire to conform one's own experience to that of the herd creates an ever-growing database of positive results.

While some patients would claim the efficacy of these drugs in easing depression, those taking antidepressants also report symptoms of feeling foggy and distant, a muted version of themselves. Patients may have only found relief in having their feelings numbed to match their dead-end jobs or loveless marriages, [17] thus crushing any desire for an actionable solution for their troubled emotions — not a cure by any stretch.

So why do doctors keep prescribing medications that only seem to deaden the emotions of patients, not truly curing them? Largely because there is nothing to cure. *Emotions are not diseases.* So, who decided that emotional health should best be handled by medication, rather than by understanding, compassion, and spiritual intervention? [18]

Listing a disorder in the manual increases diagnoses. Putting a disorder on the culture's radar [19] increases the likelihood that patients will become diagnosed, simply because the disorder is now an option from which to choose. The addition of disorders creates false epidemics, as they are now added to the symptom pool from which social contagion draws (more on this later). The more public attention drawn to a disorder such as self-harming or anorexia, the greater the number of incidents [20] result. We must make the distinction: either our society is becoming more mentally ill, we are getting better at identifying mental illness, *or* we are slowly lowering our standards for what constitutes a mental illness. [21] Psychiatrists are trying more and more to match behaviors with a disorder in the manual and not asking questions about *why* the patient is suffering as they are. Therefore, the number of diagnoses increase, as well as the numbers of patients taking pharmaceuticals for their "condition."

Children are the real victims. Children who become psychiatric patients today are likely to remain patients throughout their lives; the sooner they can become "customers," the more lucrative it is for the psychiatric industry. We will learn more in a later section about the dangers of prematurely diagnosing a child with a disorder and how damaging labels can be. I know firsthand the frustration in dealing with a strong-willed child, and all three of my kids have gone through periods of OCD behavior and hyperactivity. It's so tempting to see these normal phases of childhood and individual sinful bents as mental disorders that require treatment. But we are setting up our children for a lifetime of being part of a psychiatric machine that promises conformity when what they truly desire is acceptance for who they are.

Disorders evolve. Many disorders that have at one point or another been considered valid and legitimate are no longer part of the psychiatric landscape. Those involved in adding disorders to the list have beliefs and biases that are heavily influenced by the culture of the time. A striking example of how society and culture influence the creation of new mental disorders is when, in the nineteenth century, there were identified two forms of mental illness that were specific to slaves. Dr. Samuel Cartwright, a well-known Southern physician, labeled these disorders "drapetomania" and "dysaesthesia aethiopica." The former was a diagnosis given to slaves who tried to run away, and the latter was diagnosed when a slave became disrespectful or lazy. The cure for both of these illnesses was to be light whippings. [22] What an atrocious manipulation of psychiatry! And yet these judgments are made every single day, in offices around the world, without a single shred of biological support for their conclusions.

Imagine the damage done when a diagnosis is made incorrectly! Think about what happens once you leave a psychologist's office, diagnosis and prescription in hand: you are now a patient with a disorder that makes you reliant on a doctor's care for the unforeseeable future. [23] The diagnosis becomes your label, your mark, your identity. Now you are "disordered" — you have been held up to the standard and found wanting. The whole experience changes you on the inside, compounding the original reason for which you sought professional help. Then add to that the medicine you are now taking, which I know from experience can make you feel numb and empty and distant.

What if you had taken another route? What if, instead of making a doctor's appointment, you opened up to a friend who encouraged you and came alongside you to support you through whatever you were going through? What if your friend advised you to change jobs or have that difficult conversation with your husband or cut down on your children's activities? What if the depression and anxiety were critical to your making necessary decisions and changing your life?

Assigning a biological cause to depression can imprison a patient by factors beyond their control and discourage them from finding constructive solutions for their current emotional state by making change appear impossible. [24]

Mental suffering can be an impetus for change, not a disease to be extricated. If the biological cause could be identified, then the goal would likely be to remove it immediately; if emotional pain is merely biology gone wrong, then it must not have any purpose. [25] How freeing to know that there is nothing without purpose in God's design; even suffering leads to growth and hope.

> "Consider it all joy, my brethren, when you encounter various trials, knowing that the testing of your faith produces endurance. And let endurance have [its] perfect result, so that you may be perfect and complete, lacking in nothing." (James 1:2-4 NASB)

Why do we continually compartmentalize our health into categories:

those issues that God can fix, and those that humanity needs to fix themselves? Why do we think that we can even solve our own problems, when our sinful minds are what got us into trouble in the first place? [26]

Based on what you see in the commercials for various psychiatric medications, one could easily assume that the intent of psychiatry is to make us happy, well-adjusted individuals. Images of people creating art and dancing and spending time with loved ones fill the screen so you don't notice all the fine print. These ads paint a pretty picture of how your life could be if only you ask your doctor about X-Y-Z drug. Unfortunately, psychiatry's focus is not on all that could be right, but rather has become the study of all that is *wrong*... with us.

Psychology was never devised to make us mentally healthy; it was instead contrived to explain how people could become dysfunctional and disordered.[27] Just as medical science became preoccupied with disease and illness in order to best provide specialized solutions, psychiatry made a deep-dive into all that could go wrong with the human psyche. The result? A longer list of disorders, and still no answers why or how to treat the suffering effectively.

Because Freud had been a medical doctor, he applied medical terminology and practices to the field of psychology; words like "disorder, patient, cure, and treatment." [28] This tendency to label mental disorders with similar phraseology as physical ones remains today. The human heart may be best studied under a microscope, but the soul requires compassion and understanding.

Our focus ceases to be on gaining mental health and well-being, but on avoiding mental illness, and having a negative focus never leads to success. And as long as we allow psychiatric medicine full sway over our mental health, we will continually be susceptible to an ever-changing definition of what mental health actually is. Our ideal for mental health and well-being should always be defined by our Creator, not by a community of fellow sinners. We are simply incapable of fully understanding our own hearts, let alone healing them.

Besides, would we even know what well-being looks like? There are two philosophies in psychological science on what "well-being" entails: "Eudaimonism," or living in agreement with one's virtues, and "Hedonism," or having pleasure as one's ultimate goal. [29] Hedonism provides short-term, short-lived happiness, while Eudaimonism has happiness as a byproduct.

Drugs that mask unpleasant feelings may bring a semblance of pleasure or escape, but do not deal with the underlying cause of those feelings. Pleasure and escape do not add significance to one's life; however, purpose can lead to pleasure. [30] Illness can result from a loss of control over one's life, a lack of resources required to accomplish a goal, a sense of meaninglessness, or a lack of purpose. [31]

In order for psychology to treat a suffering patient successfully, it must be able to provide *meaning* for their suffering, as well as the tools required to overcome the obstacles that person is facing. A diagnosis is merely a detailed description of your problem, and a medication only postpones those obstacles being found, obscuring all meaning. There is no real cure to be found in a prescription pad.

To illustrate, exercise alone is more effective in reducing depression symptoms than even exercise along with anti-depressants — feeling hopeless about being depressed perpetuates the depressive state. Patients who take an active role in reducing their own depression experience better results than they would had they been prescribed an anti-depressant claiming to do much of the work for them. The best treatment plan appears to be cognitive behavior therapy along with physical exercise, as both involve self-discovery and self-realization without the stigma of a diagnosis. [32]

Removing the label and addressing the depression as a normal, temporary phase of life moves a depressed person from being a patient to being empowered.

The real questions are: *Why* are you suffering? How did your suffering come about? What led up to your suffering? How did you contribute to your suffering? What tools are you lacking? What is the meaning behind your suffering?

Instead, a label is given, and a course is set. Labels become so integrated into a person's life that they become their identity, their true self; once absorbed into the fabric of their being, labels become virtually impossible to abandon. [33]

We would be wise to interpret any diagnosis as a snapshot of a moment, not a life sentence, else it can actually solidify a false way of thinking and halt recovery in its tracks. [34]

Diagnosing solely on symptoms can get us into deep trouble. Would tests or scans be more reliable?

Tests and Scans

With physical pain or disease, doctors also rely on tests and scans to make their diagnoses. With back pain, an MRI can show a disk herniation, pinpoint the source of the pain, and provide a basis for a treatment plan.

However, the accuracy of these tests and scans are being called into question. Both the American Pain Society and the American College of Physicians agree that imaging is only beneficial when there are other extreme factors present, such as "a history of cancer, unexplained weight loss, recent infection, loss of bowel control, urinary retention, or loss of strength" and that imaging as a matter of routine can be harmful. [1]

The reason for this warning is that MRIs can see too much, and the assumption is that only textbook spines are pain free. MRIs also see into the past, revealing healed injuries as well as fresh ones with no way of knowing one from the other. Even after an acute injury has healed, your MRI or x-ray may still show signs of damage. This is due to the fact that even though the disc has healed, it will never look as it did before the injury; it will always show signs of damage. Both old and new damage can appear the same on a test. Therefore, treating a spine as if it is still injured will not be effective and may even cause additional damage. [2]

There's no way of knowing whether a fall caused the disc to herniate, or if the herniation had been there all along.

There are countless flaws in diagnosing based on imaging tools such as MRIs and x-rays alone. Structural differences are meaningless because they evolve so slowly over time and don't cause pain.[3] Your body adapts to these anomalies and variations, just like white hair or wrinkles. In fact, herniated disks, arthritis, spondylosis, and even degenerative disk disease are all common occurrences, and are considered natural aging processes in the spine. [4]

Seventy percent or more of the population has these anomalies and experience no pain whatsoever. [5] Degeneration and pain have never been definitively correlated in any scientific documentation. [6]

There are many examples of pain attributed to pinched nerves, such as sciatica and spondylolisthesis, largely due to misconceptions regarding nerve behavior. Many peripheral pains are attributed to herniated discs or pinched nerves that could not possibly be the cause. The areas affected are most often not even linked by any neurological pathway; for example, the gluteal region is not connected by any nerve to the lumbar spine, so any diagnosis that seeks to link gluteal pain to a herniated disc, a pinched nerve, or even spinal stenosis would most definitely be *wrong*. [7]

With spondylolisthesis, for example, there is most often no pain involved with the condition, and would instead cause paralysis or bowel and bladder dysfunction. [8] I think you would notice that!

In his book, *The Pain Cure Rx*, Dr. Mitchell Yass describes the intricate pathways of the nervous system, and how most of what the medical community tells us regarding back pain is impossible. He also illuminates the other implications of true injury that would not just present with pain. For a diagnosis to make sense, there would have to be more symptoms involved. For example, a ruptured disc would cause severe and noticeable symptoms that far exceed mere back or neck pain. [9]

For a diagnosis to make sense, more factors beyond imaging results and/or pain need to be taken into consideration. If your doctor is only using an MRI or an x-ray to evaluate you, their diagnosis is most likely wrong. [10]

MRIs and x-rays can *see*, but they cannot *explain*. [11]

If the current method of diagnosing worked, we would expect to see a marked decline in those suffering from pain. If our current method of treatment worked, chronic pain would be a thing of the past. The opposite is sadly true. The current opioid crisis [12] in the US is a testament to the growing number of people experiencing chronic pain. The fact that opioids are becoming less effective, and more people are actually reporting increased pain resulting from their use suggests that we are on the wrong track. [13] That a seemingly obvious solution to a seemingly obvious problem has failed miserably calls into question our very process for diagnosing disorders.

Patient History

The other main tool used in making diagnoses is patient history. Doctors try to retrace your illness' steps and find out where it first began. They usually begin with your DNA — what is in your genetic heritage that could have set you up for such a disorder? The problem with making the connection between the past and the possible future is that there is not always a clear solid line to connect them. Not everyone with a family history of heart disease contracts heart disease. Some develop cancer despite generations having been cancer-free. There is no direct and reliable cause and effect.

In our quest to find a root cause for illness, we prematurely rejoiced in the discovery of genetics. It certainly makes sense that if you have such-and-such a gene, you need to be prepared to see it expressed in the form of cancer or diabetes. We spend hundreds of dollars ordering genetic testing and devouring the data as if it were a high school class schedule: "What did you get? Oh, I got high cholesterol and cancer…" But does knowing our potential health struggles really make a difference? Are genes really our destiny? Can genes even begin to explain the complexities surrounding most chronic disease? [1]

Genes are far more complex than we can yet understand. They move and change in a constant dance of expression and repression, depending on our environment, our physical health, and our emotions. Your DNA is constantly changing. Your actions, your feelings, your experiences, and your thoughts can turn genes on and off depending on the moment. Your genes are not set in stone. Hope is written into our DNA — if you've ever felt like you are stuck in a certain pattern or doomed to fulfill a specific destiny, your genes are proof that you indeed *can* change, even at the cellular level! [2] Also, these genetic changes of expression can occur moment by moment,[3] so that you could even say we are never the same person twice!

Genetic tests only reveal the possible cast list, not who will end up with the lead roles. The information isn't helpful enough to justify the worry that usually results. It would be convenient to know the future, genetically. But the future is wide open and entirely up to the choices you make *now*.

Neuropeptides are the brain's way of communicating with the body. As they are produced by the neurons, the building blocks of your nervous system, these neuropeptides are released into the bloodstream and affect our bodies at the cellular level — there are neuropeptides associated with anger, stress, fear, for example — and these neuropeptides actually switch genes on or off. [4] What an amazing influence our emotions have on our bodies, on our very genes! A slight difference in genetic expression can determine whether a tumor becomes cancerous or remains benign, [5] so every emotion *matters*.

If you are born with the breast cancer gene, it can be tempting to prepare for the inevitable disease. And genes often win. This may be because genes respond to your emotions and mental state and, for most of us, these thoughts and emotions stay pretty much the same throughout our lives. We seek homeostasis, reacting the same way to the same triggers, making choices based on the same tendencies, gravitating towards the same types of environments and people. If nothing changes in your life – if your perceptions and reactions remain the same – your genes *will* be your destiny, choosing your future for you. [6]

How we respond now is how we will respond later and forevermore unless we make a change for the better. The good news is that even small deviations from the norm can have a huge impact on your genetic destiny. Just one minor change, a new experience, or a new thought can make immediate genetic changes that can even be passed on to future generations.[7]

A new experience can change not only *your* future but that of your children! Choosing a salad instead of a burger, taking a new route to work in the morning, going out of your comfort zone even just a little, or making a new friend can actually change your *genes*.

These changes, to be effective, must first involve beliefs. What we believe — whether or not it is true — and the meaning we assign to our beliefs can "produce significant biological changes on a genetic level." [8]

We see one of the most intrinsic markers of gene activation and expression in how quickly minor wounds heal. By testing the speed of healing and comparing it to the level of stress the participants were experiencing, researchers at the Ohio State University College of Medicine could confirm a direct relationship between stress and gene activation. [9] In fact, genetic expression takes its cues from "thoughts, choices, behaviors, experiences, and feelings" [10] — there is a myriad of factors involved in the development of disease that goes beyond simple genetics. Genomes are simply not reliable determinants when predicting chronic illness and disease.[11]

Your genes are *not* your destiny.

If symptoms, test, scans, and genetics aren't reliable criteria for making a diagnosis, what else *is* there?

CHAPTER THREE:
WHAT IF WE HAVE IT WRONG?

Medical science can tell us how the heart pumps, how tissues repair themselves, how lungs expand, and how muscles make joints move. What medicine cannot do is explain *why*, nor can it predict an outcome with precision and confidence; it can only make guesses based on statistics of past patients. Much of medical science should not be called science at all. When we put our faith in this uncertainty, we end up with hopelessness, confusion, envy (why *me?*), and despair.

When I buy a hair dryer, I want to know that it will dry my hair. I don't want to see a warning label that says, "Caution: may do one of the following: dry your hair, explode, wash your car, or make you a cup of coffee." Yet that is the message we receive from the medical community every day. "You may get sick, you may not, you may find relief from this pill or it might give your heart palpitations — your guess is as good as ours."

Now, I'm not suggesting to throw your doctor's business card away. Doctors are incredibly knowledgeable when it comes to the human body and how it functions. And medicine has its place. We have made many advancements in vaccines and cancer treatments and laparoscopic surgeries in the past several centuries; we would be foolish to dismiss the role medicine plays in keeping people healthy and alive.

The problem lies in giving medicine the only role in every play. An orchestra would be boring with only an oboe. All instruments need to be playing together in harmony for the music to capture your heart. Medicine alone cannot be the answer to our problem of chronic pain.

It makes sense to our human minds that physical pain would have a physical source; it's simpler. We love to label, compartmentalize, isolate, and organize. But as much as we crave order, we still make our first stop a medical one. Why, given that it cannot provide any input/output reliability? We *want* it to be true so badly, but are disappointed every time a surgery leaves us in more pain than before or a medication does not relieve the pain in its entirety.

With pain being defined as an emotion, it becomes clear that the mind and the body are intricately connected. If the mind determines whether to feel pain, then *how does it make its decisions?*

Towards the end of the nineteenth century, there was a surge of people suffering from "hysteria," a label given to patients who demonstrated odd behavior such as fainting, moaning, crying — an excess of emotion, basically, that was manifesting itself in physical symptoms. There appeared to be no cure for these individuals until Dr. Sigmund Freud started taking the time to listen to these sufferers. The patients soon began to reveal what lay beneath the hysteria, the "secret wishes, taboo thoughts... traumatic memories," [1] and they were cured simply by being allowed to voice what they had kept hidden.

An amazing thing began to happen. As the patients became emboldened and willing to express the truth they had previously been suppressing or resisting, they no longer needed their bodies to speak on their behalf. Speaking the truth brought about physical wellness, not just emotional peace.[2]

(If that sounds familiar, it is because John's gospel said it first: "Then you will know the truth, and the truth will set you free." [John 8:32 NIV])

Freud, and others like him, had recognized the possible psychosomatic nature of disease. The term "psychosomatic" literally means "mind/body," but it has taken on the nasty connotation that pain is "all in your head." While it's true that many doctors have used that expression, the term itself never intended to imply that pain is imaginary. While I may refer to the term "psychosomatic," it can also be shortened to its more modern label, "MindBody."

The belief that physical pain is the outward manifestation of emotional pain lies at the foundation of the MindBody approach. Removing the requirement of a physical cause opens up a host of possibilities for what kind of pain could be expressed; the mind is creative and strategic in its communicating innermost emotional needs in physical form.

Hippocrates once said, "It is more important to know what sort of person has a disease than to know what sort of disease a person has."

Some books I read in the course of my research were written many years ago, long before HMOs and HSAs. Physicians formed diagnoses with less data on hand; they had none of the modern testing equipment we have today, nor the studies on genetics we have at our disposal. Perhaps due to their limited resources, it was easier to blame emotions for a disease than admit their own incompetence. Still, medical hastiness doesn't negate the success they experienced; patients became well soon after learning that their pain was emotionally driven. How could that be, if it were not ultimately true?

Hysteria is no longer a prevailing issue in our modern culture; it has been mistakenly relegated to the failure category in the annals of historical diagnoses. However, we have not quite heard the last of its kind, as it has been replaced by other disorders for good reason. Culture itself defines which diseases are legitimate, and what may be deemed legitimate one day may fall out of favor the next, thereby continually changing the very landscape of psychosomatic illness. [3]

Psychosomatic disorders come and go as the cultural environment changes and medical advancements evolve. If a disorder gains public support and approval, the rates of that disorder will increase. [4] Each culture develops its own list of acceptable symptoms for members to choose from subconsciously to express their emotional pain. [5] The rationale behind this "symptom pool" is that because we are longing for acceptance, our symptoms, too, need to be acceptable. [6] Diseases that sound too weird don't catch on. Turning purple, barking like a dog, or growing moss on your skin aren't symptoms that would, in all likelihood, be taken seriously.

These ever-changing symptom pools explain why there may be a huge increase in one disorder or another. One disorder explodes and fills the media for a time, while others subside and all but disappear from the public eye. Think about the most common illnesses and diseases from when your parents were young and compare them to today's health crises; there is a natural ebb and flow as the symptom pools are restructured and redefined.

Most importantly, these symptom pools need to consist of symptoms that must be blamed on a biological or organic cause so that the sufferer could never be held responsible. [7]   If a disorder is seen as self-inflicted because of a mental issue rather than a physical one, or too awkward or disgusting, it defeats the very purpose for which it was "created." The disorders involving pain, fatigue, and allergies are far more popular than those involving discharges, odors, pus, and saliva.

While back pain and migraines may be the disorder *du jour* here in the United States, other cultures have entirely different symptom pools. For example, in southeast Asia, there is a disorder called "Koro, " which is the "terrifying certainty that their genitals are retracting into their body." [8]   In Korea, there is a disorder named "Hwabyeong" which involves "intense fits of sighing, a heavy feeling in the chest, blurred vision, and sleeplessness." [9] In South America, menopausal hot flashes are called "bochorno" or "shame," while in Asia they are called "second spring," and are a sign of honor. [10] We view health and illness differently depending on the culture in which we live.

What is common in one culture is unheard of in another — even though we are all essentially the same on the inside: human. The only difference between us is in the expression of our emotional pain and in which symptoms are found to be acceptable and legitimate within our society.

Mental disorders are no exception; what is considered genius or "inspired" in one culture may be labeled mental illness in another. [11] In Puerto Rico, there is a "fighting sickness" ("Mal de pelea") that is diagnosed in men who have been insulted or falsely accused; the diagnosis serves to protect the man's honor by not labeling him insane for wanting to protect his good name with his fists. [12]

In today's American culture of science and reason, we gravitate toward disorders that make logical sense — something we can see on an x-ray or diagnose from a textbook. In other cultures, these disorders are non-existent or take on a whole different appearance — for example, anorexia in Asia isn't usually connected to a desire to be thin but rather an aversion to food. [13]

Medical science is heavily influenced by culture, as is in the case of migraines: in the U.S., migraines are said to be vascular or hormonal in cause, in France, they are due to liver issues, and in the U.K., they are the result of gastrointestinal disorders. [14]

The illness or pain you develop is unique to your environment. Your symptoms encompass that which is most likely to get your feelings across and secure the most meaningful results. Canadian patients are more likely to complain of negative thoughts, while Chinese patients have more physical symptoms [15] — most likely because in a Communist regime, bad feelings could imply criticism of the government. Behavior that is not considered appropriate by a culture would never become a disorder. We diagnose what we tolerate.

Your culture influences the support available to you, whether it is emotional or physical. We should not accept a simple one-dimensional physical explanation for conditions that appear to be as diverse and unique as the sufferers themselves.

Hysteria at the time was a big deal. We may look back and mock Dr. Freud's process as primitive; however, we must be careful in doing so, as future generations will judge us in the same way. Will we be mocked for our lack of understanding of the entire body and mind as a whole, derided for using medicine when we should have used understanding?

TMS

One prevailing theory about psychosomatic pain was developed by Dr. John Sarno — I mentioned earlier his book that started it all: *The Divided Mind.* [1] Dr. Sarno has labeled the mind-driven pain cycle as "TMS" (originally "Tension Myositis Syndrome," now more informally known as "The MindBody Syndrome"). According to Dr. Sarno, TMS occurs when the brain induces physical changes in the body via oxygen deprivation to the affected body sites. Chronic pain stems from the brain's decision to cut off oxygen to the body, resulting in pain more intense than would be expected from injury alone.

Why would the body do this? It may sound absurd, but it all stems from a desire to protect the mind at all costs. Emotional trauma is far more damaging to a person than any physical injury. It's basically the old saying: "Sticks and stones may break my bones, but words will never hurt me" flipped upside down. The body opts for the sticks and stones to avoid the pain caused by the words, which usually cause more long-lasting damage.

The basic premise behind TMS is that your mind wishes to suppress a traumatic emotion, usually rage. Rage expressed would have devastating effects on relationships at work, in the family, and in the community, and may even get a person arrested! Not to mention, the person showing rage

35

would certainly have their mental health questioned. The mind draws a line that the person cannot cross; the rage must be suppressed. But the rage needs to go somewhere. So, we use the body as a release of pressure, a distraction from the original emotion, while using another emotion: pain. Awareness of this cycle results in a "cure," [2] defined as an elimination of pain, resuming normal physical activities without fear, and discontinuing all physical treatments. The idea of a cure is in stark contrast to what we are usually told by physicians — that pain can merely be "managed," not necessarily eliminated.

Why rage? What causes this rage? Sin causes us to desire what Satan desired: to be God (I John 3:10). Deep down, we feel the world is unfair, we deserve better, and we could do a better job if only we were in charge. Instead of yielding to a God who knows best, we strive against Him, even as we claim to serve Him. We are fighting for our rights while pretending to surrender. We know we must keep up the facade or else be judged by our peers, but our inner desires often sabotage genuine obedience.

You may know the proverbial story of the family who shows up at church in their Sunday best, praising God with holy smiles, everyone else unaware that they were fighting in the car the whole way there and cussing at other drivers on the road. We like to think we are submitting to God, but there's a part of us that just wants what we want. In fact, the more a person claims to "never get angry," the more likely they are suppressing a deep, hidden rage. We all have a toddler side, the side that wants to stamp our feet and demand our way. But the only way we can *keep from* acting like toddlers is to keep ourselves in check, and that is where pain comes in.

The mind knows that we cannot go around stamping our feet. We would all be taken away in strait jackets and sent to psychiatric wards! While we would definitely benefit from biblical counseling and spiritual truths, getting the emotional help we need is problematic under our current system. Due to the fact that medical insurance limits payments for psychotherapy, the mind conjures up a genius distraction. It is far more convenient to have physical pain that to admit emotional distress. [3] Physical pain, after all, doesn't require that you divulge anything personal about yourself. Physical pain is a safe way to express and acquire need. Health insurance covers physical pain to a far greater extent than it does psychological pain, and without the social stigma attached.

Once physical pain has been initiated, it often continues and increases because of the many methods available for relief. One obstacle to being cured of chronic pain is the connection that arises between medical interventions and pain relief. If you have a box of back massagers and ice packs, according to Dr. Sarno, all of that has to go. As long as you associate those devices with pain relief, you will continue to need them to feel better. You will not be able to discover the solution apart from them. These devices don't even remove the pain entirely; they only serve as additional distractions, keeping you from asking the hard questions. These tools will be literal and figurative crutches for you, and you will require more and more as the pain takes over.

Having a houseful of remedies can make a pain sufferer feel like they're making progress against the pain. Downloading a diet app on their phone can make a person struggling to lose weight feel like they are doing *something*, when in actuality the diet app remains unopened. We can say the same for the countless massagers and gadgets back pain sufferers own; not all end up being used, but none can be given away — just in case. These tools serve a purpose: they offload the responsibility onto something outside of themselves. If the pain persists, the answer must be to try a new gadget or program. A casual glance at the magazine covers at the supermarket checkouts provides some evidence of this: "Five Simple Ways to Reduce Back Pain," "The Easy Solution for Headaches," "Foods that Fight Inflammation" — people are looking for answers, preferably ones that are fast-acting and require little emotional effort.

Physical pain makes more logical sense than some abstract emotion; emotions can't be measured or seen under a microscope. The beliefs that pain can only occur when there has been an injury, that the only alternative is that "I must be making it up, I'm crazy, there's no real hope for me," only lead to more and more pain. Surrounding yourself with failed attempts, such as back massagers and chair pillows, can lead to increased despair and pain.

Because repressed rage is such an enormous threat, sleep and relaxation are considered to be dangerous states, as there is more of a possibility for exposure. Emotions, usually kept under wraps during the day, roam free during the night. In order to keep these emotions under control, pain has to increase and intensify during the night, often waking patients up from a sound sleep. [4]

There are a host of other triggers for TMS pain. Seeing items or places you associate with pain, seeing others in pain, visiting a doctor, going on vacation, or even just having someone ask how you are doing can all set off a pain episode. [5] Memories, associations, perceptions, and feelings of vulnerability or guilt can all incite a pain event. The pathways for pain become plentiful, and the more associations you make with your pain, the more entangled pain becomes in every area of your life. The process for healing involves understanding the emotional nature of your pain, dealing with those emotions that have been long suppressed, identifying and addressing possible triggers, and moving forward in self-awareness and humility.

However, knowing about your possible triggers is not enough. You must also prepare to have your progress thwarted by others; even well-intentioned physicians and friends can bring about a relapse. When your doctor dismisses MindBody pain as ludicrous or impossible, it can make you question your own judgment, and even doubt any results you may have experienced. Friends who dismiss MindBody pain can make you feel crazy and alone at a time when you crave support and acceptance. And reading about new medical discoveries or articles about your condition that deny any possible emotional connection can tempt you to renew your search for a biological "cure." [6]

As you can see, the mind is desperate to continue the deception and will use all means available to do so. The greatest trigger of all is your own subconscious desire for the pain and its "benefits" — being self-deceived is the hardest obstacle to overcome. In fact, the more you find yourself rejecting the possibility of emotion's role in your pain, the more likely it is to be the cause. Overreactions indicate you are threatened by the idea that your symptoms are emotionally caused. [7]

The emotional connection makes perfect sense, however, and applies to every one of us. Because of our need to save face, there is often no socially acceptable manner in which to express certain emotions. Honesty isn't always the best policy, socially. Admitting too much about our inner desires and needs may put us at a disadvantage with others around us, therefore accentuating and increasing those desires and needs.

So, what is a "body" to do? Chronic pain.

Emotions are energy, and they must be expressed somehow. Suppressing emotions means they have nowhere to go, and the ensuing pressure must be released somehow. [8] The answer? The physical body.

The physical body becomes the conduit for the subconscious mind to express itself. [9] What you feel in your mind, you will feel in your body.

Think about it. If you were to tell your employer that you and your spouse are arguing, the kids all need new clothes and your bank account is approaching zero, you feel inadequate, and you are resenting your coworkers for not carrying their share of the burden, how would they respond? They would probably tell you to "leave your personal life at home and get back to work." No sympathy there, no time off, no remedy. But if you tell them you injured your back and need to work from home, they are obligated to attend to your needs and assign others to help you with your workload. Your spouse will probably let the argument go, also. Your subconscious needs are now fully met, at the expense of your physical comfort. Ultimately, the mind sees mental and emotional needs as taking precedence to the physical, barring anything life-threatening. (The ego must be protected at all costs; however, even death is not out of the question if the ego is substantially threatened. We will see more of that at play in a later section.)

These thought processes are performed completely below your conscious radar. You are not deviously plotting or faking your pain. This is the way your mind takes care of *you*, and it's effective!

I have met some wonderful, loving, kind people with chronic pain. These people have never yelled a day in their life, never complained about their pain. And yet, when I mention to them that their pain may be emotionally driven, especially by rage, I see a different side to them emerge. These kind, soft-spoken individuals have practically growled at me, their eyes flashing in the very rage they deny they have. Their pride prevents them from releasing the pressure caused by the very high standards they have established for themselves. Cancer patients have been characterized as being rule-following, responsible individuals who remain loving and generous even in the midst of challenging times – there is a distinct cancer personality described as "too good to be true." [10]

It's not natural or healthy to feign external perfection, and yet we continue to do so in order to "earn" our value, even our very salvation; however, we then exempt ourselves from experiencing the grace the gospel has to offer. I've read social media posts filled with fury about people who "don't understand" and how *evil* it is to suggest that their pain isn't from a legitimate physical source. Why the anger? Because the pain is protecting them from an even more painful truth: deep inside, they know they are not *good* enough to deserve grace. *None* of us is; instead of breathing a collective sigh of relief, we continue to act as if there was some worthy part of us that caused God to pick us first for His team of holy followers.

If the MindBody explanation is wrong, then why would it be offensive? I don't get offended when people tell me they disagree with my decision to homeschool, that I'm not doing the right thing for my children. *I know what I know, so I let it go.* But what if the MindBody explanation is correct? Then the anger makes sense, actually!

If you feel the need to defend your pain at all costs, then it isn't your pain you are defending.

TMS and the Symptom Imperative

Your mind is incredibly clever, and its main goal is to provide continuous distraction. One way the mind accomplishes this is by the "symptom imperative."[11] While most pain sticks to familiar places, sometimes the same pain just isn't enough to keep you sufficiently distracted. The symptom imperative explains why your pain may move from side to side, or spread from just your elbow to your whole arm, constantly changing shape or intensity to keep your mind off of what's really behind your pain.

I tell myself, "This too shall pass" — I've had weird aches and pains over the years, and they've all gone away over time. I know my body will always try to find new distractions, so I am no longer surprised when strange and unusual symptoms arise.

Dr. Sarno's research has changed lives, and more and more doctors are beginning to follow in his footsteps. More research has been conducted on the MindBody connection in other areas of health; while TMS is a well-documented explanation for most chronic pain, there are additional tools the mind uses in its attempt to look out for our emotional needs.

Buried Emotional Trauma

We all know what happens when there is a physical trauma to your body. Inflammation, intense pain, immobilization of the injured limb or area, sometimes even unconsciousness. If we break a leg, we put a cast on it, use crutches, ask others to carry things for us and open the door for us, and rest our leg until it heals. We don't continue to walk on the broken leg; if we did, it wouldn't heal correctly, and we would become deformed and lame. But what happens when there is emotional trauma? If an emotional response to a trauma such as the death of a loved one is not repressed, but is expressed naturally, it will follow the seven stages of grief: [1] shock or disbelief, denial, anger, bargaining, guilt, depression, and acceptance and hope. Unfortunately, many emotional traumas *are* repressed, and can lead to more pervasive responses such as nightmares, mood swings, panic attacks, sleep disruption, chronic fatigue, psychosomatic illnesses, chronic pain, and depression. [2] The more traumatic childhood experiences one has, the more likely they are to have frequent headaches. [3]

Emotional trauma doesn't have to imply that you were violently attacked as a child or that you spent time on the battlefield. **We experience emotional trauma every time we choose to act outside of God's protective will.** Remember: sin hurts, both emotionally and physically, and some pain runs deep and lingers for quite a long time. We are in a spiritual battle, and we have wounds to show for it.

Why would we choose to repress our emotional pain? Because emotional injuries take much longer to heal than physical ones, and yet we often refuse to let ourselves grieve. The grief process is messy and loved ones aren't always patient or understanding enough to stick with us through the dark times. Life goes on, and we feel we must pick up where we left off before the trauma occurred... as if it never occurred. We shove our feelings down deep where we assume they will stay buried. Over time, we become bitter and angry. Our bitterness stems from the fact that we want... no, we *need* others to carry our burdens, but we don't feel we can share them because of a misplaced sense of pride and dignity, or even a fear of rejection. To remain socially acceptable, we deny the emotional pain altogether, claiming to be "fine." But "emotion is an energy that needs to flow." [4] Contrary to what you may have heard, it is not possible to "swallow your pride" or "stuff your feelings;" they must go somewhere. But where? The emotions become manifested in the physical body in the form of chronic pain. This kind of pain is also MindBody pain and is sometimes referred to as "conversion disorder" — think of your emotions being converted into physical sensations. The result is the same, no matter the source: pain. *Real* pain.

Our body takes on the role of our mind — if we are feeling paralyzed by emotional pain, that emotion can be transferred to physical body parts, rendering limbs immovable. [5] Between the seventeenth and nineteenth centuries, there were many cases where patients would present with paralysis in a limb. A reflex test can easily show if the paralysis is of a mental origin or a physical one, and many cases were indeed proven to be psychosomatic. When the doctors started performing these reflex tests, the cases decreased, mainly because if a medical condition can be shown to be psychological in origin, it is less likely to be developed. [6]

If we are feeling broken or weary of heart, our bodies take on that mantle and play the part on our mind's behalf. The body may even try to reenact the situation that caused us grief to begin with: if you fell off your bike only a few yards from the finish line of a race for which you had trained months, you may be more susceptible to sprained ankles [7] in the future, as your body tries to rehash the painful event — perhaps to learn from it or to reframe it into something more positive. Beneath the surface of our awareness, our mind is attempting to secure us the help we so desperately need. Just like the broken limb needs a cast, the broken heart needs repair. If we are too afraid or unwilling to ask for this help ourselves, our body will do it for us, while ensuring that we also save face in the process. If asking for help threatens our pride, then our mind needs to protect us from that, as part of allowing us to save face is to protect us from even knowing that we need to save face in the first place! [8] Your mind needs to *address* the pain, or else your body will *express* the pain.

When was the last time you felt selfish? Go ahead, you can admit it. You come home from a long day at work and all you want to do is sit in a chair and rest. But there is dinner to be made, dishes to wash, kids to tend to, a spouse who needs attention — what about *your* needs? It's not "nice" to tell your family to leave you alone and let you tune out the world. If you did, your spouse would most likely become angry, and an argument would not help you in your quest for peace. But yet, anger is taking root in your heart, and it needs to go somewhere. Now you feel a slight headache coming on. You tell your spouse that your head hurts, and all of a sudden, they are deferent and compassionate, telling you to rest yourself, they'll make dinner. What just happened? Did you manufacture the headache to manipulate the situation? Not exactly. You weren't even aware of the entire process, for it all took place within seconds. Your mind knew you needed rest, knew you couldn't ask for it without threatening your relationship with your family, and arranged for you to get it in the form of a headache. End scene. This little play occurs more often than most of us realize. Its efficacy rests on its flying below the radar of our consciousness. Once we realize this little dance, we can break the cycle and deal with the emotions our mind is trying to help us conceal.

Our sinful nature, in the form of our subconscious, is in control every time we aren't. And that's quite a large portion of the time! Research has shown that our lives are being run by our subconscious minds 95% of the time, maybe even more. [9]

If our subconscious is running the show, then we are allowing our lives to be run unchecked, unmonitored, and unfiltered. While your subconscious can be a huge help to you while driving or brushing your teeth — imagine if you had to *think* about what you were doing the entire time — we need to perform consistent quality checks and scans on what our subconscious has been up to.

It's not as if we can just coast in life and expect to come back to things as we left them. You'd never leave a toddler home alone, would you? You would come home to a disaster and not a few broken dishes, maybe even a house fire. Yet we routinely let our sinful nature take over, letting our thoughts run wild down sinful paths, distracting ourselves with technology and work meetings and nights out with friends so we don't have to pay attention to what we are **thinking**. And our thoughts become emotions, and emotions have to go somewhere. It's like Lucy (in "I Love Lucy" [10]) working on the conveyor belt at the chocolate factory. She gets confused and behind in sorting the chocolates — the belt keeps advancing and the chocolates keep coming and piling up, so Lucy ends up stuffing them in her face to hide her incompetence. If we aren't mindful of sorting our emotions, they end up sorting themselves, and that's how chronic pain begins.

Chronic pain is physically unnecessary. If acute pain serves as an alert to crisis, chronic pain is like a broken smoke alarm that continues after the fire has been extinguished. Chronic pain plays a critical *emotional* role, however.

If emotions aren't expressed as their emotions of origin (sadness as sadness, anger as anger, fear as fear), they take other forms. Fear can become anger, sadness can become fear, and fear can become sadness. But many times, they become something else entirely. If there is no acceptable form of expression for a particular emotion, it can become embedded in the physical body. There, it finds expression in the form of chronic pain. Why pain? Because pain cannot be ignored, as emotions generally are. Pain is a warning light, a buzzer, an alarm — and it just keeps growing in intensity until it is acknowledged. In severe cases, pain can also serve as a distraction when emotions cannot be expressed in a beneficial manner, or if the emotions are too traumatic for the mind to allow them to surface.

Your conscious mind often enlists the power of the subconscious mind in order to provide a diversion, a way to repress and escape a situation that is frightening or emotionally devastating. Your conscious mind is aware of your painful buried emotions, and in order to protect you, will conjure up a genius plan to help take your attention away from them, something that cannot be ignored or dismissed, something that will preoccupy you and fill your mind: chronic pain. [11.] It's quite a remarkable ruse on the conscious mind's part, and is indeed an effective one.

We would be wise to see pain as a call to action, but too often we allow it to distract us from our emotions entirely and allow our body to speak on our behalf. Chronic pain can be a last resort for a person whose mind is suffering beyond what it can bear, and any treatment plan needs to involve all aspects of the person: mental, emotional, and only lastly, physical. [12]

Consider a cracked water pipe in a building. Pressure builds up over time, slowly. The damage can go undetected for quite a while... until the pipe bursts. If emotions aren't allowed to flow, they will spill out into your body.

Pain can serve a purpose beyond distraction; if the patient has given up on ever being able to deal with what is troubling them emotionally, physical pain can provide a more manageable alternative. Until the patient develops the skills to address their mental suffering, their emotions can find temporary outlet in their physical bodies. [13]

If the treatment for chronic pain peripherally addresses emotional pain, the mind considers that a win. Bed rest, a vacation, concern from loved ones, hey, I'll take it! Especially if the real pain can remain hidden, and I can save face in the process.

The Story of Pain

The beginnings of chronic pain occur on a molecular level, even before the pain is felt, as the subconscious mind weighs the risks of expressing emotion versus burying them. There is a massive network of nerves and ganglia that lie along the spinal cord and extend to all of our organs, even our skin. This network is the conduit for emotion, and our subconscious relies on neuropeptide triggers to evaluate whether or not an emotion or a thought becomes consciously expressed or lies repressed and hidden. [1]

Our entire body is continually playing a role in deciding which emotions should be dealt with outright, and which need to stay buried until the mind is more prepared to deal with the fallout. And all of these decisions are made in split seconds, below your awareness, repeatedly throughout your lifetime.

The brain calls the shots and makes the final call regarding when to express emotion and when to bury it in the body in the form of pain. It all depends on what the emotions are, how dangerous the mind perceives them to be, how acceptable they would be socially, and how ready you may be to face them. Emotions repressed as a child are more easily handled as an adult. Some emotions may be devastating at any age. The mind determines the most beneficial method of handling emotions based on the individual situation.

But how does the mind decide what kind of pain to present? It uses what it has to work with: experience. If you have ever had an injury, the pain information from that injury exists in your mind's database. The next time the brain needs to inflict pain on your unsuspecting self, it will use previous pain pathways since they are familiar and are most likely to be attributed to a physical cause rather than an emotional one.

Emotional pain can be more devastating and longer-lasting than physical pain, and we are more likely to remember emotional pain in greater vivid detail. This is because emotional pain often has a story attached; the tragedy of chronic pain is that these stories often find expression through hijacking your physical pain pathways in your brain. [2]

What is an emotional story? We assign meaning to our experiences, telling a kind of story to remember them later. It's like sticking a label on a file folder or tagging a blog entry. If the story we told about a physical pain matches a story we told about an emotional pain, the two can end up being filed together. A ski accident can become filed with a broken relationship — both forms of failure, in your mind — leading to knee pain every time you experience conflict with a friend.

The Ghost of Pain Past

Even if an acute injury caused the original pain, it does not explain the pain that you now feel. Chronic pain is unnecessary to protect your body from further injury. Once a broken bone has healed, it has healed. Pain also does not come and go. Feeling pain from an old injury makes no medical or biological sense.

Chronic pain takes advantage of pain pathways already established, along with the mainstream belief that pain can reappear even when the original injury has healed. If you get a paper cut, you would think it ridiculous for your finger to hurt again once it's healed, but we somehow believe that bones and muscles, once broken or pulled, can flare up in pain months and years later.

If pain returns at the site of a previous injury, here are a few questions to ask yourself:

1. What was going on in your life at the time of that original injury?
2. What feelings and emotions were you experiencing?
3. What feelings and emotions are you going through now?
4. Do you see an emotional connection between the two events?

Chronic pain serves no purpose in the body other than to fulfill an emotional imperative. Once pain becomes chronic, the pain shifts from the pain centers in the brain to the emotional center. [3] And the emotional center can produce pain more intensely and for a longer duration -- because the pain is driven by emotion, it becomes "associated with more and more experiences and memories and therefore becomes more complex." [4] Your brain connects more and more stimuli to the pain, leaving more opportunity for expected pain, which leads to pain. For example, your neck hurt when you went to a movie theater, so it hurts every time you watch a movie on TV, then every time you sit in the armchair in front of the TV. More and more connections mean more and more pain. *Chronic pain is sustained by the emotional brain.*

The Pain Menu - Check Out Our Specials!

The specific pain you experience is also determined by a variety of inputs the mind has to sort through. In order to be accepted by the mind, pain needs to be: [5][6]

1. **Accepted** — Accepting that something is common in society at large increases the possibility that you will experience it. The more people you know with back pain, the more likely you are to develop it yourself. This may be because your subconscious doesn't want you to suffer in isolation; there should be others out there with your experience so you don't stand out as odd or crazy. If you are going to develop pain, it is most likely going to be something that many other people have — something that isn't disgusting or involving some kind of stinky discharge. For example, back pain is more acceptable than, say, anal warts. Disorders are more commonly acquired when they are "in vogue" — this is the basis for social contagion.
2. **Assumed** — "Cold weather causes colds" — even though it's not true, it becomes true because you believe it. One of these beliefs is that sleeping on a hard surface is good for back pain. Why would a hard surface be comfortable for anyone? It makes little sense, but since it's been repeated so often, it becomes true in the social consciousness. When you hear, "Doesn't that hurt your back?" or "Wouldn't all those lunges be hard on the knees?" it's easy to fall prey to the belief that not only should it hurt; it *does*.
3. **Amplified** — Watching a commercial about arthritis, you might be more mindful of how your hands feel, leaving the door open for developing pain. Even walking into a doctor's office or hearing someone else discuss their own pain can have a similar effect. When

we hear about painful conditions, our mind scans our body to see if there is any sign of them there. While this scanning can be beneficial, most often it just makes us feel things that aren't legitimately there.

4. **Available and Affordable** — If there were no pain medications, no surgeries available, and no other aids to be found, most chronic pain would vanish overnight. My mother-in-law grew up in a small village in Iran, and there was no talk of back pain at all, even though they had to walk great distances, carrying heavy loads on their heads or backs. Back pain wasn't a big deal over there because there was limited access to medical treatment and simply no time for pain!

5. **Attributed to the Physical** — Once you have a diagnosis, the connection is made between the physical and the emotional, and a pain pattern is created. That's why it's so important to understand the fallacies behind many common diagnoses and how subjective they can be — always ask yourself if the diagnosis makes *sense*.

More than one of these inputs can be at work at any given time, working in concert to solidify the belief that there is something terribly wrong with you... or there *should* be.

Our brains are heavily influenced by what we see and how we feel about what we see. When I work out at home by myself, I quit long before my muscles have truly reached failure. When I work out at the gym as part of a fitness class, I push myself harder. Seeing others successfully completing difficult moves, hearing the trainer say, "You can do it, just two more," and feeling a bit of social pressure makes me want to finish strong. But if I see one person quit, or if the trainer pauses to adjust her microphone, all at once I feel I cannot go on one minute longer. Perseverance is contagious, as is quitting.

The location of your pain is also significant for symbolic reasons. Consider:

1. Feeling like you just can't say anything right may lead to jaw pain.
2. Having the weight of the world on your shoulders can lead to pain, guess where?
3. Someone being a pain in your neck can bring on an actual pain in your neck!
4. Wanting to punch someone may lead to arthritis in the hands, as in a clenched fist.
5. Impossibly high standards can lead to food sensitivities as you "just won't tolerate that."
6. Obsessive thinking can lead to headaches.

Many aches and illnesses have traditionally been linked with their emotional cause; it is only in recent decades that we have abandoned these colorful descriptions in favor of ones that separate mind and body and allow for more concrete methods of treatment. One psychiatry professor, formerly a dermatologist, recently described eczema as a "weeping through the skin,"[7] suggesting that there is now a turn of the tide to the former understanding of illness.

The mind has a sense of humor — my husband disagreed with a business partner and wanted to tell him off — he meanwhile developed an arthritis-like pain in his middle finger!

I don't think there's any greater scientific evidence of the MindBody connection and the power of thoughts than the research done on people with multiple personalities. Did you know that if a person has multiple personalities, each personality may have a unique and sometimes opposite health profile? For example, one may be deathly allergic to peanuts while the other one isn't, one may even have diabetes, their vision may be different, there may even be scars on one personality's skin that *aren't there* on the other personality. [8]

Your personality may have much more to do with your illness than you realize! This is good news, as it is far easier to change one's thoughts than to will one's body to heal. Personality deficits may create a requirement for disease that can be eliminated once positive change occurs. [9]

The Placebo Effect

We find perhaps the best proof for the MindBody aspect of pain in the placebo effect. Countless studies have revealed that the placebo effect truly is a real phenomenon, and medical studies have to account for it, as it can influence the results.

If we believe strongly enough that something will make our symptoms disappear, even if there is no real basis for that belief, can we respond physically as if it is true? Can we make something true if we believe it with enough conviction?

Beliefs not only lead to emotional feelings, they can also have a direct impact on physical experiences. The placebo effect plays such a huge role that researchers are often at a loss as to which is more powerful, the medication or the belief itself!

In a study published in 1969, a woman who had an allergy to pollen was given an inhaler and told that it contained pollen. Her airways constricted and she immediately showed symptoms of hay fever. [1] It was then revealed that the inhaler contained no pollen at all. The woman's belief alone was enough to cause an intense reaction to a harmless mist. A similar study was done on forty asthma patients during the same decade. When told the inhaler they were given contained an allergen, despite the fact it contained only water, 48% of them developed adverse reactions to using it. They were given a second inhaler, also containing water, and were told it contained the remedy. They all experienced immediate relief of their symptoms. [2] Nothing had changed about the inhalers themselves, only their beliefs about what the inhalers contained.

There was a study performed in 1962 in Japan involving participants who were all very allergic to poison ivy. One of their arms were rubbed with poison ivy, but they were told it was a harmless leaf. Eleven out of the thirteen developed no rash at all. Their other arm was rubbed with a harmless leaf, but they were told it was poison ivy. They all developed a rash on that arm. Belief matters more than biology. [3]

The placebo effect is so powerful, it can trigger the identical chemicals and produce the same brain waves as if the body were receiving the real treatment. [4] If legitimate medications are traded in for a placebo unbeknownst to the patient, that patient's brain will continue to produce the same chemicals as if they were still receiving the medication. [5]

What we expect, we receive. The brain is incredibly powerful in that it can create the appropriate chemicals and reactions to bring about the changes it expects to take place. [6]

Just as the original disease was not only in the patients' heads, the cure wasn't either. The placebo effect's power isn't in just *imagining* you are better; you *are* better. Healing always includes physical changes. [7] Actual cells and body processes need to have changed course, which is precisely what we see in these placebo cases.

There have even been documented cases of placebo surgeries that rendered patients completely pain-free. As long as the patients could see the scar, even though nothing was actually done to the afflicted area, they experienced longer lasting results than those undergoing actual surgical procedures, [8] with none of the side effects that surgery can cause.

For a placebo to work, it has to be completely believed and accepted as effective. Even if you know that it is a placebo, you can still experience the same positive results as long as you believe it will work. For most of us in America, placebos come in the form of pills or surgeries or medical devices. The same placebos would not work at all in remote parts of the world, where superstition plays a huge role. Pills would be useless to someone who values herbs or rituals; they would be more influenced by wearing a certain medallion, plucking a flower by moonlight, or repeating a specific mantra. [9]

The cure has to be something equal to the belief system already in place in the patient. If a patient has been the victim of a curse, offering him a pill will have no effect. A doctor would have to be creative in their proposed treatment, as was a fast thinking physician who gave his patient, a victim of voodoo, an emetic so he would vomit. The doctor then secretly slipped a lizard into the ensuing stomach contents, claiming the lizard had been the cause of his symptoms all along. The man was instantly cured. [10] Even in the US, medical treatments will not be sufficient if the patient's belief about his illness does not coincide with the pathology of the disease. [11] If I don't believe that the diagnosis is correct, or if I believe that something else entirely will cure me, then no matter what treatment you give me, it will have no effect. Our beliefs can *override* our biology.

Children especially abide by the placebo effect — who remembers, "Mommy kiss it and make it all better?" Just knowing that Mommy had acknowledged the pain was enough for them to go back to playing!

If the patient becomes aware that the treatment is a placebo, their skepticism may reverse their positive results. However, even if the patient knows that the treatment is a placebo, there can still be healing if the patient is a true believer in the placebo effect itself.

Probably the most compelling example of the placebo effect took place in 1950 between Dr. Bruno Klopfer and a patient of his who had been diagnosed with lymphosarcoma. The patient had huge tumors, required an oxygen mask to breathe, and begged Dr. Klopfer to prescribe for him an experimental drug called Krebiozen, which Dr. Klopfer had been researching and testing at the time. Dr. Klopfer agreed. Within a short amount of time, the patient saw his tumors shrink and was able to go about his normal activities. However, soon reports surfaced by the AMA and the FDA claiming that Krebiozen produced only negative results. The patient's health began to decline again. Dr. Klopfer tried a new approach – he claimed that he had access to a new and improved Krebiozen that would be more effective. In actuality, he was giving his patient injections of sterile water, but yet again the patient recovered. The tumors vanished and the patient remained tumor-free for over eight weeks. Unfortunately, more reports then surfaced in the press that Krebiozen was worthless. A few days later, the patient died. [12]

Be careful what you believe! Of course, we can't make *everything* true just by willpower and belief; we will only physically *react* as if it were true — which can make all the difference between life and death when it comes to illness and disease.

Visualizations

If placebos are so effective in treating illness and disease, does this not mean that our bodies hold within themselves the actual power to heal? If we can trigger these healing powers solely through our beliefs, the implications are there that we may be able to prevent and/or reverse illness and pain altogether. How can we utilize these internal resources and apply them to more areas of our lives?

As we see in the case of the placebo effect, the human body is capable of creating its own chemicals that may, in fact, be superior to man-made medications. We could potentially eliminate the need for prescriptions altogether, if we could only find the way to tap into our own internal pharmacies. [1]

What this could mean for you is that if you change your beliefs about your medical condition, you can actually change your physical state. A word that is often seen as taboo in Christian circles is "visualization." Now, I don't ascribe to "name it and claim it" theology, and while I love science fiction, I don't think we will bend objects with our minds any time soon. But if God makes such a big deal of our thoughts, maybe they have more power than we can fully imagine.

Consider this: you're in a plane when the flight attendant's panicked voice comes over the loudspeaker informing everyone that one of the engines has failed. Emergency procedures begin and oxygen masks drop from the ceiling. Passengers panic, feeling the plane descend, all the while their hearts racing and their breathing becoming rapid. One passenger looks out the window and sees — what? The plane is still safely parked on the tarmac! It was just a drill! All those sensations and stress responses were the body listening to the flight attendant and accepting orders from her without question. The body does just that — it listens to the mind, regardless of the facts.

How many times has your heart almost stopped because you think you left your phone somewhere, only to find it in your hand? The body doesn't stop to consider the truth; it trusts your mind completely, because in most cases there isn't time to do otherwise.

To the brain, both the real and the imaginary are the same. If we visualize wellness and recovery, the brain believes we *are* recovering and sets off a chain of events in our genes to bring about that recovery. In this way, we "become what we're imagining." [2]

The body takes its cues from the mind, so again, *what are you thinking?*

Your body "aligns with your thoughts" [3] — your body is your mind in physical form, and understanding that connection can go a long way in uncovering the origin of your pain. Here are a few ways your thoughts influence your body:

1. **Negative thoughts slow down healing.**

   Negativity prevents the necessary proteins from being produced in adequate amounts for healing to take place. [4] Having a pessimistic attitude about your illness can cause it to last longer and with more pronounced symptoms.

2. **Negative thoughts can bring about disease and illness.**

   In one landmark study in 1957, it was found that depressed military recruits had more severe bouts of influenza that those who were not. The research concluded that mood plays a larger role in health than previously understood: if you want to get sick, you will, and if you don't want to get sick, you won't. [5] Illness can be seen as an escape from those negative feelings, a physical manifestation of what you are going through emotionally.

3. **Negative thoughts can increase your chances of death by disease.**

   Just being a hostile person can increase your chances of coronary heart disease up to 500%! [6] Having a family history of disease can compel you to evaluate your diet, drinking and smoking habits, and physical fitness; however, more importantly, you need to address your attitude, your emotions, and your treatment of others, as those factors are more critical in determining if a disease develops. [7]

4. **On the contrary, positive thoughts can switch genes on or off** [8] **and can produce physical changes in your body structure.**

By repeating a movement, we increase our ability to perform that movement by strengthening the connection between the brain and the muscles involved. The same process occurs even if we only *think* about a movement. [9] There are cases of athletes improving their skills drastically by visualizing success on the court or the field. People have imagined their tumors shrinking, their bones healing, their pain vanishing — and their visualizations have come true. The power lies in how emotionally you are connected to the belief that the healing will take place. Just saying the words skeptically while rolling your eyes will accomplish nothing. Emotions trigger the autonomic nervous system, which in turn, triggers the right chemicals to be produced in order for healing to be realized. [10]

I jokingly told my mother that she should visualize herself losing five pounds during her afternoon walk. I told her to say, "This walk will burn enough calories for me to lose five pounds." She called me the next morning, gleefully exclaiming that she had, indeed, lost exactly five pounds.

I tried it out myself on one of my formerly frequent headaches. I visualized opening up a capsule of pain-reliever (the blue liquid gel kind) and rubbing it all over my head from the inside. I imagined the blue liquid coating my head and cooling down my headache. Then I visualized a red decongestant pill dancing over my sinuses and opening them up, allowing fresh oxygen to flood my brain. I had never experienced such instantaneous relief. I believe that by using a known pain "cure," my mind triggered the same pain-relieving chemicals as it always had every time I had taken those specific medications in the past. Since my mind linked these pills with pain relief, my body was already conditioned to respond in kind.

The practice of visualization has been dubbed "self-directed neuroplasticity (SDN)." We can create new pathways in the mind, and destroy harmful ones, solely through cultivating new experiences. [11]

In visualization, we are creating the impetus for biological change by using our minds, bypassing the need for environmental triggers. Since the brain doesn't know the difference, we are skipping the middleman, so to speak, and going right to the CEO... and getting results.

Drugs have been so effective at curing diseases that we have become complacent to the point that we have overlooked the vast potential that exists in the human mind. [12]

Is this just hocus-pocus? Well, it depends on what you do with this information. When you are sick, imagining your white blood cells with dart guns attacking the virus victoriously can help you heal faster! But we should be careful not to elevate our own minds above that of God. We are created for the express purpose of giving Him the glory, not ourselves. Our minds are a gift from Him, and they are wonderfully made (Psalm 139:14). His design is that we put Him first in our minds and hearts, and look to Him first to grant our earthly needs (Matthew 6:33).

Children and the MindBody Syndrome

While many researchers have acknowledged the emotional aspect of pain and illness, many still seem reticent to include children's ailments in their discussions. Issues like ADD, ADHD, autism, "growing pains," and teenage depression are seemingly off-limits when discussing psychosomatic disorders. Why is that? Are children incapable of being driven to physical and psychological distress by emotion?

With the current emphasis on early diagnosis of diseases such as cancer and Alzheimer's, why wouldn't we want to identify psychosomatic markers earlier, even in our children? My best guess is that we are still operating under the belief that humans are born without sin. Our culture promotes the idea that children simply need to be understood, nurtured, encouraged, and taught; good parenting will yield good children. However, we have seen countless times how that is not that case.

When my oldest was a toddler, she discovered a new favorite game: hitting. She especially loved hitting her baby brother. I tried calmly explaining that hitting is wrong, but she would just stare at me blankly. I tried taking a favorite toy away, but she would just move on to something else without a care. I tried putting her in time-out, setting the timer for two minutes. She would sit there quietly, and when the timer would beep, she would stand up, go over to her brother, hit him, reset the timer and sit back down in the time-out chair. We even tried spanking for a time, to which she would respond, "Didn't hurt!" Nothing we did made her bend her will. Her heart was sinful, and it didn't matter what we tried; she was determined to have her way.

Even from birth, children are sinners — there is nothing more selfish than a baby waking you up in the middle of the night. Their first words may be "mama" but soon afterwards, the word "NO!" becomes their favorite. Why do we persist in excusing evil in our children under the false conception that they are born innocent? We could further analyze our motivations by supposing that perhaps we want an excuse for our own behavior — we must have been born perfect, it was just our parents' fault that we turned out the way we did, and there is no way we could or should be held responsible.

Even children, and I should say *especially* children, suffer from MindBody illnesses and pain. Have you ever wondered why young ones get sick on Monday mornings and need to stay home from school? Or why the baby gets a fever on date night? Born sinful and selfish, babies and children want what they want and they want it now. And most often, what they really want is attention. I'm all about loving on my kids and making sure they know I am here for them, that they're special to me, that I adore them; but my kids have each gone through a phase where that level of attention was not enough. They wanted *all* of me. All the time. So, they acted out in ways that were not safe, not kind, not acceptable. After a zillion time-outs and early bedtimes, they figured out that those methods would not work. What did they do next? They would get "boo-boos" and their tummies would hurt. *Mommy will snuggle with me if I am hurt*, they thought. They were right! What mommy can refuse a weeping toddler? Over time, their whole thought process was bypassed, and a psychosomatic disorder was born. My youngest started getting frequent headaches, which allowed her access to my lap whenever she desired. Trips to the doctor were unhelpful, as there was nothing wrong with her physically.

In his book *You Are the Placebo*, Dr. Joe Dispenza tells of a young woman named Laurie who was diagnosed with a rare degenerative disease ("polyostotic fibrous dysplasia") which caused her bones to be gradually replaced with a fibrous tissue that was very prone to fracture. She went from being a successful body builder to walking with a cane, for any misstep could end in a broken bone that may never heal. Her father had been violent and abusive; when he found out about her diagnosis, he left her alone, as she was too fragile for his fists. Dr. Dispenza explains how brainwaves in small children are extremely suggestible, and all of their experiences go directly into their subconscious, as they are not yet able to process them intellectually. [1] Her biology was programmed to protect her from her father's abuse! Years later, she was able to change her thoughts and attitudes toward her father and the abuse she endured at his hands; her disease reversed itself, allowing her to continue her body building pursuits and live a normal life. She no longer needed the disease to fight her battles for her.

Children aren't yet equipped to verbalize how they feel about abuse, social pressures, family conflict, and sibling rivalries. They don't have words to express their emotions and are often told to be quiet and not fuss. Not that I'm advocating letting children throw temper tantrums at will — but children need to understand that their feelings are valid. Children absorb the feelings in the household, yet they don't fully grasp the meaning behind those feelings. In homes where there is parental discord, sibling rivalry, financial pressures, emphasis on success and achievement, or strong undercurrents of anger or fear, kids pay the price — sometimes with their very lives. Children subconsciously suppress any information that would create an unsolvable situation – if they can't handle it, they bury it, leaving them vulnerable to chronic pain. [2]

I recall one morning as a child of maybe 8 or 9, waking up a few hours before my alarm for school, and panicking because I was terrified about facing another school day. I started wondering if maybe I could make myself ill. Not twenty minutes later, I had developed a fever and a horrible stomachache and had to stay home the rest of the day. I remember being unsettled because I had brought it on myself, despite the obvious benefit I had received.

Many childhood illnesses and even "growing pains" have been attributed to emotional stress in the home. I'm not saying this to make parents feel guilty. We parents are also struggling to make sense of our own feelings, so how can we expect our children not to struggle? We can't always insulate our children from heartache. But we can be more willing to talk about feelings. My kids have their share of aches and pains, and I've found it immensely helpful to open a dialog with them whenever they tell me something hurts. First, I ask if they injured themselves. Most of the time, they say no. Then I go down the usual list of suspects (are you hungry, thirsty, tired, etc.). After I've eliminated the obvious causes of acute pain, I move on to the emotional. I ask them how they're feeling, what they're worried about, if they're angry about something. That's when they open up and confess fears and anxieties they never would have talked about otherwise. It's been so freeing to our family to understand pain multidimensionally rather than just toss them a pain reliever or an ice pack. Their pain often dissipates soon after we have our heart to heart.

Children's biological states are largely dependent on those of their parents as they are unable to self-regulate while in infancy. [3] Babies mirror our sinful emotions in their biology until they are able to experience their own. What this means is that infants sin even before they know what sin *is*. That's why it is so important for us as parents to lead our children to the truth even from a very early age. We may have inherited a sin nature, but we will still be held accountable for our actions, as Jesus has provided us a way to bypass and replace that old nature with one that chooses Christ:

> "In him you were also circumcised with a circumcision not performed by human hands. Your whole self ruled by the flesh was put off when you were circumcised by Christ..." (Colossians 2:11 NIV)

We can direct our children to this new nature — it is a gift we parents give our children to have healthy relationships with our spouses, with our extended family, and with our church as far as it depends on us. When crises emerge, how we respond teaches our children how they should respond, as they are mirroring our emotions in their very biology, even from birth — our influence is *that* powerful.

I've worked with middle and high schoolers, and many of them claim to be "depressed," saying their parents are hard on them, which leaves them feeling hopeless. While this may be true in some cases, many times these kids are simply unwilling to admit that their parents aren't giving them what they want. The emotions beneath their depression are plain old rebellion and selfishness. I was a kid once, too! I know how exasperating it was to have my parents tell me "no" and how useless a tantrum would have been. But mention "depression," and parents become accommodating and empathetic.

A better way is to validate their emotions while instructing them in the truth. My teenage son was constantly getting into trouble for using his phone during Bible study. We had tried taking away his phone for weeks at a time, making him leave it at home, using apps to regulate "off times," and anything else I felt would help him control his behavior. Even without the phone, he would still find some way to be distracting. We noticed him becoming more withdrawn and sullener. Oh, it was so tempting to read articles on ADHD! I wanted to find something else to blame other than my son! No parent wants to see sin in their child; it feels like we have failed somehow to see them making bad choices. But I knew deep down there was a sin issue afoot. After a bout of taking his phone away again, my husband and I talked with him about what the real issue appeared to be: he wanted approval from the other kids in the class. After this realization, he brightened a bit and confessed he felt inadequate around the other kids and wanted some way of getting attention from them. We talked about the fear of man and how to put God first, and asked him how we could help him accomplish freedom from this temptation. Kids are good at hiding, too! When we simply punish behavior, we are missing the broader purpose of reaching their hearts.

Children need to feel safe. They are vulnerable and powerless, and fear is a huge part of childhood. I had many fears growing up, and not surprisingly was sick a great deal. Fear produces over a thousand chemical reactions, setting off a cascade of hormones and neurotransmitters that can have massive impacts at the cellular level. [4]

Teens, who are going through a host of hormonal changes as it is, are also dealing with fear: fear of losing parental approval, fear of being left out or being mocked or bullied, fear of failure in school and work endeavors. All these hormonal stressors leave teens acting out emotionally and susceptible to all kinds of physical ailments. We parents can be sensitive to their emotions first, making them feel safe and loved and thus preventing much of the negative effects of fear. Fear is actually imprinted on our genes, [5] so by nipping it in the bud now, we can benefit future generations!

If your children are too young to do this themselves, you can make a timeline for them of their illnesses and injuries and see what other events were going on in their lives surrounding each incident. One of the greatest gifts we can give our kids is teaching them how to better understand themselves and to apply truth to their times of uncertainty and fear. We need to point our children to their sin, and then to the Cross. One without the other is meaningless.

Addressing the emotional causes of pain instead of only the physical ones can free us from bondage to a very real danger: a diagnosis.

CHAPTER FOUR:
THE DANGER OF A DIAGNOSIS

When you're in pain, where do you go? To the doctor, of course. Not that there's anything wrong with wanting to rule out the possibility of a serious disease or injury, but we are so conditioned to run to the doctor at the first sign of pain that we skip right over the possible emotional causes. And that would be just fine if most doctors embraced the connection of mind and body. All too often, however, they do not.

It doesn't help that malpractice lawsuits are so abundant. For a MindBody diagnosis to be effective, the patient has to embrace the concept fully. If a pain sufferer does not accept the psychosomatic diagnoses, their pain will only increase, and they will end up accusing the doctor of faulty medicine. The doctor is in between a rock and a hard place much of the time, even if he/she accepts the premise of MindBody medicine.

As a nutrition consultant, I have often told my clients "food is rarely about food," that their emotions play a huge role in their weight loss. Most of the time, however, I would hear, "But what should I be eating?" as if they didn't even hear what I had said.

It is far easier to accept the medical claim that our afflictions are because of our physical environment and that we are not to blame. But if we aren't to blame, if we aren't in control, doesn't that leave us *more* powerless? Certainly, it would leave us angry and bitter, as it would appear we just drew the short stick in life through no fault of our own.

At the heart of the debate lies the one true question that science cannot answer: "Why do pain and illness exist?" Why *do* our loved ones suffer and die? Science has no acceptable explanation for why some die young and others live into their 90s, for why some people never seem to have any pain at all and others suffer their entire lives. We have been looking to the wrong entity for answers, when what we really desire is "validation for feelings that feel far too overwhelming to be understood." [1]

Medicine alone cannot help us answer the questions our hearts are asking; and in many situations can lead us down a dangerous path of increased despair and isolation.

The traditional approach to pain management seems so much easier to apply; it's far more socially acceptable, it's paid for by health insurance, and it doesn't involve any real vulnerability on my part. It appears to work for some people, couldn't it work for me eventually, too? What harm could it do?

Unfortunately, the medical approach misses the big picture. Since pain itself originates from the mind, why is the mind so often left out of the equation in making a diagnosis? Is the mind merely a computer, spitting out processes based on set inputs? Or is the mind a part of who we are as individuals, full of personality and emotion and creativity?

Solely pursuing a medical solution to your pain or illness will not be as effective, if even at all, without taking the MindBody aspect into consideration. If your doctor is not willing to consider the MindBody approach, then you could be subject to a very dangerous path of chronic pain, with each of these phenomena building on each other:

1. The Nocebo Effect

You've heard of the word "placebo," meaning "to please." You may not have heard of the term "nocebo," meaning "to harm." A nocebo results when you are told:

- "This is going to hurt."
- "Your break will take a long time to heal, and may continue to hurt for a while afterwards."
- "You will have to make a lot of life changes to avoid future injury."
- "You have the spine of an 80-year old woman."

- "There is simply no cure for your pain, only pain management."
- "You only have a few months to live."
- "You're going to have a difficult time running/losing weight/sleeping, etc."

Your doctor has just prescribed pain, and your mind is off to the pharmacy to fill it.

The entire medical experience is designed to perpetuate the relationship between doctor and patient. Most doctor's offices have posters of common diseases hanging on the walls, models of the back or the heart or whatever part of the body they specialize in, pamphlets for new prescription drugs complete with pictures of happy patients on the front covers, jars of sterile supplies, a biohazard trash can, and an odor of disinfectant in the air. You are usually sitting on a table with a fresh roll of paper underneath you, maybe wearing a skimpy hospital gown. The doctor walks in wearing a white coat, with a stethoscope around his or her neck. All these visuals further the belief that there is something wrong with you.

If you glance around your doctor's office and see posters of damaged spines and brochures for back surgery, your brain will make the connection between your pain and those images. Instead of just a worrisome pang, you now can imagine your very spine crumbling or the nerves being pinched, just as you see in the models on the doctor's desk. The more information you give your mind, the more specific your pain will become.

It is in our nature to worry. The more detail we have about what possibly is going on in our body, the greater our worry becomes, especially in things we cannot see ourselves. Things under the skin, in our bloodstream, buried in our tissues — these become the boogeymen under the bed, and our doctors become our dad with a flashlight telling us *there might actually be a monster after all.*

Can a simple diagnosis hurt you? Absolutely, if the physical symptoms have an emotional cause, which is more common than not.

For example, if a doctor were to diagnose you with a psychosomatic disorder, there is only a 4% chance that a physical, organic disease will be eventually discovered. This 4% chance is the same as the misdiagnosis rate that would occur in the absence of definitive diagnostic testing. Psychosomatic illnesses are usually mislabeled as organic ones initially; however, this mistake can have massive negative, even permanent consequences that most doctors fail to take into consideration. [2, 3]

The nocebo effect is incredibly strong and can be very hard to combat, even once you know the truth. Therefore, it would be less harmful for a doctor to tell you that your pain is emotionally-caused than for him to diagnose a disorder; the dangers of a false diagnosis is *that much greater* than *no diagnosis at all.*

Just because a doctor has come to a conclusion about the cause of your pain, know that he or she also is guided by opinion. Just as a creationist and an evolutionist can look at the same fossil and yet derive different conclusions as to its origin, multiple doctors can look at your back or your knees and have differing diagnoses.

There is a vast reservoir of knowledge from which the medical profession is required to draw from in making their diagnoses. Not only do doctors weigh evidence and data, they are also influenced by their own experiences and opinions. There is not one set formula for drawing medical conclusions; the same doctor can come to a different conclusion at a different point in time depending on a variety of factors that change constantly. [4]

Doctors are not infallible! False diagnoses can have catastrophic results, as was seen in the case of Sam Londe, a man in the early 1970s who was diagnosed with advanced liver cancer. He was told he would not survive, and he indeed did not. Upon his death, an autopsy was performed and it was discovered that he had only a small nodule of cancer in his liver, certainly not enough to have killed him. There was no medical explanation for his death, other than his expectation that he was dying. The belief that he was dying, shared by all those around him, became contagious to the point that he actually *died.* [5]

The words your doctor uses to describe your condition can be a death sentence or a healing balm. Look for a second opinion from a medical professional who makes you feel encouraged and taken care of, who gives you hope! If you walk out of the doctor's office feeling broken and full of despair, you are less likely to experience healing.

Interesting to note is that many "diagnoses" are actually a simple restating of the symptoms: "idiopathic rhinitis," for example, means "your nose runs for no reason." "Spastic colon" means "you have digestive issues we can't explain." If you fully understand the terms used in your diagnosis, you may discover that it was hardly a diagnosis at all, but rather a code word for "I have no clue what's wrong with you!"

Also, in the United States, we tend to revere science, so the more scientific-sounding our diseases are, the more likely we are to embrace the diagnosis. After all, it's more impactful to say you suffer from "myalgic encephalomyelitis" than to say you have "chronic fatigue." With the more medical sounding title, however, more symptoms tend to present themselves[6] as the belief more firmly implants itself in the body. If the description of your diagnosis is complex and hard to understand, your imagination will take over and liberally add to your symptoms. Any new discomfort is assumed to be part of the syndrome or disease, and the symptom list grows longer.

2. Expectation of Pain

Once you have received your nocebo prescription, the next step in the chronic pain cycle is to begin to associate pain with certain triggers. If you felt pain while sitting in a rigid chair, you will assume that every time you sit in such a chair, you will feel pain. If pain occurred once during the night, you will probably find yourself waking at the same time every night anticipating, and experiencing, pain. This works on the flip side, also -- if you anticipate relief from an ice pack or a certain position, relief will come. The key is to understand that the triggers themselves have nothing to do with the reason for the pain. The triggers are merely the pain digging its way deeper into your emotional center, allowing its roots to become entangled with experiences and memories until few things you do will *not* cause pain in some way. In this way, your life becomes smaller and smaller and the pain grows larger and larger.

If you find yourself needing certain "props" to prevent or minimize pain (pillows, custom shoes, ice packs, massagers, mattresses, chairs, and the like), then you are actually conditioning your body to feel pain when those props are unavailable. It never ends with just one pillow, does it? And the pain continues to grow and require more and more of you until travel is out of the question, and it becomes easier to just stay home in bed. The firmness of the mattress is of no consequence, "only the firmness of the belief." [7]

The expectation of pain makes the pain worse over time as well. You expect to be in pain because, well, you feel you always are. [8] Pain becomes a learned response, requiring less and less stimulus to trigger it due to the number of neurotransmitters that cause pain increasing with every pain event.[9] Cancer patients who do not expect to feel nauseated during or after chemotherapy treatments simply do not! Unfortunately, most are told that nausea is a certainty, and therefore it becomes so. [10]

Pain also leads to other pain. Your mind sees the success it has had with the pain previously, so it continues to expand its repertoire to other parts of your body. People with chronic pain rarely have just one affected body part.

The elderly population has indeed fallen victim to this expectation of pain. With all the ads on TV and online that address "senior medical issues" such as arthritis, joint stiffness, dementia, weakness, falling, and poor memory, it's no wonder that people start experiencing those effects upon receiving their first AARP mailing! Simply seeing older people suffering can increase your likelihood of these ailments, as your brain actively imagines you going through them yourself.

When I was pregnant with my first child, I was so happy and excited, and I wanted to just radiate sunbeams and rainbows. However, wherever I went, I heard moms warn me of everything that could go wrong and how I will never sleep again, how awful toddlers are, and to "just wait until they're teenagers." I could literally feel my spirits sink to my toes. I went from joy to despair in moments, and my physical body experienced the changes. I put on weight, slept less, and became depressed and fearful about motherhood. That which I expected came about.

When we cease to analyze our emotional state, simply accepting our medical destiny with absolute surrender, we render ourselves unable to heal. A diagnosis becomes a curse, keeping us locked in a cycle of disease, mindlessly accepting our fate without question. [11]

Changing your expectations and choosing to think for yourself, seeing yourself as the expert of your*self* and not accepting someone else's interpretation of your experience puts you back in the driver's seat of your health.

3. Illness Identity

Next, it is human nature to want to find connections with others who have similar life experiences to ours. Out of this desire we form support groups for our specific malady. We form friendships with others who suffer as we do, who understand what we are going through and will not judge us. Doing so is not inherently wrong; however, it can cause something called "illness identity." If all our friends have migraines, and we are joining groups for migraine sufferers, we are so closely merging our identity with our illness that we may no longer know where one begins and the other ends. I've heard stories of people sharing progress stories with their illness group, only to be told to "enjoy it while it lasts, the disease will come back" — and indeed it did. I've also heard of people being shamed for having good days, being called insensitive when discussing possible cures, and feeling like they needed to be in pain in order to be accepted. Add to that the fear that if they ever do become cured, they may lose all their friends!

If you are calling your illness "my arthritis" or "my fibro," spending time with others who suffer as you do, or participating in illness-related activities, you have an illness identity. [12] Where you find your identity **matters**; it can determine your reactions to life events, your responses to people around you, and it can set you up for a lifetime of pain and illness. I even found an ad for a Bible designed for cancer patients — as if even the Word of God has to be geared to one's identity as a cancer sufferer!

Once pain has consumed your life, there seems to be very little that remains of your life before pain. An illness identity can lead to distortional thinking — patients have been known to insist that they are still sick even when their symptoms have improved. [13] A phenomenon called an "infirm career" develops where a patient so deeply "owns" their disease that no proof of healing is enough to convince them that they are recovered. [14] An illness identity can lead some to talk about their illnesses and pain with as much fervor and intensity as they would a job promotion or a trip to Europe. [15]

5. Secondary Gain

At this point, a genuine fear starts to emerge that has two distinct sides — fear of never getting better and yet fear of what healing would look like:

- Although a large part of you may be longing for the day when you can go skiing again or wake up without a migraine, there is also an element of relief that you don't have to help a friend move or host Thanksgiving or lead a small group due to your pain.
- People show genuine concern for you because your suffering is visible and obvious; without the pain, you may worry that their concern would disappear altogether.
- Others usually don't expect much from you when you are in pain, and accommodate your needs by providing a special chair or pillow or by bringing your meals to you.
- You are free to complain or voice frustration, with the excuse that you are in pain.
- Illness can give you a pastime, make you feel cared for, help you hold onto a relationship or avoid it, arise out of self-hate or shame, and give you a way out. [16]
- You may be receiving compensation for your pain that you would

have to give up, which would require going back to work. If you haven't worked in quite a while, feelings of inadequacy may be present, leading to fear and anxiety, leading back to pain.

All of us want to be treated with compassion, but not all of us know how to ask for it -- or that we even deserve it.

If a patient is facing a crossroads or a conflict that seems unresolvable, and subconsciously desires a resolution that may not be considered feasible or acceptable, illness can provide that resolution, as well as a plausible explanation for it. [17] For anything from reconciliation with an estranged loved one to retirement from a long-disliked profession, illness can be a means to an unexpressed, yet desired end.

Lest you conclude that these phenomena only occur to very emotionally weak and unstable individuals, it is actually quite the opposite. It takes a strong intellect to be able to concoct a fitting pain manifestation. Neuroses are more often chosen by highly intelligent individuals with high moral character, thus showing that only the very strong, self-confident and sane are capable of developing a conversion disorder, as well as requiring it in the first place. [18] Your neurosis is testament to your sanity, not your lack of it.

Secondary gain can also precede the pain, bringing it into being. For example, you are asked to sing on the worship team. You love singing, but really don't want to *add another commitment*. So, you make some excuse, saying that you have a cold ("cough-cough") and maybe when you're all better you will consider it. Weeks later, the music director approaches you again, asking if you are ready to join the team. You begin to cough, not as a ruse, but for real! From that point on, you begin to cough every time you enter the church building, then every time you think about church or spend time with church members…and so on. A symptom you invented to "gain" an excuse became real, and will remain in place until the original emotion is dealt with.

This secondary gain is a trap, however. If it has become the only way to experience the love and attention you need, then you will have "a stake in staying sick." [19] When you are ill, others allow you certain graces – you are freer to cry or to complain or to express emotion in general. If you are unable to grant yourself permission to participate in those same activities while healthy, you will find yourself needing illness more frequently. [20]

Chronic pain is a work of genius by the subconscious. MindBody pain has been around since the Fall, and it's been an effective tool for many to cope with emotional pain, repressed memories, anger, fear, and other unbearable situations. One of our basic human responses to psychological problems has always been to convert them into physical form in order to provide an outlet and a coping mechanism. [21]

The strategy is to provide a solution while saving face and preventing detection of the underlying cause.

The more legitimate your symptoms, the less likely you will be held responsible for them. If an organic disease can be blamed, *you* cannot be. The subconscious is highly motivated to only produce symptoms that are legitimate and will leave you above reproach.[22]

If the sufferer could be blamed in some way, it would defeat the purpose of the disorder in the first place. Even compulsive behaviors and addictions are generally blamed on biology, rather than seen as a result of poor choices. Thus, the intellect behind this amazing facade must be sophisticated indeed, as emotions and circumstances change and become more complex over time. This need to save face and avoid personal blame for their condition has led people to become incredibly defensive of their pain and disease. They long for proof and justification for their pain, and anyone who suggests an emotional component is accused of insensitivity and being un-Christian. The anger stems from a deep need for the pain, even as they simultaneously despise it.

Emotional expression is discouraged in a performance-based society. If people are not free to express sadness or anger in open, healthy ways, illness provides an alternative outlet. [23.] If the only thing that is holding you back from performing a certain function or participating in an activity you claim to enjoy is an illness or chronic pain of some kind, then there may be an emotional reason behind your abstaining from those activities. Are you afraid of failure? Success? Are you trying to save face in some way, and needing an illness to accomplish that goal?

- A former football star is sidelined by a torn ACL the week before the big game.
- A ministry leader has to step down from her duties due to chronic migraines.
- A high school student comes down with the flu the morning of the AP Calculus Exam (this was me!).

These are common occurrences, as we are so afraid of revealing our true emotions, thus needing a more believable and external reason to avoid something we fear. The timing of every injury can become suspect when you consider how clever the mind is, and how desperate it can become in its attempts to save face.

Is there harm in the traditional approach? There certainly can be. I have a wonderful relationship with my doctor, and receive annual checkups, so I'm definitely not advocating avoiding the entire medical establishment! However, it should never be the end of the story. Searching for a strictly physical cause for your pain is not without long-lasting effects, and can lead you down multiple rabbit trails as your symptoms change over time…and they will.

The Catalogue of Psychosomatic Disorders – New and Improved!

As time goes on, the list of psychosomatic disorders grows and evolves. There are two main reasons for this: culture shift and improvements in technology.

First, changes in culture affect which disorders become the norm. When computers came on the scene, so did a rise in carpal tunnel syndrome, something almost unheard of in the time of typewriters or even quills! Cultures that are poverty-stricken do not have compulsive hoarding disorder or anorexia nervosa; affluence and prosperity bring with them their own unique conditions.

Doctor and patient also each play a role in which disorders become mainstream. There is a sort of dance between doctor and patient – if one changes their opinion about whether or not a disease is organic or not, the other will also change theirs. The entire history of psychosomatic medicine has been laden with this gradual evolution of symptoms due to this mutual influence. [1] Doctors are just as susceptible to societal pressure as are their patients.

When I was a teenager, I complained of feeling bloated and lethargic. I was diagnosed with an abundance of *candida albacans*, and told to eat a completely yeast-free diet. Back then, the only food item I could find on my acceptable foods list was rice cakes (which today wouldn't even end up on that list most likely). I honestly tried to comply for the first week, but got so agitated emotionally that I gave up. Interestingly, my bloating and lethargy vanished. If the cure is painful and difficult to maintain, often the body will opt for a different disorder altogether. These days, there are so many grain-free and yeast-free options, I may never have broken free from believing there was a physical cause for my discomfort.

68

As the mind adapts and forms new disorders, the medical community responds, as do the food and pharmaceutical industries. The more allergy-free options available, the more common food allergies become. And so on and so on, in a never-ending cycle. Supply and demand.

The second reason for the evolving list of psychosomatic disorders is the latest research and improvements in technology that are continually being made. As we are able to see more and more detail of the human body, it makes sense that we now have more opportunities for more specific and targeted pain. Instead of a vague hysteria or fatigue, we can now pinpoint the exact vertebrae or gene or cell cluster that is causing our agony. As the brain is given more information, the pain is given more freedom to thrive. All the more reason why receiving a diagnosis, along with a list of common symptoms, simply gives more territory to the enemy — it's not unusual for patients to take on new symptoms immediately following a diagnosis being made.

What may begin as a soreness or even as a sharp pain in a general area in your back becomes more and more specific as more is learned about the supposed origin of the pain. You may have only felt pain upon bending, but now that you've seen the rupture or herniation, you have pain almost constantly. The more we see, the more we can feel. Reading up on our illness and learning other possible symptoms also increases the likelihood that we will add those symptoms to our experience. The more we know, the more we can apply.

We are also able to see more results of aging. Arthritic bones, diminished cilia, weakened muscles — they must *hurt*, right? If you don't know what I'm talking about, do some research into the many critters that live on our eyelashes; you may just start to feel them if you focus hard enough. That's what advanced testing can do — make you feel things that should not be detectable, merely by the power of suggestion and imagination.

Our being able to see more has only played into our growing desire for perfection. The more we are able to "fix" what's "broken" the more broken we will seem. We crave smooth, blemish-free skin, six-pack abs, straight teeth, and perfect vision. The same desire for perfection has now been translated to our spines and even our bloodwork results. Imaging technology has actually been blamed for the growing chronic pain crisis, as it has contributed to false beliefs about what should and should not cause pain.[2]

If we believe perfection is possible, then anything less must be painful and a sign of weakness. Have you ever gone to a department store makeup counter and looked into their high-powered, brightly-lit mirrors? Every pore and follicle are magnified; it is quite a frightening sight! Of course, that's the whole point: to show you your flaws so you become willing to spend a small fortune to cover them up. The parallels here to modern medicine are unnerving.

Interestingly, the incidence of chronic pain has increased almost in proportion to the increase in the use of imaging in diagnoses. Surgeries to fix the damage seen on the images are ineffective, implying that the connection between what is seen on the images and the pain itself was grossly misunderstood. [3] If your only symptom is chronic pain that you have had for years, and you haven't had a recent accident, succumbing to tests and scans is not advised, as there is nothing to be gained from them. [4]

Not only is more chronic pain being diagnosed due to advanced imaging techniques, there is actually no advantage to the diagnoses, as the pain is still increasing in the population. It doesn't take much to deduce that increased knowledge leads to increased pain.

Sometimes the more you know, the more confused you become. There will be no end to tests and scans, as the search for a legitimate cause of pain will never end. Our drive for perfection will never be satisfied. Understanding the flaws in the idea that there could even *be* a perfect standard of health frees us to accept our own uniqueness and experience actual health, not just textbook conformity.

We continue to place blind faith in tests and scans, believing that the more we know the wiser we will become. We have been here before, and the last time didn't end so well! (The Tower of Babel, remember?)

Every year, my family goes to our doctor for physical exams. One time, after I had lost 20 pounds, my blood test showed my glucose levels to be alarmingly high. The results startled me, as I hadn't eaten any sugar at all for six weeks, and only very hearty grains. Then it occurred to me — as I was losing the fat, it was breaking up and flooding my bloodstream, along with it all the toxins and garbage I had been eating before my weight loss program. Of course, it would show up in a blood test. And true to form, the following year my blood test was completely normal.

If lab results are snapshots of what is going on in your blood at any given time, how reliable are they for making diagnoses? I'm glad to have a doctor that is more holistic and laidback in her approach — I could have been on the road to a nocebo effect had she told me I had "pre-diabetes" the moment she read the test — but many patients are not so fortunate. How much stock should we place in blood tests and scans?

First of all, it's important to understand the ranges set for "normal." How are those numbers determined? Are they based on true health standards, the average numbers of any given population, or on the desire to sell more medication? The ultimate question to ask is whether or not people are getting *better*. [5]

Second of all, keep in mind that the more we see on a scan or in a blood test result, the more prone we are to detecting something wrong. Your body contains a certain number of precancerous cells the majority of the time which your immune system is continually seeking out and destroying. Does seeing these cells provide a benefit at all? The medical community would, of course, insist that early detection saves lives. What is not reported is the number of unnecessary surgeries and treatments resulting from the early detection of cancerous cells that never would have become life-threatening, that would have been handled just fine by the immune system.

Here is an all-too common scenario: you are told that a recent screening test suggests you may have cancer, and are told you need a biopsy. The biopsy comes back positive so you begin treatment, whether it be surgery or chemotherapy or both. You remain cancer-free for years following, and you fully believe it is due to the early detection and prompt intervention. What you don't realize is that it was more likely a "pseudodisease" – even though it appeared to be cancer, it most likely would never have become cancer if it had been left alone. [6]

Tests can also lead to impulsive decisions to take medical actions that may cause harm because treatments based on early detection often don't require much energy to implement, but they are also more unpredictable the farther in advance you perform them. [7] Being able to see a small bundle of cancerous cells in your breast, while knowing you have the breast cancer gene, may cause you to see a mastectomy as the logical next step, even if it never would have come to that if left untreated.

There is a time and a place for medical tests. Doctors love them, as they provide a paper trail of evidence for their diagnosis, and they get paid for doing them regardless of the outcome. But tests don't tell the whole story, as they are meant to find meaning in a sea of complex factors. Tests only view one piece of the puzzle, and they are specifically looking for something *wrong*.

"To a man who only has a hammer, everything he encounters begins to look like a nail." [8]

While neglecting our body can lead to illness and disease, so can having a preoccupation with it. Being overly concerned with every heartbeat, every breath, every sensation can cause the body to have a physical stress response and the mind to suffer from anxiety or depression or even hypochondria. Wouldn't ideal health be better defined as less of a preoccupation of what is going on inside our bodies, rather than more? [9]

Why Pain Increases

Whenever I meet a new person, I look them up on social media. Not because I particularly like social media, but because I am curious to see if we have any mutual friends or interests. Right in line with the idea that all actors are within six degrees of separation from Kevin Bacon, [1] most of the people I meet are friends with at least someone in my friends list.

The brain, too, likes to make connections; between events, feelings, places, people. Messages the brain receives are placed into a specific contextual framework, and pathways will form between related ideas and thoughts. I ate a bowl of quinoa once and got horrible heartburn. An internet search informed me that quinoa can often give people heartburn, so my brain made that connection. From then on, any time I would eat quinoa, I would get horrible heartburn. Oddly enough, my son began to get heartburn as well. Until one day, I read an article about the health benefits of quinoa and decided to give it another chance. No more heartburn for either of us. The connection between pain and quinoa apparently wasn't as convincing to my brain as were the benefits of quinoa. My son's pain pathway had been merely piggybacking on mine through power of suggestion, and both were overridden.

These connections are the cause of much of our pain increasing over time, as more and more information is linked to the pain sensation. The Hebbian theory of how brains learn can be summarized by saying that neurons that "fire together, wire together." [2] The more messages of the same type the brain receives, the more it expects, which is probably why we aren't constantly surprised every day by everything that happens. But just like we may tend to ignore those routine occurrences over time out of an almost boredom, and need variety and novelty in order to stay engaged, the brain also craves more and more stimulation. Drug users crave a greater high, compulsive shoppers crave a better bargain, and gamblers crave higher jackpots. We are never satisfied with anything the world offers, as we are created to find our joy in God alone. Our brains are a perfect microcosm of that discontent in action.

I was watching a friend of mine, who was sitting with his arm around his wife's shoulders, rub her arm with his thumb, over and over, in the same pattern, in the same exact place, for what seemed to be our entire conversation. My eyes could not stay away from his thumb and her arm, as I could not help but think how painful that must be, how her skin must be literally wearing away. Doing the same thing repeatedly creates discomfort and then numbness; you will need something to change in order for you to *feel* again.

If you think the same thoughts over and over, you will create the same connections in the brain which will elicit the same feelings, which will result in similar behavior throughout your life. Your brain will begin to crave more intense thoughts and feelings in order to maintain the same level of stimulation. If you are an angry person, you will need to get angrier over time in order to "feel" angry. Just like any other addiction, emotions will require more intensity in order to be felt. [3] This includes pain -- especially since physical pain is so directly linked to emotional pain. Whichever came first, they feed off each other, and together produce more intense pain levels than would ever be expected in the case of actual injury or disease.

You may be familiar with the term "change blindness." Here's how it works: you may have a pile of papers next to your phone in your kitchen. This pile has been there for as long as you can remember. Over time, you actually cease to *see* this pile, as your brain logs it as part of the furniture, so to speak. You may even tidy up your kitchen and not even touch that pile, as it no longer registers as something to be tidied. Another example is that even though your nose is continually in your line of vision, the brain no longer notices it. These phenomena are similar to how the brain works in the case of pain. The level of pain needs to continually be increased in order to "see" it.

Not only does the level of pain need to increase, but more sources of pain may need to be added. A pain in the knee will no longer be enough, so a pain in the hip emerges, then maybe foot pain — there is usually enough of a connection that the added pains "make sense." "Oh, my knee pain must have caused me to walk differently, thus causing my other pains."

Pain cannot be taken at face value. Our central nervous system can overreact and register pain as being worse than it is or it can even perceive pain that has no physical cause. [4] In people suffering from the same ailment, one person's agonizing pain may be another's mere annoyance. Yet another may feel no pain at all. Ignoring the emotional component behind pain makes no sense whatsoever in light of these discrepancies. Doctors and researchers who observed soldiers wounded during the Civil War concluded that pain is personal, subject to change depending on the situation, and rooted in subjective human perception rather than in any objective factor. [5]

Feel the Pain to Heal the Pain

If pain is subjective, then shall we dare hope to overcome it entirely? The key is to do the opposite of what we are doing now: stop trying to avoid the pain, and *feel* it. Perhaps you've heard mention of this approach in the realm of sports medicine. Athletes, when training, endure quite a bit of pain in order to improve timing, build muscle, and increase flexibility. If they were in the habit of avoiding pain, they would never succeed in their sport of choice. They learn to experience the pain and reframe it as a positive thing rather than something to fear, and as a result, the actual pain sensation decreases.

Pain becomes more powerful the more we push away from it. Swelling and inflammation are possibly more often caused by this subconscious, or sometimes conscious, resistance. [1] Being fearful of pain leads to pain. Fear can actually become trapped in your muscles, creating tension and, eventually, chronic pain. [2] Once you experience pain, the emotion most commonly tied to that pain is fear of it ever happening again. The memory, along with the emotions associated with it, are stored in every cell of your body. Fall down the stairs once, and every time you see a flight of stairs, your body will react as if you are falling once more. It is only in the retraining of the mind to reframe these pain triggers that you will break that connection.

When a loved one dies, those left behind often find themselves reliving the loss on the anniversary of the death every year. The catch in your throat, the loss of appetite, the tears that wouldn't stop flowing, are all retained in your body like an emotional bookmark. My grandmother died September 12, 2017. Every September 12th since, my mother find herself sobbing uncontrollably, regardless of how she may be feeling otherwise. Her body remembers.

Your body stores memories of past trauma in order to protect you, to alert you when a situation is looking all too familiar to one that harmed you in the past. Chronic pain can manifest itself when there are suppressed memories of childhood abuse, so paying attention to specific symptoms can be useful in determining if there may be something in your past that you have subconsciously buried. Once the emotions are dealt with, the physical pain usually vanishes. It's as if your body gives you a choice — remember in the mind or remember in the body. Either way, nothing is truly forgotten. For some, the physical pain is far more bearable than having to deal with a terrifying event from their childhood.

Scientists have linked physical pain to social pain, as the same regions in the brain are affected by both.[3] We inadvertently link the two as well, in the way we describe the way we feel: "he left me with a broken heart," "she's being a real pain in the neck," or "he stabbed me in the back." We describe our emotional pain with the same terms we use for physical injury.[4]

The same principle applies to social pain: the more you avoid it, the more you will experience it. If you risk nothing, you gain nothing. Avoiding personal pain usually leads to deeper rejection. We avoid getting hurt in relationships by trying to control others — whether it be by avoiding them altogether, by only choosing relationships that are "safe," or by pushing people away by bad behavior, or by becoming needy and clingy. You don't need a great imagination to see how any one of those scenarios will play out. Only in humility and vulnerability will true relationships form. Leaning into the fear and the possibility of pain can eliminate the pain altogether.

We DO Have It Wrong About Chronic Pain

Knowing more about our bodies has not made us healthier. The more we know, the more damage we tend to do to ourselves out of fear — unnecessary operations and procedures, medications and supplements we think will prevent the worst-case scenario, and overall just living in terror of what we believe might be inevitable anyway. We are becoming obsessed with rituals and routines that promise health, all of which do nothing but rob us of it in the long run.

Medical care has become a form of bondage, leading to overmedicalization, painful and dangerous side effects, high medical costs, and a worsening of symptoms due to the inevitable depression, fear, and hopelessness that go along with a diagnosis. It is believed that more than 30% of medical intervention in this country is unnecessary.[1]

The more we intervene medically, it appears the worse off we are becoming. The mainstream view of medicine is falling short, and is potentially causing as much harm as it does good. Again, their failure is largely due to their reductionist view of the human body: we are all just a sum of our parts, nothing more than a body inhabited by a mind, with both remaining fully and completely separate.

The medical reductionist approach suggests that if there is damage, one would simply be able to repair the damage to bring about relief and healing. This approach makes complete sense at first glance. But relief from pain doesn't happen in most cases, so the theory must be wrong. The reductionist theory must be held to the same standards as all science; if our current method of treating pain does not work, we must look elsewhere for answers.

The classical view of the body is that it is just matter responding to electrical stimulation with no internal intelligence, whereas the new understanding of the body is that the mind is intelligently and elegantly working behind the scenes to direct all of the body's processes, uniting every cell in a harmonious dance of life. [2]

If there is proof of an intelligent design in our bodies, there is proof of an intelligent designer. Taking the mind out of the body is a mere stepping stone to taking the Creator out of the creation. If our bodies are random sets of cells just following programmed genetic orders, then there is no need for us to find meaning in our lives. Meaning is a moot point, survival becomes all that's left to consider. While there may be a medical *explanation*, there is always an emotional *reason*.

(Now, I'm not opposed to pharmaceutical drugs. When I have a cold and can't breathe through my nose in the middle of the night, it's far easier to take some medication than to contemplate my emotional health — that can better take place in the light of day after a good night's sleep. The key is not to rely on them for true healing; crutches don't heal broken bones but they sure help you get around.)

The "Stress" Compromise

In order to give a nod to the emotional component of health, many physicians have settled on a compromise: stress. They acknowledge that stress can exacerbate symptoms, can cause a handful of physiological responses, and can lead to emotional distress. Could "stress" be an acceptable middle ground?

Research estimates that the majority of people seeking medical treatment suffer from extreme emotional stress, proving more and more that there is an established link between emotional and physical health. [1]

Modern doctors have replaced the term "hysteria" with "stress." The word "stress" is itself too vague a term to really be useful at all. What is stress? Merriam Webster defines stress as "the burden on one's emotional or mental well-being created by demands on one's time" [2] — can that be all it is? I have many demands on my time, but not all of them give me stress. More likely, the lack of control in being unable to choose *not* to perform a certain task produces more stress than the task itself ever could. [3]

Perhaps a better definition of stress would be "the rage we suppress when required to do something we despise." If you enjoy your labors you may feel tired at the end of the day, you might feel a bit rushed or overwhelmed, but you will not feel stressed. But once asked to work alongside a coworker you don't like, or given a deadline you don't agree with, stress shows its ugly face. If I'm given a day alone at home, I may happily choose to clean the entire house while listening to my favorite music. But if I'm hosting Thanksgiving and I really would prefer not to, cleaning the house can make me feel angry and resentful.

No one likes to feel backed into a corner. I will gladly give large amounts of money to worthy causes...until the government forces me into it with new taxes. I will happily bring you a meal or clean your house if you are in need...until you expect it of me. At its root is pride — I want to be the one to offer! You rob me of that pleasure when you demand things from me, and my pride takes a painful hit.

Another factor at play is how we think about the situation we find stressful. What are your expectations? Do you feel adequate to accomplish the task? Do you feel as if you deserve a positive outcome? These thoughts can create stress if your results don't match your expectations. If I feel inadequate in performing a certain task, being asked to do it can cause stress. My fear of being exposed as "less than" can be a huge impetus for stress, as my pride is at stake. However, if the task is something I excel at, I will eagerly take it on.

Stress can also send your senses into overdrive. My own version of the famous quote: to a man with a shield, everything is an arrow. Rather than consider circumstances wisely and objectively, you would prefer to just beat up anything that threatens you: it "holds grudges, feels pain and suffers, or can't get beyond its victimhood." [4] Choices made in hyper-vigilance are often foolish and sinful.

In this overprotective state, emotions can become jumbled, so simply lumping them all together under one easy word, "stress," is not helpful. Like a tangle of necklaces, we have to take the time to isolate each individual chain in order to better understand the source of our emotional discomfort. Pride, selfishness, fear, anger, sorrow — all may have "stress" as a symptom or outcome, but are to be each dealt with differently.

The same activity can produce joy or rage depending on our attitude towards it. We choose how we respond to stress, either as a victim or as a victor. If we are accustomed to hopelessness, we will assign meanings to events that perpetuate that feeling of despair. These habitual responses determine the degree to which an event is stressful or enjoyable. [5]

From start to finish, stress is a choice: you choose what stresses you out, and you choose how you respond to stress. It might be helpful to envision a toddler and the kinds of things that cause him or her to "melt down": being tired or hungry (fear that needs won't be met), being restrained or restricted (desire to be in control), or being told "no" for any reason (physical desires). Your stresses will fall into one or more of these categories. We expect to be treated a certain way, and when we are not, we become *stressed*.

On a biological level, if you have certain expectations for your day, or even your life, and these expectations are not met, your very immune system responds. A day that may begin with countless possibilities may become drudgery if you have demands imposed on you against your will, leading you to feel less than at your best. Stress can make you tired, give you pain, blurred vision, and stomach discomfort; negative expectations can affect your levels of cortisol and prolactin, the hormones responsible for regulating your immune system. [6]

The more pressure there is to impress and succeed, the greater the need there will be to hide failure and shame. Oddly enough, the majority of chronic pain sufferers are in their 40s and 50s. [7] Why would that be, if deteriorated spines are blamed for back pain? Wouldn't the elderly be the ones most affected, seeing as their bones are the most aged?

However, once you consider the great deal of stress that this middle-aged group is under — worrying about retirement, taking care of aging parents, still raising children — it should come as no surprise! Chronic pain tends to taper off in older age, as the demands placed on the elderly become greatly diminished.

The medical community loves to throw around the word "stress" — it serves as a catch-all for symptoms that have no explanation. I'm actually glad they are considering it at all, because that means they're on the right track. For years, health insurance actuaries have determined your illness risk by assessing certain stress factors in your life — if you've recently become divorced, lost a spouse, had a child — they see the connection as well!

And sure, stress does lead to medical conditions. Just not the way we thought. It's not as vague a process as it appears to be; stress is merely a group of sinful thoughts and emotions masquerading as environmental factors, something that can be excused and blamed on something other than self. We become stressed when we have to do something we **don't want to do**. The medical conditions that result from a life of chronic stress come about not just because an elevated heart rate and sleeplessness aren't good for you long-term; those very health issues develop as a means for you to have a way out of those activities you dislike.

If you've gotten to a point where you just can't take any more, pain takes over and gives you a way out, protecting you from taking on more than you can handle and even compelling you to take a break from work altogether. [8]

If the body were merely a vessel for the mind, there would be no such thing as stress-related medical conditions. Just as poverty-stricken lands have no use for self-storage units, cultures who know how to express their emotions in a healthful manner have no need for chronic pain. The mere fact that we can definitively trace our health back to an emotional cause, even a vague one such as "stress," should call into question the entire Descartian understanding of the human body.

(Note: "Stress," as it is discussed here, is not to be confused with *anguish*. Emotional trauma can take on many characteristics of stress, but differs in the same way that acute pain differs from chronic pain.)

There is plenty of evidence claiming to connect stress to medical conditions like high blood pressure, ulcers, and heart disease. Stress becomes a biological factor like dust mites or oxygenation rather than a mental response to natural circumstances. The vaguer the cause, however, the less likely there will be an appropriate and effective solution. Therefore, stress cannot be an acceptable compromise, as it does not go nearly far enough in identifying the problem *or* the solution.

When it comes to our health, we cannot accept guesses and compromises.

When you are in pain, you want answers. You want a treatment plan that will *just work*. With so many pain relief methods on the market, shouldn't there be one that rises to the top as being the most effective? One back pain sufferer insists that a hard bed has helped her immensely, while another swears by nightly ice packs. Or physical therapy. Or a change in diet. Or any host of gadgets or herbs or oils or medications that have "helped" in some way. But if the remedies for pain are so personal, could the causes also be...personal?

To answer this question, we must go back to the very beginning...to the Garden.

PART THREE:
WHAT FIG LEAVES AND
CHRONIC PAIN
HAVE IN COMMON

CHAPTER FIVE:
HIDING

Imagine walking in the Garden of Eden with God. Personally, I'm not a big fan of the Great Outdoors. So, I have to imagine a garden with only friendly bugs and nothing squishy or slimy. It's hard for us to picture a place of total peace and comfort, with no fear of predators or bad weather, a place of perfection and pleasure. But think beyond the external sensations you would feel in a garden like that; think of what it must have been like to *know* God — to understand Him, to hear Him when He speaks. I always have wondered if they laughed together, if He revealed mysteries to Adam and Eve about His character, if He taught them things about their world that we are barely scratching the surface on now. To have a mind open and able to comprehend all that God shows us; that would be a deeper pleasure than the smell of flowers or the buzz of hummingbirds.

Perhaps Adam and Eve were content to avoid the Tree of the Knowledge of Good and Evil as long as they did because it seemed superfluous. They knew Good, and they had no frame of reference for Evil. When your stomach is full, even the most glorious of smells don't appeal to you. Their hearts were full of God's presence and they lacked nothing, so they desired nothing. Until.

Satan cannot invent anything new. He can only distort what *is*. The Tree alone couldn't tempt them, so he lied. He told them that not only could they know God, they could be *like* God. Have you ever had a friend who you admired immensely? Just imagine someone telling you that not only can you spend time with this wonderful person, you could be just like them, an object of admiration yourself! Suddenly, your loyalties are torn. From praise to pride in a flash. Adam and Eve were hooked.

That first bite must have tasted amazing. All sin does at first. Thoughts must have been running through their minds like, "Why did God forbid this? It's amazing! Satan must have been telling the truth about God not wanting to share this knowledge with us!" I wonder how it felt to have that knowledge just POOF! appear in their minds. What a mind-blowing, jaw-dropping experience that must have been. However, Genesis 3 suggests that their new awareness was not as satisfying as they had been led to expect. Notice all the verses that were *not* written about how they went on to compose great musical masterpieces and literary works with their advanced knowledge, or how they felt the power of self-realization and the joy it brings. No, none of that happened. The knowledge they gained did not bring them anything but shame.

All at once they knew Evil. While we aren't given any kind of description of what that looked like for them, I can only guess it was terrifying. Just as my teenage daughter went from being a passive, relaxed passenger in my car to gripping the door handle with terror after watching a movie about deadly car accidents in Drivers' Ed, they, too, must have had their eyes opened to all that human beings would be capable of doing, all the temptations we could now face, all the wrongs we could do. The worst part of that realization would most likely have been the chasm they now saw between themselves and God. Once their eyes were opened to Good and Evil, they were closed to the intimacy they had shared with their Creator. How can they, now filthy and wicked, ever dare to approach Him again? They now understood the word Evil, the word Death was not something they were eager to experience, and there was no word for Forgiveness yet mentioned. There was only one response they could think of, only one course of action that their now sin-laden minds could concoct: to hide.

> "So when the woman saw that the tree was good for food, that it was pleasant to the eyes, and a tree desirable to make one wise, she took of its fruit and ate. She also gave to her husband with her, and he ate. Then the eyes of both of them were opened, and they knew that they were naked; and they sewed fig leaves together and made themselves coverings." (Genesis 3:6-7 NKJV)

Can you picture that moment? Looking down and feeling ashamed of what moments ago was something quite natural? With no other woman to whom to compare herself, Eve most likely compared herself to her husband, maybe wondering what was wrong with her that she looked so different? Her feet, covered in moss and soil from her walk to the tree, may have suddenly looked dirty and filthy. She may have noticed sweat on Adam's brow for the first time and found him not as attractive as she had moments ago. Their eyes were opened, all right, but that just meant they could see the negative side of what before had only brought them joy and happiness.

Both of them could sense the new separation from God and from each other that unleashed a whole onslaught of feelings such as jealousy, bitterness, hatred, lust, and fear. These new sensations flooded over them, making their hearts race, their palms sweat, and their heads ache. Did they feel the change on a cellular level? Were they just waiting for death to come? They probably didn't even know what the word meant, as they had never seen it for themselves.

I know they felt it on a spiritual level, that's for sure. God was no longer a heartbeat away, their protector and companion; now they felt He was their enemy, their predator. Oh, how far they had fallen!

We can learn so much about ourselves from their actions in that moment. They, who had a closer relationship with God than any other human before or since, had the impulse to run and cover themselves with the nearest thing available. Fig leaves. I don't personally have much experience with fig leaves, but those who do tell me they are not soft and luxurious. They **hurt**. They probably only chose them because they were large, and fewer would be required to form an outfit. I would guess that sewing them would have been a challenge. It certainly took longer than a few moments — did they have to learn the art of sewing first? And without instructional videos, no less. And maybe at this point, the foliage had become mixed with sweat and had become itchy. And now that they had to contend with physical pain, the stems probably poked them and even made them bleed, something they may never have seen before. Not to mention, movement would be a problem — it wouldn't take much for the leaves to tear. They would have to have known that these new robes would not last more than a day or two; that they'd have to make them again and again if they were to stay decent. All these new experiences and sensations, as well as the amount of effort they had to put into this covering, and not feeling able to ask God for help or turn to Him, all probably made them feel full of despair.

And then God comes on the scene. I wonder if He purposely waited for the fig leaf overalls to be fully completed. Here He comes, walking in the garden in the cool of the day, as the three of them had once done together.

Only this time was different. Adam and Eve were hiding among the trees of the garden. The first attempt at camouflage. God asks where they are — not because He doesn't know, but because *they* need to know. They need to realize where they are… and where they *aren't*. They aren't where they used to be anymore: with Him.

Adam tells God that he was naked and hid. God gives them a chance to own their actions, but in turn, they blame forces outside themselves — Adam blames Eve, really blaming *God* for giving such a woman to him, and Eve blames the serpent, again blaming God for something that he purportedly had made. They blamed Him for evil itself, for the first time doubting His goodness.

And now the curse. One by one, they receive their punishment — Eve, in the form of painful childbirth and a desire for a husband who would rule over her, and Adam, through subpar working conditions that would only cause him pain and hardship.

Humbled, sorrowful, and still itching from the fig leaves they had covered themselves with, they hung their heads before their God. Graciously, He made them tunics of skin, thus bringing about the first death in the Garden, and symbolizing the death of Jesus that would be the ultimate covering for sin, once and for all. But then they had to leave, cast out into a world that no longer was familiar to them. Notice God didn't leave them alone; He was still present in their lives and in their children's lives. But they no longer had the same access to Him, nor did they understand Him anymore.

I often wonder what would have happened if God had just not put that fool tree in Eden. But Scripture doesn't give us any indication that His doing so surprised or frustrated its original inhabitants. The problem lies in our trying to understand God with our new sin nature; our minds are distorted and cloudy, just like waking up from a dream that you can no longer recount. Perhaps He allowed sin to enter His new world solely to showcase His justice and mercy, attributes we would never have seen otherwise.

Our minds are victims of the Fall just as our bodies are. And we are still hiding from God, even those of us who know Jesus as our Savior. It's in our sinful nature to hide.

Since sin has infused our very nature down to our core, we know we are not worthy of a relationship with a holy God. Still, we try to convince others and ourselves that we are better than we are in an attempt to avoid the truth. So, we seek to blame something or someone else for anything in our character or behavior that falls short. I eat a donut; I blame stress and the fact I had a coupon. I leave my shoes on the floor for someone to trip over; I was in a hurry. I spent too much at the store; I was depressed and needed a pick-me-up. Instead of addressing my gluttony, my laziness, my greed, I hide behind, "Hey, everyone does it, I had a good reason, don't judge me."

None of these excuses or diversions touch the heart issue, however. Hiding never brings us closer to our God. They are just fig leaves, and they hurt.

The fig leaves we use today vary from person to person. Anything that gives us a covering, a disguise so we no longer have to be seen. Walls that we build. Excuses we make. We may become materialistic, judgmental, self-absorbed, or cruel. Maybe our leaves are made of good things like service projects or ministry or church activities. Like any good magician performing sleight of hand, we direct attention away from where the action is taking place to present a spectacular display of whatever it is we want people to see in us.

Anything can be a fig leaf. Your children, your marriage, your job, your hobbies, and your health can all serve as masks of concealment.

Many of us even fall prey to sewing our fig leaves from what we have been deceived to believe to be medical disorders: depression, chronic pain, food allergies, and ADHD. We have been led to believe that these trials are merely physical, products of the curse, nothing to be done, that's just the way life is until Jesus comes again. What if I told you that most of the common complaints we experience are of our own design? Not that we make a conscious choice to suffer, but just as our hiding instincts in the Garden led us to pick up something as ridiculous as foliage to cover ourselves, our subconscious grasps at whatever it can find to disguise the real condition of our hearts.

I'm aware that much of what I will share with you contradicts all you have been told about modern medicine. I'm no conspiracy theorist, mind you, but we are fighting a spiritual battle, and one of the most effective tactics — maybe the only tactic — of the enemy is to deceive us into thinking we aren't fighting him. As long as we are focused on disease and pain as the enemy, Satan is free to roam about unnoticed, putting up strongholds in our lives deadlier than cancer but that spread just as quickly.

Most believers jump right to the verses in the Bible that deal directly with healing. There are plenty! While there are no "Ten Steps to Healing" spelled out in the New Testament, the Bible provides us with some principles often overlooked in our quest for relief. Principles that can help us heal from, and even prevent, much of what afflicts us.

Adam and Eve each lived several hundred years after the Fall — the Bible doesn't mention Eve's age, but Adam died when he was 930 years old. I'm willing to bet that his hiding instincts didn't just vanish the day he left the Garden. He most likely passed them on to his descendants, and they became more and more creative in hiding as the generations unfolded.

We know that Cain hid the truth from God about killing his brother, King David tried to hide his affair with Bathsheba, Rachel hid her theft of her father's idols, Achan hid his stolen booty and cost Israel the battle of Ai, and so on. Fast forward to today: we haven't learned our lesson; we've just become more adept and creative in our hiding tactics.

There's an old saying that goes something like this: "The best way to conceal something is to hide it in plain sight." Wearing our pain on the outside to disguise the pain we feel on the inside is nothing short of genius.

There's that other old saying, "Your sin will find you out." (Numbers 32:23 NKJV) So why do we continue to hide them at all?

What is Hiding?

Hiding isn't always a bad thing. We hide those things most precious to us, such as our bank account details, our credit card numbers, and our safe deposit box combination. We also hide things we perceive as dangerous to others, such as guns and prescription medications. While these forms of hiding are useful and even beneficial, other forms of hiding have the opposite result. We hide our insecurities, our fears, our shame — things we are afraid will expose us for who we really are inside. Personally, I close the door to my messy laundry room when people come over, and I cross my arms over my midsection when I'm feeling overweight. Hiding things I am ashamed of makes me feel like maybe I'm not so bad after all; what you can't see can't hurt me.

Why shouldn't we want to hide? Isn't it justifiable to want to protect ourselves from hurt or judgment? If we were created to live independent of others, then hiding would be the best course of action. However, we were created to live in community with others and in communion with God. While I am not suggesting broadcasting to the world that you once wet your bed in fourth grade or that you have an irrational fear of dryer lint, there are times in which revealing deep secrets is critical to establishing intimacy and trust with others. We are called to "bear one another's burdens" (Galatians 6:2 NKJV) and the only way we can do that is if we reveal what our burdens are. The problem is that we often only dance around the subject; we talk about "stress" when we mean we have maxed out our credit cards and are in danger of losing our home. We use terms like "struggling" and "frustrated" when we mean we are so at the end of our rope that isolation from the world seems like the only way out. Even at our lowest places, we still want to hide the true depths of our condition. Social media allows us to dress up any situation, put a filter on it, and make it into a funny meme. Lonely? Socially awkward? Depressed? Sure, you can talk about it; just make sure there's a punchline. We're so busy hitting the "like" button and laughing at the joke we miss the person behind the post.

Hiding is in our nature; it was the first action we took after we sinned in the Garden, and it's our knee-jerk reaction to just about every situation we encounter. We don't even realize we are doing it — like breathing, it's become so automatic that we cease to notice when we do it. Our subconscious learns to take over and manage those things we do repetitively, just to save us the trouble of having to be aware of every part of our routine. I don't even remember making coffee in the morning, or brushing my teeth, or washing between my toes in the shower — those are just things I *do* every day, so my subconscious helps me out so I can think about other things like my to-do list for the day. Muscle memory is a part of that process; you don't have to think about how to tie your shoes or put on your socks (or even not to do those things in that order). You just *do* it. The same goes with hiding. Yet you can become aware of any of those rote behaviors if you really concentrate. Just try teaching a Kindergartener how to tie their shoes and you will come to see you actually don't know how to break it down into steps as well as you thought you could. Focusing on a subconscious act can be confusing and a bit disorienting at first, so if you find yourself doubting everything you are doing as you become more aware of hiding behaviors, you're not alone.

Hiding, at its root, replaces the *fear* of God (meaning awe and respect) with the **fear** of God (meaning terror). Sinners have much to **fear** with God, as He is holy and will not tolerate sin.

> "Behold, the day of the LORD comes, cruel, with both wrath and fierce anger, to lay the land desolate; and He will destroy its sinners from it." (Isaiah 13:9 NKJV)

> "Now consider this, you who forget God, lest I tear you in pieces..." (Psalm 50:22 NKJV)

> "'But I will punish you according to the fruit of your doings,'
> says the LORD; 'I will kindle a fire in its forest, and it shall
> devour all things around it.'" (Jeremiah 21:14 NKJV)

While these verses are accurate depictions of God's hatred of sin and love of justice, they are not to be read in isolation of the rest of His Word. The wicked have much to **fear**, yes! But you who have been redeemed have only peace and safety in the arms of a loving Savior; you are spared from His wrath. Justice has been paid, you have been set free. Now His wrath is focused on those who would harm His children; His justice is *for* you, no longer *against* you.

> "If God is for us, who can be against us? He who did not
> spare His own Son, but delivered Him up for us all, how shall
> He not with Him also freely give us all things? Who shall bring
> a charge against God's elect? It is God who justifies. Who is
> he who condemns? It is Christ who died, and furthermore is
> also risen, who is even at the right hand of God, who also
> makes intercession for us. Who shall separate us from the love
> of Christ? ... For I am persuaded that neither death nor life,
> nor angels nor principalities nor powers, nor things present
> nor things to come, nor height nor depth, nor any other
> created thing, shall be able to separate us from the love of God
> which is in Christ Jesus our Lord." (Romans 8:31-39 NKJV)

Once we are saved by the blood of Jesus and are covered by His righteousness, our **fear** should turn to *fear*, a gratitude and acknowledgement of His holiness and His mercy in saving us from certain death. The gospel is simple, and yet it is one of the most difficult concepts to understand.

We are sinners; we deserve death, but Jesus died in our place. Do you believe you are a sinner? Do you believe you deserve death? Maybe that's the easy part of the gospel for you. Maybe death seems like a welcome friend, a way out of all the shame you feel. Some struggle with admitting guilt, some with accepting forgiveness. Whichever you struggle with, freedom can only be found by accepting the entire gospel, not just the parts that are palatable and easy to swallow. Redemption literally means the repaying of a debt, so to be redeemed you have to acknowledge that a debt was owed and that someone *other than you* paid it. Redemption does a number on pride.

We are now covered in robes of righteousness with the promise that God will never give up on our becoming holy. That's a blessing, as our pride is still waging a battle within us, and we continue to glue fig leaves to those white sparkling robes paid for by His blood! He doesn't see our sin when

He looks at us, but that doesn't stop us from trying to hide it anyway, perhaps to convince ourselves that we didn't really need His help after all. I remember in middle school when the teacher would scan the room for a volunteer to come do a math problem on the board in front of the class; everyone would suddenly find their shoes most fascinating, anything to avoid eye contact with the teacher. We didn't want the entire class to know that we weren't grasping the concept being taught; we wanted to be liked and have the teacher praise us, and we knew none of that would happen if we got a hold of that chalk — our failings would be revealed once and for all.

It's not just our sin that we try to hide; we hide our need for God out of a **fear** that He will reject us, or make us give up things we enjoy, or maybe go on the mission field, tithe more, or befriend that new family at church — things we really don't want to do. We doubt God's goodness. His wrath terrifies us, His love intimidates us, His holiness humbles us. We think we must be better off on our own, anything but having to come into contact with a God who has the power to undo us. Just like those underground bunkers American families made during the Cold War, we wall off a part of ourselves that we think we can run to when we feel threatened, somewhere we think God won't see.

Our underground bunkers may manifest on the outside in obviously sinful ways, while some are more subversive. Children are wonderful examples of both extremes. Some rebellious teenagers hide from their parents by slamming doors and defying orders, anything to separate themselves from their parents' authority. At the other end of the spectrum, children may also rebel without the appearance of rebellion. Passive aggression, "forgetting" to do chores, and muttering under their breath are all subversive ways to reject their parents' authority while still presenting themselves as the model child.

At times we wear our sin proudly. Blatant rebellion, overt defiance that we hope will keep Him at a distance. However, the most common forms of sin in the church are the passive, sneaky kinds. Confession is rarely done corporately, and when it is, there is usually an uncomfortable silence, all of us hoping we have lived our lives in such a way that no one will volunteer us to go first. We **fear** that a spotlight will appear above us if we were ever to confess even the smallest of sins. "Aha! I KNEW it," everyone will gasp in astonishment, and our reputations will be ruined. We Christians may know intellectually that we are sinners, but we don't necessarily want everyone else to know it, too.

The Church has made it easy to hide. Sermons have become more self-help oriented with watered-down scripture and questionable applications, community groups have become less about sharing emotional pain and more about putting on a good face and bringing your best homemade dessert, and church-wide events have become more elaborate and demanding, requiring us to be on our game at all times. And of course, there's what I call Bible verse duct tape — if you slap enough Bible verses on a situation, it should fix it! So instead of empathy with others, we bring out our favorite verses:

"All things work together for good!"

"You can do all things through Christ!"

"Cast all your cares on Him!"

Slap. Slap. Slap.

It's no different from the passage where James warns that faith without works is dead:

> "If a brother or sister is without clothing and in need of daily food, and one of you says to them, 'Go in peace, be warmed and be filled,' and yet you do not give them what is necessary for their body, what use is that?" (James 2:15-16 NASB)

The Unusual Suspects

When presented with a list of seemingly unrelated items, it may be difficult to find a connection between them. A string of bank robberies may appear random, for example. However, when you look closely enough, you may find a hidden subset that links them – all of the banks had different security systems, but all of those security systems used the same computer software.

We don't all hide the same way — our "security systems" are all different and unique. But they all have something like software in common; look at this list of common disorders:

- Compulsive Hoarding
- Compulsive Shopping
- Overeating
- Depression
- Anxiety
- Chronic Pain
- Headaches

- Food Sensitivities
- Chronic Fatigue Syndrome (CFS)
- Psychiatric Disorders
- Arthritis
- ... and more

What do *these* things have in common? The root causes of these and other disorders have always eluded science, even though they attempt to draw various connections between biology, environment, nutrition, sleep, stress, genetics, and more to explain the rising numbers of people suffering from these conditions. As a certified nutritionist, I, too, attempted to draw similar lines and offer remedies to those I counseled. Nothing fully took away their pain. I knew there was something behind all these disorders, something much simpler and yet perhaps more difficult to accept. I also saw how even empathizing with pain sufferers didn't make things any better. Something was behind the pain.

Have you ever had one of those itches that seem to come from your bone itself? The kind where you scratch and scratch but your skin just aches and become raw, while the itch persists? If you've ever experienced that, you know how maddening it can be! These physical manifestations are only the "itch;" they are not the real problem. No amount of medical or psychological intervention will fully take them away.

The more we focus on the ever-growing list of health issues springing up in the church, the more we overlook the source: we are afraid of being known. We don't want anyone to see our sin, our flaws, our needs, our secret pains and fears, and our true nature.

We tend to believe that to be a Christian means having no problems, or at least only acceptable ones. Like health issues. Those don't get the Bible verse duct tape treatment like the others. *Those* needs are prayed over, tended to in the form of meals and household help, and addressed in support groups within the church. Do you see why it is so much easier to hide behind needs that people actually will care about?

So, we modify our sin into more spiritually acceptable manifestations. We choose fig leaves that are in fashion, that everyone else is wearing. Just ask Waldo; [1] it's easier to hide in a crowd where everyone has a similar uniform. These are the fig leaves of physical and emotional illness and chronic pain. No one would suspect that anyone would use pain as a disguise; after all, pain hurts! But remember what I told you about the subconscious taking over those habitual actions — you aren't even aware of what you are doing when you open the door to pain and let its roots take over your life. We will slowly open another door, the one that leads to awareness and, in time, healing.

Being known is what we were created for, what every cell of our body is designed for. If we aren't free to reveal ourselves in a loving environment, our minds will devise a way to enjoy the benefits of being known without the risk. A "need" that masks the true need. So, you can have the compassion without the conviction, the help without the humbling. The immediate gratification can be intoxicating and can certainly feel genuine… enough. All sin seeks to glorify self. Our ego has always been the favorite child, the one we feed at the expense of our physical and mental health. That's why it seems so counterproductive that we could cause ourselves pain, when in reality it's reasonable collateral damage in the war to protect our pride.

The gospel gives us access to our Father, not through a human priest, not through rote actions and memorized prayers, but to Him directly, immediately, and intimately. And being known by Him allows us to know others fully and to be fully known by them as well.

Jesus told the Pharisees in Luke 19 that if the disciples ceased praising Him, "the stones will cry out!" (v. 40 NASB) If you refuse to be known, your very body will cry out.

Where We Went Wrong

It's easy to imagine why Adam and Eve would want to hide following their deliberate sin against God. They, as they say, "had one job," and they blew it. For us, living in full knowledge of the forgiveness and grace offered to us by the Cross, it's more difficult to understand why we would have anything to hide from. We know that God knows our sin, and we know He has forgiven us. There are, unfortunately, many truths we *know* that we do not yet allow to penetrate our lives. We know that speeding is against the law and we could get a ticket. Why are we so surprised to see the flashing lights in our rear-view mirror? We know that if we study for a test, we are more likely to get a good grade. And yet, we binge watch our favorite show instead of opening a book. What would cause us to live in a way so contrary to what we know as true?

Were humanity mere automatons, we would operate solely on logic. Computers don't ask "why," they don't complain, and they don't take things personally. Our illogical behaviors stem from the fact that we have desires, opinions, and preferences: we have *emotions*. We wouldn't think to hide were it not for our feelings of shame, fear, sorrow, and pride.

Modern scientific education emphasizes our random beginnings through a series of random evolutions of one thing into another more complex thing, haphazardly changing into more advanced organisms with nothing to guide them but some convoluted concept of survival of the fittest. According to modern science, hiding would have to have benefitted us somehow in our ancient past; a mechanism to promote survival. Were all hiding equal — hiding from prey just makes sense, after all — I would agree; but where is the advantage of hiding our needs from others who might help us? And why would we want to hide from our Creator who offers us peace and protection?

If hiding is designed to avoid danger and provide some sense of protection, how could it be that it has such negative physical and psychological consequences? Why do the results of hiding end up being the very things we were hiding from?

The emotions themselves that drive our hiding seem, at first glance, to be unnecessary to our survival. Why do we need love to feel a commitment towards our offspring? Wouldn't it be enough simply to desire the continuation of the species? Why do we need sorrow when it so often puts our lives on hold? It would be simpler to live in a world without complex feelings; decisions would be easier to make, relationships would be based on compatibility rather than attraction, tasks would be managed on time, and wars would never be fought. Emotions cause us to care about what others think about us and can carry us away into deception. Life would be easy without all the drama that comes with feelings.

Emotions must serve a purpose in God's creation; He has them, too. God experiences love and sorrow and anger and joy. We are *meant* to feel. Without feelings, life would be easier, for sure, but it would be awfully dull. There would be no happy tears, no remorse-laden apologies, no passion, no dreams. Emotions are God's gift to us, and they are meant to make life full and rich.

So, what happened? Where did we go wrong?

Everything changed the moment Eve's lips touched the fruit of the forbidden tree. Her heart no longer beat for her Lord and her husband; Self took over the throne of her life. Love for God became self-love, praise for her Creator became self-adoration. The true sin of the Fall was **pride**: believing we knew better, that God wasn't good, and that we could do this whole "life" thing without Him.

To go it alone, and to prevent the shame that would surely come as a result, we had to break off the parts of ourselves that made us like Him. We

95

had to harden our hearts and steel our minds. We had to deny our feelings, or they would break our hearts. We dropped them like a bag of rocks, considering ourselves free, little knowing we never can really put them aside. God's image in us is not something that can be discarded.

Truth is, we look ridiculous. Have you ever asked a pouting toddler if she's upset, and had her answer, "No!" We laugh at the spectacle, but perhaps deep down we identify with the desire to conceal our feelings.

The more you deny having certain emotions, the more likely it is that you are harboring them on a deeper level. The fact is, we *all* have them. It reminds me of when my children were little — after a bath, they would wrap a towel around their head and run around the house, fully convinced that no one could see they were naked! We would love to remain in the bliss of self-deception, thinking we are doing a marvelous job of covering our unpleasant emotions, but we are fooling no one.

Despite our attempts to block unwanted emotions or feelings, our bodies are still influenced by them on a neurological level. We may experience changes in heart rhythm, facial expressions, body temperature, and other biological changes that often go unnoticed but which cycle back and affect us emotionally, influencing our ability to reason and make decisions. You cannot escape buried emotions, they will always find a way to become expressed. [2]

So, where do these emotions go? And if we are doing such a great job at hiding them, at least as far as we know, what's the big deal, anyway? The problem is that *they do not stay hidden*. Repressing negative emotions and memories only turn that pain inward, where the body then transfers it to the muscles and joints. When we incur physical pain, it is merely the manifestation of the tension we attempted to repress, directed inward rather than outward. [3] Repression is never an effective solution for managing emotions, even though it may appear to work for a period of time. It is only a matter of time before it finds an outlet.

Repressed memories eventually come to the surface or drive us mad. Repressed emotions do the same. Hidden emotions become external pain. Which is easier to bear, chronic pain or vulnerability? For most of us, we would gladly take the pain! To be truly vulnerable is to see ourselves as we *fear* God sees us: as damaged and unredeemable. What a mercy that He doesn't look at us that way!

The Psalmist asked God to reveal those hidden emotions, knowing that

God knows us better than we can ever know ourselves: "Search me, God, and know my heart; test me and know my anxious thoughts" (Psalm 139:23 NIV).

If we refuse to allow God to reveal these hidden emotions, we may continue in ignorance, but I guarantee you others will see them... in our actions. Hiding's clever disguise of pain and illness can only do so much to prevent our sin from being brought into the light.

While a balloon that has been pierced by a pin allows air to escape slowly and almost unnoticeably, sin escapes like the air out of a whoopee cushion — noisy and shrill! Hiders become just as whiny and unpleasant:

- "grumblers and faultfinders; they follow their own evil desires; they boast about themselves and flatter others for their own advantage." (Jude 1:16 NIV)
- "discord, jealousy, fits of rage, selfish ambition, slander, gossip, arrogance and disorder." (2 Corinthians 12:20 NIV)
- "'If anyone is unwilling to work, he shall not eat.' Yet we hear that some of you are leading undisciplined lives and accomplishing nothing but being busybodies." (2 Thessalonians 3:10-11 NIV)
- "A constant dripping on a day of steady rain and a contentious woman are alike..." (Proverbs 27:15 NASB)

Your emotions will reveal themselves in your actions, and any sinfulness you thought you were hiding will be made known for all to see.

The Truth About Fig Leaves

I have used the term "fig leaves" when referring to these disorders and for good reason. When we begin to realize that these disorders originate from our desire to hide, we can find true relief and healing from them. Fig leaves are actually the perfect symbol for what is going on beneath the surface:

1. **Fig leaves hurt.** Sure, they look harmless, but they are itchy and rough like sandpaper. My mother grew up in Mashhad, Iran, abundant in fig trees, and when I told her I was using the imagery of fig leaves, she said, "How appropriate! Those things are so uncomfortable!" Imagine yourself covered in them! But to Adam and Eve, those scratchy leaves seemed a better alternative to being discovered naked. Chronic pain hurts, obviously. But for many of us, our subconscious still considers pain a better choice than

97

openness and vulnerability.

2. **Fig leaves don't truly cover you.** I'm pretty sure there were some holes in Adam's armor. Just as leaves hand-stitched together set you up for plenty of wardrobe malfunctions, chronic pain and illness never mask the real problems underneath. Anger and hurt will eventually surface, bitterness will catch up to you, and fear will still control you. I'm not sure how cold it got in the Garden after sin entered the world, but I do know that rustling leaves provide little warmth or protection from the elements. Pain cannot protect you; pain solves nothing in the end.

3. **Fig leaves limit movement.** You aren't free to take up gymnastics or racquetball while wearing a figgy skirt. Leaves could rip, fall off, or expose sensitive areas. Likewise, chronic pain limits your ability to seek real solutions to your problems. Pain isolates you when you need relationships, keeps you from activities you may enjoy, and makes you feel inadequate when you most need to feel approval. Pain hurts you beyond the physical; it binds you to itself and prevents you from escaping its clutches.

4. **Fig leaves don't last.** Eventually they will dry out and crumble and fall off. You will constantly need to find new fig leaves to replace the dying ones. You can't wash them and you can't repair them; they will wear out. Chronic pain is the same way. While your back pain may have done the trick initially, soon people will stop caring and doctors will stop trying so hard to find a solution. New pains will have to appear to keep your emotions contained.

Fig leaves show the contrast between our attempts to cover up our sin and God's complete obliteration of our sin. Remember, He removed Adam and Eve's fig leaves and replaced them with animal skins, an act that required a sacrifice, the first death in the Garden. These were the same animals that had been named by Adam, who fellowshipped with them and offered them their companionship. Adam and Eve *knew* the ones that had worn the skins they were given. Just as we are called to *know* the one whose sacrifice we now wear in the form of spotless robes. Our attempts to hide hurt *us*. His gift of healing hurt *Him*.

Does thinking about God's sacrifice frighten you? Maybe make you feel obligated or humiliated or exposed? If a fellow human were to offer to die for us, we would not be able to bear the burden, let alone the death of an Almighty God.

When my husband and his father were living here in the United States waiting for the rest of the family to join them from Iran, my father-in-law would refuse to eat kebabs, saying, "How can I enjoy this meal knowing my family cannot enjoy it also?" My husband tried to convince him that his suffering did no good, that eating the kebabs was not an act of cruelty to the rest of the family. My father-in-law's reaction might sound ridiculous, but that's exactly our reaction to Jesus' sacrifice. We still feel we need to suffer, to make up for the pain He endured. It does us no good, and it undermines what He set out to achieve: our healing and our freedom.

Can We Truly Hide Ourselves from God?

> "'Can a man hide himself in **hiding** places So I do not see him?' declares the Lord. 'Do I not fill the heavens and the earth?' declares the Lord." (Jeremiah 23:24 NASB)

God sees our hearts and knows our innermost thoughts. Why do we convince ourselves that we can cover up our sin and present ourselves to Him on our own merits? Satan desires to defeat us and render us useless; what an ingenious method hiding is! Just as in the parable of the talents, we are afraid of God's wrath, so we hide all that He has given us rather than risk failure or shame (Matt 25:14-30). But yet the one who buried his talents lost everything! What consequences are we to face if we continue hiding?

1. **Growing physical pain.** Pain does not yield territory; it seeks more and more. What begins as back pain soon spreads to the shoulders and the knees and the head and beyond. One food sensitivity becomes a list of dozens. My mother at one point was allergic to 178 foods! Consider a life that will grow increasingly smaller and frailer. Think about opportunities lost, relationships collapsing, freedoms diminished. What Satan promises, he never delivers. Hiding only ends in more pain.

2. **Growing chasm between you and God.** Have you ever tried to maintain an intimate relationship, all the while keeping a secret? Topics of conversation are limited, as you wall off more and more of yourself in an effort not to reveal the truth. Lies beget lies, and soon it becomes too difficult to make eye contact or to even be around that person. That's exactly how it becomes with you and the Lord. Confession doesn't come easily, praise is more and more difficult, and soon you find you are barely praying at all.

3. **Growing more and more deceived.** Hiding begets hiding, and when

you are hiding, you can't see clearly. Over time, you will become more easily hurt and offended. You will become more blind to your faults, find more faults with others, pass more blame, withdraw from those who would contradict or confront you, and eventually be unable to tell truth from lies.

Focusing on self makes you small, for what can you learn from yourself that you do not already know? What can you gain from yourself that you do not already have? The Bible tells us to focus on Christ and keep our minds fixed upon Him:

> "Set your minds on things that are above, not on things that are on earth. For you have died, and your life is hidden with Christ in God." (Colossians 3:2-4 ESV)

> "You are my hiding place; You preserve me from trouble; You surround me with songs of deliverance." (Psalm 32:7 NASB)

Did you catch that? We are to be hidden IN God, not FROM God. Imagine hiding in a dark, damp cave, shivering and afraid. Now imagine cuddling up in a soft blanket, warm and cozy. The two types of hiding could not be more different! Hiding in God means to have Him cover up your sins with His precious blood, rather than trying to cover them ourselves.

The Bible talks about several things we are to cover ourselves with:

- Sackcloth, the outer symbol of humility and repentance. (Isaiah 32:11)
- The Armor of God. (Ephesians 7:11)
- Love. (Colossians 3:14)
- The new man, the renewing of your mind. (Ephesians 4:24)
- Christ. (Galatians 3:27)

Our fig leaves may have become our second skin, and they have definitely involved a sacrifice on our part; just not the right one. God himself provides the sacrifice and the covering we so desperately need:

- He has covered us with His blood and clothed us in righteousness. (Ephesians 2:13, 2 Corinthians 5:21)
- "For in the day of trouble he will keep me safe in his dwelling; he will hide me in the shelter of his sacred tent and set me high upon a rock." (Psalm 27:5 NIV)

- "He will cover you with his feathers, and under his wings you will find refuge; his faithfulness will be your shield and rampart." (Psalm 91:4 NIV)

Now doesn't that sound more comforting than fig leaves?

How Do You Know You're Hiding?

We are in a spiritual battle for our minds and hearts. If we hide, we lose. We may think we are comfortably far away from the battle, but in actuality, that just makes us prisoners of war. If we decide to fight, we must know how our Enemy functions. His primary method of attack is in our thoughts. That's why the first line of defense is in taking our thoughts captive, as if they are literal enemy soldiers attempting to climb our walls and besiege our city.

> "For though we live in the world, we do not wage war as the world does. The weapons we fight with are not the weapons of the world. On the contrary, they have divine power to demolish strongholds. We demolish arguments and every pretension that sets itself up against the knowledge of God, and we take captive every thought to make it obedient to Christ." (2 Corinthians 10:3-5 NIV)

It's easy to see how our bodies have been impacted by sin. We have pain and disease to show for it. It's also easy to see how our souls need a Savior. We have sinful behaviors as evidence. The hard part is seeing how our *minds* have been affected by sin. Our subconscious thoughts have been modified from their factory settings; we have a program constantly running in the background that is infected by the sin virus. In this program, sin goes undetected until we bring our thoughts out into the open and see them for what they truly are.

As long as you are alive, you will have thoughts. "Taking every thought captive" (2 Corinthians 10:5) is not a weekly practice, but a moment-by-moment one. Sure, you will get better at it, but you cannot take a day off — Satan sure doesn't! You will be swatting at those little fellas until Jesus comes again. And some will get through, planting their flags in the form of beliefs taking root. If we don't take our thoughts captive, they take *us* captive. And sinful thoughts lead to sinful behaviors that lead to *pain*.

Even though your mind appears to have a "mind of its own" (forgive the pun), it is still a part of *you*. You are not a mere bystander incapable of intervening in this whole process. Imagine your brain as an autopilot, and this autopilot is hard-wired to your sinful nature. If you are not in the driver's seat, paying close attention to your emotions, your brain will take over. And the decisions it will make will be selfish, tending toward self-protection and toward hiding. Hiding is what we do when we are not abiding in Christ. Hiding or Abiding. There is no middle ground.

When you are hurt or angered by an injustice and you don't take those feelings directly to the Cross, your inner thought life will take over and it will sound something like this:

"I can't believe what she did. She is one to talk! I know I'm not perfect, but hey, I do my best. And I have to work within certain limitations that no one seems to appreciate. She isn't worth my time; in fact, forget her!"

That certainly doesn't line up with the whole "turn the other cheek" (Matthew 5:39) idea, does it? Our thoughts rarely mirror those of Christ's when left unexamined.

Even if you are reading the Word daily and attending church and Bible studies, you are not hearing what you are listening to unless you are putting it into action. James cautions us to not only be hearers of the Word, but doers; if we are only hearing the Word and not obeying it, we are "like a man observing his natural face in a mirror, for he observes himself, goes away, and immediately forgets what kind of man he was..." (James 1: 23-24) Using a driving analogy, when you are distracted by being on the phone or texting, you may still see the road, but you don't truly *see* it, not enough to respond in time to avoid an accident. You're simply not processing what you see. [1]

What better time to turn to the Word than when we have been offended or hurt? How many times do we sit in the pew at church and take lengthy notes on forgiveness and love, all the while thinking of how badly others need to be hearing the message and missing it ourselves?

How can we tell if we are looking without seeing? Here are a few things to look for:

1. **The whole world stinks.** My dad tells a story of a man who had gotten some very foul-smelling Limburger cheese on his mustache. He walked into the living room and exclaimed, "Something stinks in here!" He marched into the dining room and hollered, "Something stinks in here, too!" Finally, he went outside and yelled, "The whole WORLD stinks!" If you find that everyone around you is annoying or judgmental or hurtful, look at the one person they all have in common: you.

2. **You haven't changed much in quite some time.** The world should change you. You should be able to look back over your life and see how far you've come. If you are in a similar place to where you were years ago, then you may be ignoring the truth in some parts of your life. Wilderness living is no fun; it's time to move on to the Promised Land.

3. **You hate it when people give you advice.** And they always seem to be giving you advice, have you noticed? Everywhere you go, someone is making a suggestion or commenting on something that's worked for them. Wait a minute. Could it be there's a reason behind this onslaught? Maybe everyone else sees something you are missing. Try something new and listen this time; you may just hear the solution to a problem you never knew you had.

4. **Your world has gotten smaller.** You may have had to not-so-gracefully unfriend certain individuals, as they were getting too close for comfort. Instead, you are choosing friends who agree with you, at least to your face, and sticking to social media where you can reveal only what you want others to see about you.

5. **Your prayer life is less than satisfying.** Your list of needs far outweighs your list of praises, and the needs never seem to be met, so why even pray? You lack the passion you once had for spending time with God, and He seems more and more distant with every passing day.

6. **You feel the need to "Christianize" your thoughts.** It's far easier to maintain a strong Christian facade if you can transform even evil thoughts into more spiritual sounding ones. Don't want to go on the mission field? "My mission is here to my family, that's where God is calling me." Don't want to serve in children's ministry? "I believe it's important for the younger women to step up; I'd only be a stumbling block if I volunteered." Don't want to reach out to a family in need? "It's not my spiritual gift; I will be in prayer instead." Deception can be thickest when it uses Bible verses to lure you away from actual faith and obedience – Satan knows the Bible, too!

Coming into Focus

Looking without seeing causes blurry vision. Our vision lacks focus; not only do we focus on the wrong things, we neglect focusing on the most important thing of all: Jesus.

The Bible doesn't just mention the importance of thoughts — we are given **commands** regarding what we focus on and how we think:

- Abide in Christ and you will bear much fruit (John 15: 7-8)
- Don't allow your heart to be afraid or troubled (John 14: 27)
- Have the same mind of Christ (Philippians 3:15-16)
- Be anxious for nothing (Philippians 4: 6-7)
- Keep on confessing your sins (I John 1:9)
- Keep His commandments (I John 5:2-3)
- Abide in the doctrine of Christ (II John 9)
- Set your mind on things above (Colossians 3:2-3ff)
- Meditate on truth and purity (Philippians 4: 8-9)
- Rejoice always and pray without ceasing (I Thessalonians 5:14-22)

We are told not to *allow* our heart to be troubled, implying that our emotions are under our control! 2 Corinthians 10:5 says that we are to take "every thought into captivity to the obedience of Christ" (NKJV), implying that we are capable of doing so. We are not victims of our feelings, tossed by the waves of our emotions. Rejoicing, confessing, and meditating are not optional, and they are not dependent on how you feel. Obedience is the way to renew your mind, one day at a time, one thought at a time.

Just the other night, my youngest daughter protested that she needed to watch TV before bed in order to "not have sad thoughts." I called her on it and told her she was responsible for her own thought life, TV or not. It reminded me of myself and all the ways I justify my thoughts by mumbling to myself, "I was having a bad day," or "I was hangry [hungry + angry]." None of these are valid excuses. I am responsible for what thoughts I allow inside my mind. That's not to say that Satan won't try to whisper in our ears, convincing us that his words are our own. We need to discern the moment Satan's voice becomes ours.

When we nurture those thoughts, they become behavior, and behavior becomes character. A driver who focuses on oncoming traffic rather than the lane ahead will end up in a head-on collision before too long. Similarly, focusing on anything other than Christ will lead us down a path of self-destruction and physical pain.

Our thoughts affect not only us; they spread to those around us. Our pain affects our family and loved ones, as they suffer along with us — sometimes out of their love and concern for us, and sometimes because we are hurting them with our toxic emotions! Our children are watching how we handle trials; generational sins flourish when we hide from the truth. David's sin with Bathsheba created the perfect breeding ground for David's son Amnon to engage in sexual sin with his own sister (2 Samuel 13). Perhaps if David had been more forthcoming with his own struggles, he could have prevented his son from falling into the same trap. Our hiding harms everyone with whom we come into contact; our faces may be buried in the sand, but our backsides are sticking out for all the world to see. We set out to fool the world, but we are only fooling ourselves.

The two main emotions behind hiding are pride and anger. We feel entitled to certain comforts because of our pride and when we don't get them, we get angry. We want others to respect us and praise us, but we only present them with a shadow of who we really are; when they compliment our facades, it doesn't feel genuine to us, so we despise the praise. Instead of humble confession, we return to pride as a dog returns to its vomit (Proverbs 26:11). Pride and anger are part of a vicious cycle; how can we escape from it?

Pride

Arrogance is what we usually are thinking of when we think of pride — someone bragging about how great they are and making everyone around them feel inadequate. And false humility also makes us feel uncomfortable, as if the "humble" person is always looking for a compliment. Or we view pride as a good thing, a warm and fuzzy feeling we should get when we've done something well or worked hard.

In reality, pride is at the root of every negative, sinful thought. God desires us to be like Him; pride wants to *be* Him. Be careful what you wish for — being God doesn't remove responsibility in your life; it makes you responsible for *everything*. Being God doesn't mean you can get whatever you want; you just have to pay for it. Oh, and create it. And fix it if it gets broken. Pride is an illusion, and it is a promise that never delivers.

What does the Bible say about pride?

- Pride goes before destruction. (Proverbs 16:18)
- Pride brings you low. (Proverbs 29:23)
- Pride defiles.

> "For from within, out of the heart of men, proceed the evil thoughts, fornications, thefts, murders, adulteries, deeds of coveting and wickedness, as well as deceit, sensuality, envy, slander, pride, and foolishness. All these evil things proceed

from within and defile the man." (Mark 7:21-23 NASB)

- Pride is worldly.

  "For all that is in the world, the lust of the flesh and the lust of the eyes and the boastful pride of life, is not from the Father, but is from the world." (I John 2:16 NASB)

Pride is deadly. Boasting about oneself can lead to a devastating loss of relationships, can tarnish our witness, and is summarized in one word: evil (James 4:16). The only thing we are allowed to boast in is God Himself, with the express purpose of giving Him the glory:

  "Thus says the Lord, 'Let not a wise man boast of his wisdom, and let not the mighty man boast of his might, let not a rich man boast of his riches; but let him who boasts boast of this, that he understands and knows Me, that I am the Lord who exercises lovingkindness, justice and righteousness on earth; for I delight in these things,' declares the Lord." (Jeremiah 9:23-24 NASB)

- We are not to boast in our brother's misfortune (Obadiah 1:12)
- We are not to boast in the Law. (Romans 3:27)
- We are not to boast in our gifts or blessings. (I Corinthians 4:7)
- We are not to boast in our ministry. (I Corinthians 9:16)
- We are not to boast in our appearance. (I Samuel 16:7)

Pride has been called "the original sin" because it is the motivation behind Satan's Fall — "I would be like God" — the same line he fed Adam and Eve in the Garden (Genesis 3:5).

How do you know if you struggle with pride? Simple: You're alive. No, really, it's a no-brainer. But here are some other ways to be sure:

- You have ever said, "I would never do that." (Not about skydiving — about something you find distasteful like stealing or adultery or eating non-organic produce.)
- You have certain standards that you expect yourself to meet. If you like things "just so" and feel uncomfortable when they aren't, you are proud. This is the pride that masquerades as a low self-image. Perfectionism often leads to inaction and despair. And it's only a matter of time before you hold others to those same impossible standards.
- You look down on others different from you. Whether they are

poor or disabled or simply wearing last year's shoe style, you feel a twinge of discomfort when they're around.

- You don't take criticism well. Even if it's not intended to be a criticism, you may perceive a slightly negative comment as an attack on your character.
- You are easily hurt. Someone doesn't invite you to their party and you're undone. A friend takes too long to reply to your text and you give them the silent treatment. Pride brings you low, even to the point of throwing a tantrum over something minor.
- You feel the need to defend yourself. You may have difficulty apologizing, or you may be quick to justify your choices.

Pride whispers that you can be perfect. Romans 3:23 tells us we *all* "fall short of the glory of God" (NKJV). Yet we keep trying to elevate and enthrone ourselves. I tell my kids that Self is a tyrannical ruler; it's never satisfied. "Self cannot satisfy self, no matter how frequently it feasts." [2] Self's burden grows heavier and more oppressive, while Jesus gives us a yoke that is easy and a burden that is light (Matthew 11:30). Self demands we meet our own requirements, and we are always adding more and more to the list. Jesus sets us free from those requirements, as He has satisfied all of them on the Cross — Jesus alone is worthy of the title "King" in our lives.

Anger

Pride naturally leads to anger, as being on the throne is a thankless, unfulfilling job. We can't meet our own needs, let alone our own desires, so we are constantly lacking; that makes us angry.

> "What causes fights and quarrels among you?" (James 4:1 NIV)

This is an age-old question, and the answer is simple:

> "Is it not this, that your passions are at war within you? You desire and do not have, so you murder. You covet and cannot obtain, so you fight and quarrel. You do not have, because you do not ask. You ask and do not receive, because you ask wrongly, to spend it on your passions." (James 4: 2-3 ESV)

We all have desires, and most of them are sinful if we can bring ourselves to admit it. We want what we want and we want it *now*, no matter who we have to hurt to get it. Just because we aren't physically violent doesn't mean we aren't wishing harm on others in our hearts. And let me be clear: we are *all* angry. The more adamantly you deny your anger, the angrier you most likely are. We are angry because we have all been born into a sinful nature; it's in our DNA to be angry. The Bible even says, "In your anger, do not sin" (Ephesians 4:26) acknowledging that we *will* be angry. And not all anger is bad; anger can serve as an impetus to defend the falsely accused, to correct social injustice, and to protect victims of crime. Anger is a useful emotion, and denying it can harm your health, as we have seen. But when anger festers and becomes unforgiveness, when it demands its own way, when it puts self on the throne — it becomes sinful, giving an opportunity to the devil to take more and more control of your life (Ephesians 4: 26-27).

How do you know if you are angry? You may not always *feel* angry. Or maybe you've been angry so long, it has become the status quo. Or maybe you equate anger with turning red in the face and smoke billowing out of your ears, yelling and shouting obscenities. Don't be mistaken. Anger also lurks in the silence, in the raised eyebrow, in the carefully crafted prayer requests, in the passive-aggressive ways we refuse to extend grace to others. And worst of all, anger hides behind "righteous anger" which so often isn't the case but makes us feel justified for banishing others from our lives or unfriending them on social media.

- How do you handle not getting what you want?
- How do you speak to a customer service department who is not being helpful?
- How do you handle receiving the wrong meal at a restaurant?
- How do you react when the "wrong" presidential candidate wins?
- How do you respond to criticism from someone you don't respect?
- How do you behave when you have to wait for a longer time than you expect or pay more money than you think is fair?
- Do you genuinely rejoice with others who succeed where you have failed?
- Do you graciously allow other cars to merge in front of you on the highway?

If you answered that you respond peacefully and joyfully to all the above situations, I have news for you: you are either reading this book in Heaven or you are in denial. While your face may wear a smile, and your tone of voice be melodious and full of sweetness, there is anger in your heart simply because you are a sinner.

Does that mean we simply accept the way things are? Absolutely not! As Paul asked in his letter to the Romans, "Shall we continue in sin that grace may abound? Certainly not! How shall we who died to sin live any longer in it?" (Romans 6:1-2 NKJV). Just because we are sinners doesn't mean we are free to sin — in fact, we are free *not* to sin! Before Christ, we were slaves to our anger; we probably didn't even recognize sinful anger for what it was, as it was seen as a natural reaction to being offended or hurt. There was no war between our flesh and our spirits, as we were dead on the battlefield.

Now we are alive again, and we need to be armed and ready to reenter the battle. Fighting against the anger will never be enough; the only way to combat unrighteous anger is to desire something *more* than you desire your own way. The battle is not just yours; it is the Lord's. We fight not for public approval or an external morality, but for His glory. Matthew 6:33 says to "seek ye first the kingdom of God, and His righteousness; and all these things shall be added unto you" (NKJV). That doesn't mean that if you pretend to put Him first, you'll get your way. Putting His kingdom first overshadows all earthly desires and causes us to no longer want them. Putting God first doesn't mean putting our way last; it means eliminating our way from our wish list altogether.

What would that look like in your life? What things are you pining after that you never seem to gain? What is causing fights and quarrels among you?

What are We Hiding From?

We've established that we hide from unpleasant emotions and sinful thoughts, all of which stem from anger and pride. We've also identified that false **fear**, rather than true *fear*/awe, paralyzes us to the truth and creates an environment in which anger and pride flourish. We **fear** God's holiness, as we know that He is a just God, but what keeps us from taking that step from terror to trust?

Let's go back to what we briefly touched on earlier. There are three specific things we fear about a holy God:

1. **Rejection** — What if He won't accept us?
2. **Responsibility** — What if He asks us to do something we don't want to do?
3. **Repentance** — What if He asks us to give up the sins we so cherish to stop doing something we want to do?

1. Hiding from Rejection

Adam and Eve hid from God in the Garden of Eden because they were afraid of being rejected by their Creator. They knew they had failed Him, and armed with their new sinful nature, attributed motives to God such as they themselves would have in His position.

Created in God's image, we crave relationship with Him and with other believers, just as the Trinity enjoys a relationship between the three Persons. We fear losing that connection and mistakenly believe that our being accepted is entirely up to us.

God loved us when we were unlovable. Nothing we could ever do could earn His love, and nothing we could ever do could cancel out His love. We can't even accept His gift of salvation without His first changing our hearts and opening our eyes. As humbling as that is, understanding His sovereignty is key to understanding that we can *never* be rejected by the One who created us, chose us, and predestined us to be His child. If we had any role in the process of redemption, if even a tiny bit of it depended on us, then fear has a foothold. Knowing that we are beloved and set apart regardless of our sinful nature, regardless of our failures and flaws, gives us a security in His love that cannot be shaken or changed.

So many of the world's religions are man's attempts to earn God's favor. Follow these steps, obey these rules, stick to these guidelines, and you will be on your way to earn His approval. Maybe. All these attempts speak to this fundamental fear we have of being rejected. We *want* to earn it, because that means we have some say in the matter, some semblance of control.

We can say the same for our relationships with others. We believe it is up to us to earn favor with the people around us. If I were to ask you what kind of friend you were looking for, chances are you would describe someone who is honest and open — *real.* But we spend so much of our time acting the complete opposite! "That's just the way it is," I often hear. Doesn't anyone question *why*? I liken it to middle schoolers at a dance. The boys all line up on one side, the girls on the other. Neither will speak to the other because they're afraid of being rejected. All it takes is one brave soul to get the ball rolling, to act genuine.

I still have a personal social media account, but I no longer spend any time looking at it if it's not absolutely necessary. I was becoming caught up in the endless parade of happy moments and perfect portraits. Some people I had befriended were my close friends in real life, and I can attest that their lives are nothing like the images they post. Oddly enough, I like them better with their visible flaws and quirkiness. Why do we feel the need to share only the good times? I, too, was falling prey to the deception, carefully editing my posts so as not to offend others or appear inept or foolish. On the flip side, there are those that appear to enjoy posting only tragedy and trials, but there's an element of bragging even in the sorrow — "See what kind of life I am enduring and yet I am strong, yes, a perfect example for others to follow am I!" I was seeing every blessing, every act of service, every meaningful encounter with friends as something I needed to display. "Checking in" at church activities, posting filtered photos of an open Bible (or even of an especially healthy meal — eek, that was totally me!), and sharing family photos where everyone was smiling (not all the ones of the kids fighting, of course) became my way of proving my worthiness to the world. Despite what we see on social media, it simply isn't natural to share the same things with everyone you know, as if all of our acquaintances need to know the minute we buy a new car or eat ice cream or organize our pantry. Heaven forbid we post something and get no response at all!

Suppressing the truth about who you are and how you feel can be so confining that it can elicit spontaneous "out of character" outbursts. If you've ever caught yourself mouthing off to another driver or a customer service representative, you most likely have not been truthful in your relationships. We too often neglect to tell the truth to one another because we don't want others to think less of us. Truth tellers aren't very popular! (Galatians 4:16)

Where is the authenticity? It's buried behind a wall of fear that others will see who we truly are and *reject* us outright. Physical pain has nothing on the heart-wrenching agony that accompanies rejection.

I was a bit of an odd kid and faced a lot of public ridicule. I remember one time in middle school: I had decided I was going to sit with a group of kids in the cafeteria at lunchtime. I didn't have a real concept of "popular" or "unpopular" at the time; I just knew that these kids were having a good time, and I wanted to be a part of the fun. I carried my lunch over and sat down in an empty seat amidst the group. In unison, they all looked at me, picked up their trays and left the table, leaving me alone and confused. I had just been rejected, not for anything I had done, but for the mere fact that I hadn't been deemed worthy of their group. I couldn't understand why; my parents always told me I was funny and pretty and smart and I believed them, as children do. But here was the "proof" of my falling short, of my inadequacy, of my failure to make the grade.

We all have stories like that in our past. Maybe it's a parent who left, a painful break-up, a best friend moving away and not staying in contact. All these stories touch on a fear that has been there since the Fall; that if we can't even hold on to a human relationship, how can we be assured of the love of our Heavenly Father? If we are rejected by other sinners, how can He NOT reject us?

So, we fake it.

We smile and nod, raise an eyebrow, force a giggle. Small groups, small talk, small worlds. We leave no room for honesty, replacing it instead with social niceties. Of COURSE, you look lovely in that dress, I was JUST thinking about you, oh yes, we SHOULD get together. Without honesty, however, there is no intimacy. Without intimacy, there is no relationship. And without relationship, there is no risk of rejection.

Shame causes us to avoid being known by others, to seek out dark hiding places where we can conceal our innermost sins and protect ourselves from being hurt, rejected, or judged. We are afraid that if we are discovered, we will be discarded. [3]

Do you see how this leaves us empty?

We either spend our time pretending we fit in or we avoid fitting in all together. Memes poke fun at this tendency of ours to hide our real feelings: "I'm sorry I was late. I didn't want to come." That's something I've wished I could have said in certain situations! There's actually a party banner that says, "Please leave by 9." (I'm tempted to order one.) Even some of our apparel choices are designed to keep people away unless they share our personal tastes, thus ensuring that only the "right" people approach us. When I'm wearing a shirt reflecting my fandoms, I know that like-minded people will give me a nod or a compliment, and if anyone rolls their eyes at me, I know it's only my favorite TV show they've rejected, never *me*.

Do you feel you can truly be yourself? Or are you afraid you won't be accepted as you are? Can you admit your flaws to even your closest friends? To yourself?

Over time, this burden of phoniness wears on us. And wears us down. The truth must be revealed and if we will not be the ones to share it, our bodies will. Hiding negative emotions while maintaining the illusion of health and happiness on the outside is next to impossible. [4]

I was talking to a stranger the other day who was telling me about her chronic pain — she made the comment, "When I tell people about my pain and they act all uncomfortable, I can tell I don't need them as friends, anyway." Her words hit me hard. Of course! If you have a chronic pain or illness, and you mention it to a new acquaintance, they may reject you. Great! At least you've ruled them out as a possible friend from the get-go. You've now officially avoided getting rejected later on for something more vulnerable like your personality or your beliefs. It's a clever tactic that you aren't even aware of; sort of like a screening process to eliminate the possible haters.

The result, however, is isolation. Isolated people are three times more likely to catch colds and viruses, and 2-3 times more likely to die from an illness! [5] We are created to live in community and connection with others; it is essential for our physical health.

Community is also critical for our spiritual health and emotional health. By not giving others a real chance to get to know you, you are eliminating potential friendships that can help you grow. My closest friends are those who are comfortable speaking truth into my life — they tell me when I'm being selfish or foolish or just plain stupid. It doesn't feel good at the time, but their words spare me countless hours of wandering on the wrong path!

> "Faithful are the wounds of a friend, but deceitful are the kisses of an enemy." (Proverbs 27:6 NASB)

This world is full of pain. Sin has caused us to fall out of relationship with ourselves, others, God, and nature itself. We are living with our hearts out of rhythm, but the good news is that God is restoring us daily into alignment with Him, and that means all other relationships will follow suit.

People will hurt you; some intentionally, some not. They will judge you, they will be unkind, they will bully and mistreat you, they will slander you, there will be *pain*. Others' treatment of you is largely beyond your control, but you alone choose how to react to the painful acts of others — whether to run or hide or retaliate or forgive.

Actions stem from thoughts, so how we respond to others begins with how we think about others in general. Having unreasonable expectations and assigning motives are the top two ways we jeopardize true relational intimacy:

1. What are the **expectations** you may carry around for how others should treat you?

Having unreasonable expectations of others leads to disappointment and resentment. What we expect of others falls into two major categories: areas in which we are successful and areas in which we envy others' success.

Being successful at a behavior or skill can lead to pride and, if success comes easily for you, the assumption that success should be easy for everyone. Certain skills come easily for some and do not come at all for others. Not everyone was raised in a family that taught manners or common courtesies. Others may bear burdens so heavy that they overlook social niceties. Also, as you've heard before, the world does not revolve around you. People make mistakes; they snub you and make jokes that hurt your feelings, they forget your birthday, and they leave you off of the group text. Very little of what other people do is a personal attack on you; they're just human beings and sinners. Just because you would never forget an anniversary, you bake homemade cookies for every newcomer to your neighborhood, and you sign up for nursery duty every Sunday doesn't mean that others even have those kindnesses on their radar. Holding your own social morality high as a standard that all others are expected to reach only feeds your pride; it also sets you up for failure, as not even you can meet your own standards all the time. Also, we secretly expect more from others than we are willing to do ourselves. We get angry when another car cuts us off in traffic, but yet we engage in the same defensive driving tactics when in a hurry. We want others to be happy and encouraging at all times and yet put up with us when we are in a bad mood. We may claim to uphold a standard of behavior, but it's only a smokescreen designed to hide and excuse our own shortcomings. When we fail, in order to maintain our reputation, we must make excuses or hide the truth — that we, too, are sinners like everyone else.

The flip side of pride-related expectations in this case is jealousy-caused expectations. Being envious of others often requires us to dehumanize them entirely. Instead of learning from them and finding out how they lost the weight, got the promotion, or aced the test, we create an entirely new set of demands for them. Not only must they meet *our* standard, they must exceed it beyond all reason. That business owner in your church who drives the fancy car? "Why should he only give $100 to the widows' fund? No, he should give at least $1000; he's got the money! Anything less would just prove he was a selfish heathen." The gorgeous mom of four who sits in the front row dared show up to church with a wrinkled shirt? Tsk, tsk, she should know better. Having such unreasonable expectations of those we envy may make us feel better in that they can never measure up, but it requires that we hide our true fears of not measuring up ourselves.

Forcing others to meet our expectations comes from a need to be validated, praised, and honored. If the measuring stick is of your own design, you can control who measures up and who does not. Surrendering to God's standard means possible rejection, that you won't be able to meet it on your own merit. So, we set ourselves up as bouncers of our own private clubs, determining who gets in and who is sent away. Our selves are firmly on the throne; our standards become the law we hide behind.

I visited a high school the other day right after the afternoon bell had rung — kids flooding the halls, each with their own insecurities and anxieties. I admit I had a little panic attack just remembering my high school years, but I realized I no longer needed these kids' acceptance. I could smile and keep eye contact with even the burliest guys and the most popular girls. If one glared back, I simply didn't care. Most of them smiled back, however — something about a smile makes it difficult not to respond in kind. It was quite a different story from when I was one of them years ago, when I felt invisible and rejected constantly. I had my oldest daughter with me, a freshman in high school herself, and I could see her fear like a mirror through time. The only real difference between us was our expectations. I needed nothing at all from these kids; she desired contact and approval.

Not only do we judge those close to us, we take it a step further and *pre*judge complete strangers. Most of us would label ourselves as open-minded, reasonable people. I consider myself to be tolerant of others, allowing everyone an equal opportunity to be my friend. However, there are teeny tiny things I notice in the general public that really turn me off. For example, I despise cussing. And coarse language. And phoniness. So, if I meet someone that engages in those behaviors, I tune them out. I justify myself by saying that I don't want to fellowship with darkness or some such nonsense, but in reality, I just don't want to bother with the drama. I would prefer to associate with people who don't challenge me, who agree with me in all things, and who enjoy the things I enjoy. Wow, how boring is that! Let alone, next to impossible!

When we think highly of ourselves, it becomes so easy to think less of others. Likewise, if we think too lowly of ourselves, it becomes natural to bring others down to our level. Neither extreme is justified: "I say to everyone among you not to think of himself more highly than he ought to think…" (Romans 12:3) — pride is not allowed — and we are also called "holy and acceptable to God" (Romans 12:1); self-hatred is not acceptable either. We must view ourselves only as Jesus sees us: sinners saved by grace, not by our works, redeemed to a right relationship with God the Father.

Adam and Eve had one rule and they broke it, yet we create an infinite number of rules for others and set ourselves as judges over them. Only by stepping down off the Judge's Bench and taking our place among the accused can we hear the words: "The debt is paid, case dismissed, you are free!"

The only approval and validation that will ease our souls is that of Jesus Christ. His "yoke is easy and [His] burden is light" (Matthew 11:30 NASB). His Law is the "rejoicing of [your] heart" (Psalm 119:111 KJV) and full of "delights" (Psalm 119:143). Our law brings death and condemnation; His brings life.

2. Do you ever **assign motives** to others' actions?

Our fear of rejection can also lead to our rush to reject others before they can do the same to us. As with having wrongful expectations, we seek to find fault with those around us to justify ourselves. We long to declare others "guilty!" and have them face scrutiny so we can skulk away in the darkness and continue living in an illusion of piety and perfection. Just as a detective making a case against a suspect needs to identify a crime and opportunity, they must also determine the motive behind the crime. Juries can't easily convict a defendant without a clear motive, and if we hope to pass judgment on those who have hurt us, then assigning a motive is essential.

Even the simplest of disagreements can become intense warfare solely by assigning motives to actions. If you feel hurt by someone, it's easy to assume they meant to hurt you, that they never liked you in the first place, that you were wrong to trust them, that it's your duty to warn others about them… on and on and on… it will never end. But sometimes an action is only that. An action, taken by a tired or stressed out individual who may not even be aware they hurt you.

You can probably relate to being behind an incredibly slow driver, and as you pass them in frustration and impatience, see that it's a sweet little old man behind the wheel. I know that as I get older myself, I have a lot more compassion toward the older generation — that could be my dad! My impatience always melts away as my heart softens toward them, but I admit I say a prayer that they will stay safe on the road.

My friend from my small group shared a morsel of wisdom she heard: "It's hard to hate up close." How true that is!

Our reactions to others can tell a lot about ourselves. If we too easily reject others or too eagerly seek approval from others, it could mean that we are deeply afraid of rejection.

Applying the truth, what does Jesus say about rejection?

- **Jesus was rejected.** "He must suffer many things and be rejected by this generation" (Luke 17:25 NIV). "The stone which the builders rejected has become the chief cornerstone" (Mark 12:10 NKJV). He bore the shame of worst kind of rejection, false accusations, mockeries, abuse, and torture so we would never have to bear it ourselves.

- **Jesus will never reject His children.** "For the LORD will not reject his people; he will never forsake his inheritance" (Psalm 94:14 NIV). He chose you from the beginning of time, and He is faithful to accomplish HIs perfect purpose for you. Human rejection stings for a while, but you can be assured your Heavenly Father will never turn you away! (Romans 8:1, 33)

2. Hiding from Responsibility

We also hide from responsibility. I'm not referring to paying the bills or doing laundry; it's an owning of your own actions and feelings. It's knowing yourself and allowing yourself to be known. When we say someone is responsible, what do we mean? We are saying that that person *responds*. When there is something that needs to be done, they do it. When there is a conversation that needs to take place, they are present and willing to speak. When there is conflict, they do not run from it. They respond.

God has given us clear guidelines in His Word on how to respond, first to Him, then to others.

Respond to Christ

Our first responsibility is to Christ. He is the only one to whom we are ultimately accountable. The ways we are told to respond to Him are quite simple: *Trust and Obey*. "Trust in the LORD and do good" (Psalm 37:3 NASB).

Trusting and obeying are difficult when you are hiding from the one you are to trust and obey. Jesus tells us to abide in Him (John 15:4), which means "to submit to," [6] "to remain stable or fixed in a state" and "to continue in a place." [7] I believe that the submission and the remaining in one place are irreversibly tied to one another. Remaining fixed in a state of union with Christ is essential to our obedience to Him and our trust in Him. Abiding with Christ also eliminates the **fear** of His holiness:

"Now, little children, abide in Him, so that when He appears, we may have confidence and not shrink away from Him in shame at His coming" (1 John 2:28 NASB).

The first four commandments in Exodus 20 involve our response to God. No other gods, no carved images, not taking the name of the Lord in vain, and honoring the Sabbath day are all summarized by Jesus in the words: "Love the Lord your God with all your heart and with all your soul and with all your mind and with all your strength." (Mark 12:30 NIV) Love is our motivator for obedience, and should flow out of an intimate knowledge of Christ, not out of a self-protective desire to comply in order to escape punishment. Rather than fixating on all the details of the Law or on how society at large defines Christian behavior, we are to focus on Christ Himself: "Set your mind on things above" (Colossians 3:2 NIV) "... for where your treasure is, there your heart will be also" (Matthew 6:21 NASB).

What we focus on determines how we behave – if we are paying attention to the needs of a lost world, we will be eager to serve others. If we are meditating on the beauty of God's creation, we will be more likely to create beauty ourselves.[8]

Abiding is to be our response to God, and out of abiding comes an ability to respond further in obedience and trust.

Respond to Others

The final six commandments deal with our response to others. We are told to honor our parents, be truthful, refrain from stealing, coveting, adultery, and murder. These can be broken down to our responsibility as citizens, as spouses, and as believers. These commandments were summed up by Jesus in Mark 12:31: "You shall love your neighbor as yourself."

- **The Citizen's Responsibility is Obedience**

> "Now, Lord, consider their threats and enable your servants
> to speak your word with great boldness." (Acts 4:29 NIV)

Even during the persecution of the early church, the disciples opted to pray for boldness rather than deliverance. Yet so often, we choose instead to run from our troubles, perhaps under the misconception that the fruit of the spirit "peace" means that our lives need always be peaceful.

> "I have told you these things, so that in me you may have
> peace. In this world you will have trouble. But take heart! I
> have overcome the world." (John 16:33 NIV)

Did he just use the words "peace" and "trouble" in the same passage? It is possible and even promised that we can have peace amidst trouble. The key is in understanding Who is in charge and *letting* Him be in charge.

God has placed us exactly where we need to be. He has appointed leaders over us that He hand-picked, yes, even our boss who seems to delight in making our lives miserable. God is sovereign, and every little detail has been selected and approved before making its way into our life's experience.

We can wage an inward war against our employers, our government, our teachers, our parents, and the world at large, but I assure you it will come to no end. Our battle should not be of our own choosing; we fight in the Lord's army, and He chooses our war strategy, giving us our battle garments: the armor of God.

> "Finally, be strong in the Lord and in his mighty power. Put
> on the full armor of God, so that you can take your stand
> against the devil's schemes. For our struggle is not against flesh
> and blood, but against the rulers, against the authorities,
> against the powers of this dark world and against the spiritual
> forces of evil in the heavenly realms. Therefore, put on the full
> armor of God, so that when the day of evil comes, you may
> be able to stand your ground, and after you have done
> everything, to stand. Stand firm then, with the belt of truth
> buckled around your waist, with the breastplate of
> righteousness in place, and with your feet fitted with the

readiness that comes from the gospel of peace. In addition to all this, take up the shield of faith, with which you can extinguish all the flaming arrows of the evil one. Take the helmet of salvation and the sword of the Spirit, which is the word of God. And pray in the Spirit on all occasions with all kinds of prayers and requests." (Ephesians 6:10-18a NIV)

We are not to waste our energy on things that matter only to a dying world.

"But one thing I do: Forgetting what is behind and straining toward what is ahead, I press on toward the goal to win the prize for which God has called me heavenward in Christ Jesus." (Philippians 3:13-14 NIV)

There will be times that God will call us to right an injustice, however, and in those times, we must be ready and courageous to stand firm. The wisdom lies in knowing what battles we are called to fight; raging against injustice in general will do no one any good, while stepping out in obedience when called to the front lines to do a specific task will yield eternal blessings.

Obedience is always for our good. A map is designed to help us find our way, not to get us lost. Laws are meant to protect us, consequences to teach us, and order to comfort us. Take a moment to read Psalm 119 and ask yourself if your views on God's Laws at all match with the Psalmist's.

- **The Wife's Responsibility is Submission**

One of the toughest teachings in the Bible is that of submission. Wives are commanded to submit to their husbands (Ephesians 5:22), and as much as we may search for them, there don't appear to be any exceptions.

I grew up in a home in which submission was modeled. My mom was obedient and loving to my dad, and my dad protected and adored my mom. My mom was in charge when my dad was at work, but the moment he arrived home, she passed the baton on to him. They supported each other's rulings in matters of discipline, and they were a true team, putting forth a unified front. I am blessed to have seen the real reason for God's command for submission; it just works.

When I got married, however, submission was a real challenge for me. My husband had come from a Muslim background and from a culture where men are rulers of their homes. He had some bad habits at first that made it difficult for me to submit. He would make decisions just to show me he was in charge, and sometimes those decisions were not wise. It took everything in me to not argue and fight him on these decisions. I knew I had to take God at His word, however. So, I put Him to the test. One day, my husband called me and said he had decided to buy a new truck. My insides were a mess because we did *not* have the money for a new bicycle, let alone a new truck. Our current cars were in good condition, so we didn't even need a new vehicle. I said a quick prayer and answered, "I don't think buying a new truck is a wise choice, but I will respect your authority should you choose to buy one." He was silent for a while and said, "Ok, I will." I hung up the phone and tried not to hyperventilate. I was so frustrated and thought how unfair it was that God should put husbands in charge when they so often were not sensible! (I confess that was petty.) When he came home later, he said, to my surprise, that he had decided not to buy a truck after all. He told me years later that my answer had changed his heart. Just knowing that I was putting our future in his hands made him feel that much more responsible for his choices. If I had argued with him, he may have bought the truck to spite me. God proved faithful! When He told us wives to submit to our husbands "as to the LORD" (Ephesians 5:22 ESV), He meant that He would fill in the gaps and protect us as a true Husband should. [9]

How is your submission? Are there areas of your marriage that you just will not yield to your husband? Times you refuse to let him lead you? Although these areas may give you the appearance of safety and security, they are really puncturing holes in your marriage that leave you vulnerable to spiritual attack. When we oppose our husbands, we are standing in the way between them and God. Once we get out of the way, they will be more likely to see the path ahead.

We wives don't want to let go of the control we think we have. But it's an illusion! We think if we let our husbands start that new business or take the kids camping or buy a new sailboat that our worlds will come crashing down. Read the command again: "Wives, submit to your own husbands, **as to the Lord**" (Ephesians 5:22 NKJV *emphasis mine*). When we choose not to submit to our husbands, we are choosing not to submit to God Himself. God is the one who has the ultimate control over our lives, and if we follow Him, He will accomplish His purposes. That may include bankruptcy, injury, loss, and heartache. Are you willing to let go and allow God to work through your obedience? Or do you want to stand in His way, choosing instead to fight for the fistful of dust that is the control you have in your home?

Migraines, fibromyalgia, Irritable Bowel Syndrome, and chronic fatigue syndrome are mostly female disorders. [10] Why is that? Could it be that we women desire to rule over our husbands and resent the command to submit to them? There has been so much injustice towards women in years past, maybe we feel entitled to a revolt; not by taking a stand, but by taking a seat!

- **The Husband's Responsibility is Leadership**

Husbands are commanded to love their wives. If I asked you if you loved your wife, most of you would say, "Of course! I married her, didn't I?" But let me ask you some probing questions:

- How often do you "forget" to do a chore she's asked you to do?
- How often do you ask her how you can serve her?
- How often do you go to battle for her, defending her honor or taking on a task she feels inadequate to do alone?
- Do you ever tease her for being emotional or confused by something you find simple?
- Do you spend at least 20 minutes a day listening to her tell you about her day?
- Do you respect her time and efforts by putting your own laundry away, putting your dishes in the dishwasher, and coming to the dinner table on time?
- Do you make her feel like she is the only woman in the world?

Love is sacrifice. Love is willingly and joyfully serving, even when you really want to be doing something else.

Men have a unique role in a marriage as a provider and protector. This role becomes burdensome when men try to do it alone (back to the whole pride thing). Feeling the weight of responsibility for a growing family can lead to fear of failure, inadequacy, and humiliation. I've often wondered if men develop chronic pain as a test — how well can the family cope without me? What would it look like if I couldn't provide? It's easy to say that you would still be loved and respected even if you were in a wheelchair; it's another thing to accept that love. If your identity is your ability to pay the bills, and you are afraid of the day when you won't be able to do so, you are falling into the pride trap. It's not all about you. Just as women are called to submit to their husbands as to the Lord, you are called to lead your family in the same way that you are led: fully cared for by a loving Father who will never leave you or forsake you, a Father who promises to provide for you out of an overflow of abundance and the cattle on a thousand hills (Psalm 50:10). When you worry, your vision gets blurry. You see your family members as burdens, your job as a trial, your future as not so bright. Anger seeps in, and with it, chronic pain.

Happily married men are healthier than single or divorced men, however, *dependent* men — men who have abdicated their leadership role in the home — are "more likely to develop a number of diseases, including prostate and other cancers." [11]

God's way just works, and it's better for our health!

- **The Believer's Responsibility is Love**

Life has demands, and they never stop coming. Like we talked about in the chapter on stress, these demands can be a source of joy... or they can be an unbearable burden. And at the heart of these demands is the most frustrating of all: other people.

I've never been a people person. All the personality tests I've ever taken resulted in "introvert" and "task-oriented" and "thinking over feeling." Armed with these labels, I saw my lack of empathy as part of my personality, so others should just deal with it. It was only in the past few years that I realized that I am not called to be an introvert OR an extrovert, but a *servant*. Introverts avoid people, extroverts seek their approval. Neither extreme is biblical. Casting labels aside, we have a responsibility to lay our lives down for others, even if it means going out of our comfort zone. For a person who is more introverted, this may mean attending a community group and meeting new people. For someone tending toward extroversion, this may mean meeting one on one with a struggling friend and just listening without offering advice or cracking a joke.

Seeing yourself as a servant sets you free from the need to impress, as well as your expectations of others. That barista who messed up your drink, the man with way-more-than-15 items in the express lane, the toddler who is kicking your chair in church, and even the professor who gave you a failing grade for what seemed like no reason are all people we are called to serve in love. Turning the other cheek should be more than lip service; it should be a lifestyle.

I don't have the right to not be a people person. Once Christ's love fills our hearts and we completely experience His compassion and mercy, we are compelled to love others; not on our terms, but on God's.

- **Taking Responsibility for Yourselves**

Having most diseases blamed on biological causes can offer us a degree of comfort — we can achieve wellness without having to work hard or make difficult sacrifices, as they would be meaningless anyway. [12]

While it would make life so much simpler if we could blame all our problems on our biology, we must take responsibility for ourselves: our reactions and our attitudes. Think back to when someone said something that hurt your feelings. Taking responsibility requires stepping on the brakes and taking a time out. It means asking the tough questions, "Why did this hurt my feelings?" "Did I do anything to provoke their words?" "How can I best respond to maintain this relationship?" Reacting is not responding. To react is just to let the sinful nature's knee-jerk reflex take over — it doesn't really engage who you are as a person, your individual-ness. Without self-analysis, your reaction is counterintuitive; it will never improve your situation, your relationship, or your understanding. Responding is also not simply following the rules out of fear — that's basically the same as not responding at all. A correct response involves knowing who you are in Christ and trusts Him enough to step out in obedience to His will.

How well do you respond to criticism? To conflict? To confrontation? Do you make excuses or have others fight your battles? Do you blame others for your actions?

Taking responsibility for ourselves is a key element of maturity. Without it, we have no clear edges; we are not unique or set apart from the rest. We go where the wind blows, follow the crowd, and blur the lines between self and non-self. Our selves become smaller and smaller, and we perceive more and more threats to self, as our walls grow higher around us and continually move inward, cramming us into an ever-shrinking space of fearful existence.

Auto-immune disorders have been traced back to an inability of the immune system to determine the difference between what is a threat and what isn't — self and non-self — those very lines that we blur when we don't take responsibility for ourselves. Our thoughts and our confusion as to who we really are and what our purpose is, communicate to our immune system.[13] Avoiding responsibility can lead to our body becoming so out of sync with reality that it attacks itself!

Blaming others for your problems has been shown to increase the levels of pain and dysfunction, [14] as have other negative behaviors such as being rigid and stubborn, interrupting, having a high opinion of yourself, assigning motives to others, projecting, engaging in negative self-talk, reading others' minds, and being judgmental. It wasn't for no reason that the Bible condemns these attitudes; it is for our own good that we cast them off, instead taking up our Cross in humility and gratitude, seeing ourselves the way Christ sees us, as deeply loved and forgiven sinners saved by grace.

How do you know if you are being responsible? When you no longer feel the need to run the other way from an uncomfortable situation or relationship, when you cease your striving against the divine design for your relationships, when your comfort zone is anywhere and everywhere, and when you are enjoying intimate closeness with your Heavenly Father.

God's Word demands a response. If we simply read the Word and do not do what it says, we are "like a man who looks at his natural face in a mirror; for once he has looked at himself and gone away, he has immediately forgotten what kind of person he was" (James 1:23-24 NASB). Do you know what kind of person you are?

3. Hiding from Repentance

What is repentance? Have you ever had someone apologize to you by saying, "I'm sorry you were hurt" or "I'm sorry you took it the wrong way." They technically apologized, but what we really were looking for was repentance — a turning from sin, a heart change, a renouncing of old ways and committing to do things differently. That's what we want from others, so why do our apologies often attempt to justify ourselves by shifting blame, making excuses, and minimizing the offense?

Many of the principles in this book may make sense to you in theory. Maybe you have even had a loved one come to mind who you think could benefit from this information. But can you see yourself in these pages?

I was struggling in my prayer life, finding myself always distracted and droning on and on about needs and requests, not finding the motivation to praise God in earnest. I had set aside the time every morning to spend with God, reading the Bible along with my devotional book of choice. I had even taken to memorize verses, writing them down, keeping a prayer journal, all those wonderful things that spiritual people tell you to do. But my prayer life was pathetic. One morning, I heard God say to me, "Get. On. Your. Face." Um, what? I admit I ignored Him for about a week. I could not believe that it was really God speaking to me; I was sure I had misunderstood. But finally, I thought, what have I got to lose? So, I knelt down and put my face to the floor. Suddenly, I could almost see the throne room of God, and I felt humbled to the point of tears. I hadn't been able to pray because I had forgotten to Whom I was praying! Confession just poured out of my mouth — for my lack of trust, my pride, my bitterness, my selfishness — I just couldn't seem to get to the end of the list! And then I could praise — praise is acknowledging who God is, while firmly understanding how unworthy we are to even be in His presence. Confession brings about praise.

Sin and confession are mortal enemies. There is no way that sin will allow you to be that humble and vulnerable and admit you are sinful. Sin will give you excuse upon excuse why everyone else is to blame, that you couldn't help it, that you would be an incredible Christian "if only." Do not fall into this deception. Confession is the only way to true healing and avoiding it will only lead to more pain.

Confess your sins to God. (1 John 1:9) Confess just means "to agree with," so we are agreeing with God that we are sinners. There's no point in arguing with His assessment of you; He knows you better than you know yourself (Psalm 139:1).

Confess your sins to others. "Therefore confess your sins to each other and pray for each other so that you may be healed" (James 5:16 NIV). This verse occurs in the passage on what to do if someone is sick in the congregation; the emphasis is on confession and faith first, then healing. Does this mean you rent out a billboard to list all your sins? No, you need to first confess to whoever you have hurt, make restitution if possible, then confess to a body of believers who agree to hold you accountable for whatever sin in your heart led up to the offense.

Repeat. Yeah, you're pretty much going to be doing steps one and two for the rest of your life. Best to make a daily habit of it!

Fleshly desires that are allowed to fester in our hearts tend to fester in our bodies as well. "Can a man walk on hot coals without his feet being scorched?" (Proverbs 6:28 NIV)

Is there any part of your life, any desire that you have not fully yielded to God? What's the first thing that comes to your mind, the thing you are quick to dismiss, "Oh it couldn't be *that*." For the longest time, I would pray that God could have my entire life, anything He wanted. Except one day, He showed me a door inside my mind. Just like He asked Adam and Eve a question to which He already knew the answer, He asked me, "What's behind that door?" I hemmed and hawed, tried changing the subject, even tried to distract Him with eloquent praises, but He called me on it, and asked again: "What's behind that door?" I finally broke down and told Him it's my room of things I refuse to give Him. Wow, when I said the words out loud (in my head), I was mortified by how awful it was to hold *anything* back from Him! I flung open the door in shame, and He showed me that when I close off rooms to Him, I miss the opportunity to be filled up completely with Him. Those things I had walled off came creeping out, and in the light of His love, they were but vapor. Surrender in the form of confession may seem unbearable, but it brings healing.

If you are only working on your image, you are overlooking the real work that needs to be done: on your heart — and you risk being *exposed* in the *assembly*, according to Proverbs 26:25-26 (NIV).[15] I don't know about you, but I'd rather be almost too eager to confess up front rather than risk the truth coming out some other way!

Hiding from God is at the root of all our pain, both emotional and physical. When we conceal our innermost thoughts and emotions, we seal off access to the parts of ourselves that need healing, forcing the pain to manifest itself in our physical bodies.

What does that look like? What kinds of disorders can be attributed to hiding? And what can we do about them?

How We Hide

You are not your body. Lose an arm, you are still you. No matter what happens to your physical frame, your essence remains the same. Yet we define ourselves mostly by our bodies. When asked to describe ourselves, we usually first select adjectives that describe our outward appearance: our race, our gender, our build, or our hair color. Those descriptions do play a role in our personality, it's true. Your body isn't just a vehicle for your mind to get around. However, your body plays a more profound role in your identity: it displays on the outside how you feel on the inside. Listening to your body can provide insight as to what you are thinking and feeling, the inner struggles and secret sins you would prefer remain hidden.

That's why the wrong diagnosis can do so much harm; it ignores *you*, the best clue there could ever be in finding out where the problem lies!

We are going to dive in to investigate several common diagnoses, but first:

A Word About Labels

We love labels. Think about the ways we choose to label ourselves and one another:

127

- Astrological signs
- Personality Types
- Introvert/Extrovert
- Color of hair (e.g. "blondes have more fun")
- Race, Heritage, or even hometown
- Alma Mater or Profession
- Generation (e.g. "Baby Boomer," "Millennial")

These labels seek to quantify us, but they actually only limit us. For example, I always thought I had to choose between introvert and extrovert; why? Can't I sometimes want to be alone while other times want to be with others? Jesus certainly had times of solitude while other times He was surrounded by people. Sometimes desiring to separate ourselves from others is sinful! The whole premise behind the distinction between introvert and extrovert is ridiculous.

My daughter was telling me about the terms "E-boys" and "emo's" — when I was growing up, we had "skaters" and "punks." If you didn't dress and act according to a set type, who *were* you?

When does an attribute become an identity?

Having a learning challenge becomes "I'm dyslexic." Choosing not to eat animal products becomes "I'm vegan." Not "I choose" or "I feel" but I *am*.

Why are we looking for our identity in our circumstances, our environment, our preferences, and our choices? I am a woman, but I am unique to every other woman out there. I am a mother, but I am not like other mothers. Sure, those things describe aspects of me, but they should never define *me*.

Your symptoms are not your identity. You may be struggling with something now that you may not struggle with in the future. Be careful not to make your struggle *who you are*.

Our identity can only come from our Creator, and He calls us *His*. Our identity in Christ eliminates all labels:

> "There is neither Jew nor Gentile, neither slave nor free, nor
> is there male and female, for you are all one in Christ Jesus."
> (Galatians 3:28 NIV)

We should throw off all worldly labels, as we are not to be defined by the world, but by Christ. Besides, if I am growing to be more like Christ, shouldn't I be asking what His personality type is?

Diagnoses could definitely become labels to hide behind. Symptoms are just that: symptoms. Different conclusions about symptoms can lead to very different results:

- Assuming all illness and pain are physical leads to disappointment, as there is no reliable relief.
- On the contrary, assuming that all disorders stem only from the mind can lead to judgmental thoughts and condemnation.
- Only by bringing both mind and body under the submission of a spirit fully yielded to Christ can we see the bigger picture.

We all hide, we all have pain. I hope you are beginning to see how pain is not the exception, rather the expectation. "There is no one righteous, not even one" (Romans 3:10 NIV). The question is not whether you are hiding, but *how* you are hiding.

Chronic pain and illness are just a few tools the body uses to hide. If you are physically healthy, that's wonderful! You're still hiding — you just may be using a different brand of fig leaf. Therefore, a word of caution: if, when you read the following list of disorders and become angry and defensive, you *have just found your fig leaves*. However, if instead you find yourself condemning those who suffer from them, *you, too, have found your fig leaves*.

CHAPTER SIX:
COMMON DIAGNOSES

If the MindBody approach were more easily accepted by the medical community, I would estimate that upwards of 90% of diseases would no longer be named as such. Medical understanding evolves over time, so today's picture of health may be tomorrow's health crisis and vice versa. One example of the ever-changing aspect of disease is my diagnosis of mitral-valve prolapse (MVP) in the early 1990s. I had to take antibiotics prior to getting my teeth cleaned as well as carry around a medical warning card at all times. Ten years later, after the evidence bore out that most of us had some degree of MVP, I was told I no longer had anything to worry about. The definition of disease is not static.

Today's common diagnoses have not always been so common. The list of chronic conditions will change over time to include new disorders, while others will drop off completely. Ulcers used to be a big deal in the 1980s, but very few people complain of them today. Attributing a condition to stress or another emotional factor usually has that effect — the pain loses its power.

The following diagnoses are common today, but they may not be years from now. There may be newer, more terrifying ones, especially as technology advances. We will probably always have a running list to choose from, as health-related hiding disorders have always proven to be the most effective.

Back Pain

Millions are spent every year in the search for relief from back pain: special cushions, massagers, ice/heating packs, chairs, rollers, and braces; not to mention multiple surgeries, steroid medications, physical therapies, and other costly "remedies." And yet, for most sufferers, the pain never completely goes away.

For those of you who suffer from back pain, you know it to be debilitating, frightening, and excruciating. The fear of moving the wrong way and inciting another painful flare-up never quite diminishes. Every activity is overshadowed because pain might not be far behind.

The medical community is quite honestly baffled by back pain. With a broken bone, the treatment is clear: set the bone and let it heal. Most patients respond the same way to a set bone; however, with back pain, surgeries often result in as many types of patient responses as there are patients. [1] For some, the pain goes away completely, others have diminished pain, still others encounter pain in an entirely different part of the back, and so forth. So, if patients have such differing reactions to a clear "fixing" of the problem, is it possible that the problem was not as accurately identified as was previously thought? Could it be that back pain does not come from spinal anomalies as we assumed?

For the sake of argument, let's suppose you have fallen from a ladder and injured your back. Back injuries are no different any other injury; there is inflammation for 3-7 days, followed by a remodeling period for several months in which the pain gradually vanishes.

Now let's say it's been 8 months or more since your fall. You may not even have felt pain for a few months. But then you get up on the ladder again to hang Christmas lights and POW! You assume you must have twisted the wrong way or reawakened your previous injury. You treat it with ice and rest and painkillers, and in a few days, you are back on your feet, good as new. But something odd has happened in your brain. There is now a direct pathway between your being on a ladder and being in pain. Not only that, other activities will start to exacerbate your back pain. You worry that your injury has never healed properly. You head for the doctor's office and have a battery of tests, all of which reveal a herniated disk on the L4/L5. Aha! So *that* explains it. Your doctor tells you to avoid certain movements, try ice packs, and he writes you a prescription for a steroid, saying that if this doesn't work, he recommends surgery.

How did you end up here? Could that fall really have destined you to a life of pain? How does that happen? You were always in good health, active, independent; how could the slightest movement now cause you such agony?

The explanation is simple. First, let's look at what is happening inside your mind during this whole process.

When you fell off the ladder, you felt vulnerable and afraid. It hurt you physically, but it also hurt you emotionally. No one likes to feel vulnerable, and we usually get angry when we feel dependent and needy. Our physical bodies and our minds are so inseparably linked that what happens to one happens to the other. So, the next time you ascended the ladder, the memories surfaced, and they took the form of the original physical pain. Think of it this way: when you look at vacation photos of the time you climbed a 14-er, you actually can feel the blisters! Memories are stored in the body as well as in the mind.

While other emotions tend to be viewed only as existing in the mind, the emotion of pain is unique in that it appears to have a direct connection to some kind of physical damage in the body; however, this is only because the brain has connected them mentally, not because any real connection exists. [2]

Even though it is merely a memory of the pain, the pain nonetheless exists and must be addressed. If you choose to address it as if there is damage, the pain will become embedded in your mind as resulting from damage. If you address it as memory, as emotion, the physical pain will more easily be eliminated, just like pulling out a weed by the roots is more effective than simply pulling off the top.

In order for pain to exists, there needs to be thought (mental), feeling (physical), and emotion (emotional). The experience of pain relies on all three of these factors in order to bring about the sensation of pain; there can be no pain if any of these factors are missing. [3] Physical sensation alone is not enough to produce actual physical pain. Therein lies the mistake of modern medicine — a basic misunderstanding of the purpose of pain and how it connects and relates to our mind and emotions.

Beyond the first 3-6 months post-injury, if there is still pain, it is labeled chronic. [4] This term merely means you still feel pain; it does not explain *why* you still feel pain. Chronic pain is not a diagnosis; it is a *symptom*.

The presence of pain in the absence of other symptoms is not diagnostically significant. If the only evidence against you in a murder trial were your fingerprints on a subway railing, I would hope the jury would throw the case out!

As my husband was a back-pain sufferer, I've heard all the possible causes: weak muscles, inflexibility, lifting incorrectly, too firm or too soft a mattress, and aging. Fred Amir, in his book *Rapid Recovery*, asks the questions that need to be voiced:

1. Broken bones heal, so why would the spine be any different?
2. If back pain could be eliminated or prevented by strengthening muscles, why do bodybuilders still complain of back pain?
3. If back pain is caused by moving the wrong way, wouldn't gymnasts be the biggest sufferers of back pain?
4. And if back pain is caused by spinal degeneration, why is the majority of people with back pain under the age of fifty? [5]

The human spine is NOT fragile, as many would conclude after hearing the list of spinal disorders and pains that plague our community. In fact, our bones are stronger than steel, with the thigh bone being able to bear the weight of well over nine tons! [6] These incredibly strong bones are capable of healing and going on to support you almost as if nothing had happened. If you cut your arm, the wound heals; even if there's a scar, the skin still holds firm, and the damage is repaired. Back injuries heal, and even if they leave a "scar," there is no reason for ongoing pain.

Why do doctors continue to make these diagnoses? They simply are working from the medical model where the mind and the body are two separate entities. Here are some questions you can ask your doctor:

1. How certain are you of this diagnosis? [7]
2. If you treat people based on these results, do they improve? [8]
3. Do any of the remedies (massage, electrical stimulation, heat/ice) you recommend change my body structurally, and if not, how can they be effective? [9]

It is a rare thing for two doctors to prescribe the same treatment plan for the same type of pain. Random and inconsistent therapies only prove the inadequacy and ignorance of the medical community in the area of chronic pain. [10] The fact that there are so many methods of treating back pain proves that the medical community does not understand what causes chronic pain.

Sometimes tests and scans can prove inconclusive. In these cases, doctors often blame your pain on "inflammation," which makes sense! Being in pain can feel like you are on fire! But real inflammation does not present with pain alone. There would be swelling and heat as well as pain and redness, and inflammation itself results from acute injury, as it is the first step in the healing process, followed by repair and remodeling. Inflammation should only last between 3 -7 days, and remodeling is complete within 6 months. Again, if you have pain beyond 6 months after an acute injury, your pain is labeled chronic, and chronic pain is emotional pain. [11] The idea that inflammation can come and go is frankly ridiculous and unproven. Now, your mind can create symptoms that resemble inflammation, but if it is not from an acute injury, it is not legitimate inflammation. The term "chronic inflammation" makes no real sense medically — and while I am fully supportive of eating the foods prescribed on an "anti-inflammatory" diet, I don't adhere to the premise behind the diet. Inflammation that exists beyond the healing of the initial injury fits the criteria for psychosomatic pain and is best addressed emotionally, not dietarily.

Another diagnosis often made involves a delayed reaction to moving incorrectly. This diagnosis cannot be true because, unless you have muscle soreness because of an intense workout, there is no physical cause for pain that appears days later. [12]

My husband recently fell off a ladder while installing our new garage door opener. While he was sore, mostly on his backside, his back didn't hurt from the fall. He could lift weights and move normally the following day. Several days later, he received some disappointing news about a work situation, and his back pain flared up. Before he learned the truth about delayed pain, he would have assumed the fall had caused the pain, and he would have returned to the former bondage of believing he was broken and damaged, that he should limit his activities and as a result, his life. Instead, he could address the need behind the pain; the need to express his disappointment without shame or fear. His back pain was no longer required.

Questions to Ask Yourself

1. If you have been diagnosed with back pain, can you trace it back to an injury? How did you feel about your injury, and what else was going on in your life at the time? If you can't trace it back to an injury, make a note of events occurring at the time the back pain began.
2. Has a back-pain diagnosis actually helped you? Has your pain gone away, or is it merely being "managed"?

3. How can seeing too much on an MRI be a problem?
4. What emotional benefits are you receiving from your back pain?
5. What emotions are you afraid to express?

Arthritis

One ailment that has been long blamed on chronic inflammation is arthritis. Arthritis is typically an "old age" complaint, but arthritic pain doesn't have to be an inevitable result of aging. Osteoarthritis is merely the gradual wearing of the joints due to a lifetime of use. [1] It is a natural part of aging, like white hair or wrinkles.

If a patient presents with pain in their joints, and the doctor finds evidence of arthritis on imaging tests, the diagnosis is made and a treatment is prescribed. But why would arthritis hurt? In fact, arthritis occurs too slowly over such a long period of time, and as long as the joint is functional, meaning if a doctor can move the joint for you and it has the full range of motion, there is no connection between your pain and the arthritis. [2] The changes made to the joints have been so gradual that you wouldn't be able to detect them or feel them at all. [3]

Even if you *could* feel it, any sensation would actually *decrease* with age, as your bones have completed their adaptations and have stopped making changes. [4] Arthritis is a benign occurrence that results from the aging process.

Not too long ago, bony outgrowths on the spine called osteophytes were blamed for pain as they certainly appear painful! However, there has since been discovered a new way to view these protrusions — as the spine ages, the body naturally seeks to stabilize the vertebrae, and osteophytes are a beneficial adaptation. [5]

Unfortunately, you'll have to tab through more than a dozen pages in a web search before even finding articles discussing their beneficial support; the rest of the search results are all devoted to surgically removing them.

Arthritis is a normal adaptation to aging and should never be painful. However, anger and resentment can make joints stiff, as we may be subconsciously clenching our fists! Joints respond to your emotions just like every other part of your body:

> "Then the king's countenance changed, and his thoughts troubled him, so that the joints of his hips were loosened and

his knees knocked against each other. "(Daniel 5:6 NKJV)

Carpal Tunnel Syndrome

First discovered in the 1800s, Carpal Tunnel Syndrome (CTS) was observed only after an injury of the wrist, not as a result of overuse by repetitive motion.[6] There has been a huge rise in CTS in the last few decades, with surgery being largely ineffective. In fact, a medical journal in 2001 published a study that reviewed predictors of successful surgical outcomes; it was discovered that surgeries would be less successful if there was alcohol use or "the involvement of an attorney." [7] "Involvement of an attorney" is a factor in how well a patient heals after surgery? How could that be, unless the pain were emotionally caused?

I worked at an insurance company right out of college, doing data entry for eight hours a day. I loved my coworkers, my boss, and my office environment, and never once felt any pain in my hands. Soon after I was married, I began working full time at an office supporting a sales team. The job was stressful, there were some interpersonal conflicts, and my marriage wasn't doing so well. Even though my work on the computer was minimal, I started having CTS pain and had to order special ergonomic wrist rests for my keyboard and mouse. I was resigned to wearing a brace for the rest of my career. When I left my job and became a full-time mom, however, the pain vanished — even though the housework I was then doing far surpassed computer work in terms of wrist strain: scrubbing toilets and sinks, cooking, carrying children, vacuuming — yet my wrists never gave me a moment's trouble again. I was happy; therefore, the pain was unnecessary.

Just as guitarists build up calluses on their fingertips from the strings, your body accommodates repetitive motions. Muscles become stronger, joints become more flexible. Carpal tunnel syndrome and other pains associated with repetitive motion are contrary to how the body naturally adapts to how it is used. The body was made to move — if you stop moving, your body will adapt to immobility!

There are as many joint pains as there are joints. Most joint pains are over-diagnosed as being from an injury that hasn't healed or a tear of some kind. If you don't recall a trauma or if you have passive range of motion (meaning your joint can be moved by another person), then there is a good chance that the cause of your pain is not the result of a tear, either rotator cuff or meniscal. [8]

One of the many myths about chronic pain is that it can be the result of an injury that hasn't healed properly. Other myths include: [9]

- If my joint causes me pain, I should rest and not move it.
- The greater the injury, the greater the pain, and vice versa.
- The existence of my pain proves that I have an injury.
- The only solution for my pain is medication or surgery.

Belief in these myths can increase your pain, so be careful what you believe.

Questions to Ask Yourself

1. When did your pain begin? What else was going on in your life at the time?
2. Are there any activities that do not give you pain?
3. What is your attitude towards the activities that give you the most pain?

Psychiatric Pain

There is a strong desire in all of us to be *normal*. When it comes to emotional and psychiatric pain, what *is* normal? How can we possibly define it? With each person being uniquely designed by a creative God, I don't believe it's possible to restrict all the possible qualities we each possess into a set framework of "normal." How does normal even feel? We know when we *don't* feel normal, of course. When we have been crying nonstop for days. When we are easily angered and can't seem to "get it together." When we just can't think straight.

We want someone to tell us that there's a reason we are acting and feeling the way we are. Better yet, we want there to be a solution, something outside of us. We also want to feel that we belong to a greater whole, that there are others who share our sorrows with whom we can both commiserate and rejoice. We are looking in the wrong places.

Being given a "serotonin story" necessarily negates all other possible explanations for your depression. You are now locked in to a biological mindset, no longer looking for answers or possible changes you can make to improve your life. [1] Hopelessness leads to greater feelings of depression in an endless cycle from which there is no reasonable medical escape. Your depression has become merely a sensation to eliminate, rather than a feeling to understand.

Anxiety

Just what is "anxiety"? It seems like we use the term to describe how we feel about everything from awkward social situations to Monday-itis. But what does anxiety look like? Just as the brain decides whether to feel pain, it decides whether to feel anxious. The error lies in the processing of events; if a normal, everyday event is processed incorrectly, the brain can interpret it as threatening and deadly. [1] A knock on the door can mean that a loved one may be coming for tea or it can mean an unannounced visit from social services. Going to the mall can bring feelings of joy and excitement, or it can bring feelings of terror and panic, depending on how the brain perceives the actual event.

How do these errors in processing occur? How does a thought become a fear?

Most of us experience *passive* anxiety, or general worry. It's passive because we aren't actually aware that we are worrying; it's assuming the worst is most likely to happen, so why try. Usually paired with depression, this kind of worry causes us to live in a state where our brains are not thinking constructively to solve problems because we doubt the possibility of solutions. We believe we are totally off the hook for the results, as they were inevitable and could not be prevented. When we worry, we cannot solve problems. Your brain can only process one line of thought at a time. [2] Worry begets more worry; our thoughts become less and less productive, and we find our lives sinking into mediocrity.

For some of us, however, this worry has taken on a more distinct form, a state of high alert. A certain amount of fear can seem necessary to help us stay on the right path, like triple-checking the alarm clock or calendar, just to make sure we don't miss that critical appointment. Or white-knuckling the steering wheel to keep from driving off the road. But are these behaviors necessary? What would happen if we *let go*? Would we really do something out of character like oversleeping or forgetting the meeting? Would we suddenly swerve into oncoming traffic? No. Our subconscious mind loves to take over and handle these things, if we would only just relax and let it. Fear is not necessary for us to be responsible, wise members of society, and understanding this fact is critical to letting go of fear as a whole. [3]

The problem comes when this fear becomes a way of life and leads to anxiety. Far beyond worrying about making a social blunder, we fear our own fundamental imperfection, and this terrifies us. Rather than turn to

God's redemptive power for our sanctification, we believe we can take matters into our own hands.

Therefore, we create a life revolving around unbreakable rules, and we then add more and more rules to insulate ourselves from the chaos we fear so much — and the more rules we make, the less in control we feel, so we keep adding rules and rules and rules…. To feel safe, we must keep our rules at all costs and, in fact, everyone else needs to keep them, too! (Doesn't this sound eerily familiar to the Pharisees in the New Testament?) The problem with this attempt to control our surroundings is that it leads to anger when others — and we ourselves — don't live up to these high standards we have created. We feel helpless and angry at not being able to enforce rules for others, especially when we cannot even enforce them in our own lives. [4]

This type of anxiety may have started from a feeling of weakness or vulnerability, but it quickly evolves into an "out-of-control strength to not act out rage," [5] with the only thing standing between us and an angry outburst is the physical pain that inevitably comes to the rescue. People with this type of anxiety tend to become narcissistic, expending so much energy on trying to meet their own emotional needs, that the needs of others, even their very feelings, become inconsequential. Even career victims are narcissists, as their only concern is safety — operating under three incorrect beliefs: I must perform well, I must be treated well, and life must be easy. [6] Since these beliefs will never be played out in reality, the individual is constantly on the brink of insanity even though they never show it on the outside. Once in a while, the pressure becomes too much — panic attacks can be a glimpse into their inner turmoil.

Eventually, this level of frenzied worry will wear you down and lead to an emotional paralysis. Anxiety robs you of your identity and purpose, and blinds you to the resources God has provided for you, even God Himself. Just like a child who loses sight of his parent in a busy mall, we are paralyzed, seeing everything around us as a threat. We simply don't know what to *do*.

Pregnant women learn to control the pain in labor by focusing on one spot and not breaking that eye contact even for a moment. It shocked me to discover how well that simple trick worked! I found I could endure my labor pains well enough… until I looked away; then the pain came flooding in and overwhelmed me.

Our need for a Father, a Shepherd, is encoded in our DNA. When our eyes are not focused on Him, our bodies and our minds simply cannot function. We are created to rely on Him for all our needs, but when we allow this anxiety to take over, we seek comfort and security from objects, other people, and routines, avoiding anything that could cause us harm.

The sad news is that all of those safety-seeking behaviors actually perpetuate anxiety. The brain needs to create new connections in order to override that panic instinct. [7] If anxiety is the school bully, we need to stop hiding in dark hallways or giving him our lunch money; we need to stand up and face him. How? By seeing our situation as an opportunity; we've been curled up in a ball, hopeless, sure that help will never come. But if we were to look up, we would see our Savior, right there all along, beckoning us to rise and follow Him. Going through tough times with our hand in His retrains our mind to see events through His eyes, thus breaking the anxiety cycle.

The Bible tells us to be anxious for *nothing* (Philippians 4:6); therefore, our modern definition of anxiety being biological or physiological directly opposes Scripture. As long as we entertain the belief that anxiety is something that happens *to* us, and not *by* us, we will never experience freedom.

Depression

Depression is not to be confused with grief or sorrow; these are normal reactions to loss and tragedy. Depression refers to the chronic state of feeling unmotivated, less-than, weary, foggy, and trapped in a world that no longer holds meaning or joy. Feeling detached from life and from others can lead to all kinds of self-destructive behaviors such as overeating, shopping addictions, substance abuse, and cutting.

If not dealt with properly, depression will affect more than the mind and the emotions, it also "reduces natural killer cell activity," a key component of the body's immune response. [1] A depressed mind leads to a depressed immune system, sapping you not only of your will to live but possibly even your life itself.

Why are so many of us depressed? Even among those taking antidepressant medications for over a year, 65-80% remain depressed. [2] Could it be that our basic understanding of depression has been wrong all along?

We are told that depression is caused by a chemical imbalance in our brains, and that explanation appeals to us because it means we don't have to look at the real cause for our emotions going haywire. We don't have to deal with painful memories or face what is wrong with the way we are living.

Although long debunked as a "mental illness," depression is another phenomenon that is still considered by many to be something beyond their control, something that just "happens" to them. It would seem insensitive and un-Christian to tell a person suffering from depression that they are at all responsible for their emotions. Even while the theory of chemical imbalance is being systematically dismantled by medical research, it is still the pervasive view among the general public.

Often it is the desire for sympathy that causes a depressed patient to cling to a clinical diagnosis, out of fear that the real reasons will only lead to humiliation and criticism from others. Understandably, quite the reverse happens: if others don't know what you are feeling, they cannot truly empathize with you. They will see you only as a medical case, not as a hurting soul. Depressed people hide from connection with others, the very thing they need most of all. Their isolation leads to their becoming over-protective, over-sensitive, and overall not very fun to be around, thus isolating them further. [3]

Depression and pain can serve similar purposes; both can be warning signs that there is a disconnect between external experiences and internal beliefs.

- Depression is usually a warning sign that something in your life needs to change, so why mask it or treat it medically? If you are working in a job that bores you to actual tears, depression can lead you to seek elsewhere for employment. If you are overweight and feeling bad about the way you look, depression can motivate you to seek fitness advice. Looking to medication and psychiatry instead can postpone necessary decisions and cause you to remain stuck in a bad situation for a longer period of time.

  By dismissing depression as merely a chemical imbalance, you are ignoring your ability to change your life; you are yielding the greatest control you have and deciding to become powerless instead. [4]

- Depression can also serve as an emergency brake in a car running out of control; if your thoughts are running full steam ahead toward self-destruction, depression can provide a type of sedative to numb the pain and slow you down:

Depression can be a valuable tool used by the subconscious to suppress your energy, thus preventing you from doing something self-destructive like committing suicide. [5] Taking medication to reverse depressive feelings can actually give a person the energy needed to take harmful actions like killing themselves! [6]

Depression, like anxiety, takes many forms. Not everyone who is depressed shows it on the outside, and some seemingly happy people would admit to being depressed. The solution to depression is not to "fake it until you make it" — it's dealing with the root thoughts that are to blame, and to replace them with thoughts that will produce true joy and healing.

It is a misconception that depressed people *act* depressed. Many have given up on the inside only, continuing the outward façade of happiness, fulfilling their responsibilities, but with deep-seated rage simmering underneath. [7]

Depression has been called "anger turned inwards," and many believe this means you are angry at yourself; however, you need not be angry at yourself for your anger to be turned inwards. Anger at others or at God that is stuffed down and hidden produces symptoms of depression just as easily. And why do we get angry at others or at God? Because we feel entitled to something we do not have, or we are asked to do something we do not want to do.

Your biochemistry does not control your attitude; they mutually influence one another. [8] The story you attach to your depression is powerful, as is deciding that the story is no longer doing you any good. [9] Depending on what you believe about your circumstances, you can either become locked into a narrative of depression or an epic tale of victory over adversity. You can alter your biochemistry by changing the way you view your life.

While I was writing this book, I had several bouts of despair. I was convinced that I was unworthy to be writing on this topic as I don't have a PhD, I hadn't written a book before, and I'm just a nobody. I almost gave up countless times. I avoided my computer, closed the door of my office, and became depressed. Avoidance of the issue led to bad habits like eating too much candy, buying things I didn't need, skipping my workouts because I just didn't feel like it. I was trapped in a spiral, heading downhill fast. I grudgingly decided to practice what I've been preaching. When I traced those feelings of inadequacy back to a lack of trust in God who had called me to write this book, I regained my focus and my enthusiasm. I may be a weak vessel, but He is strong enough and big enough to fill it and to accomplish

His ultimate purpose through me. *Avoiding my calling was undoing me; obedience was my rescue.* Almost immediately, my despair lifted.

Even anger at yourself, while it sounds noble and hints of saint like martyrdom, is a form of pride because it implies that you should have known better, that the bar should be set higher for the likes of someone like you, that mistakes and poor decisions are for *other* people, never *you.*

We Christians need to see depression for what it is: putting self on the throne. Self is a tyrant, always demanding more and more, never offering us anything in return aside from what we already have. We end up feeling unfulfilled, just like a snake eating its own tail and never having its hunger sated. **Depression is an opportunity.** Just as the desert wandering of the Israelites served to not only remind them of their own lack of faith but also to instill in them a hunger and thirst for the Promised Land, your wilderness of depression can bring you a new perspective on the contrast between a life lived for yourself and a life lived as God intends.

The world tells us to take up new hobbies or a service project to combat feelings of depression. These are not bad ideas, but the only reason they are effective is that they take the emphasis off of yourself and direct them onto something else. You are always worshipping something — what or whom you worship can make all the difference between a life of despair and a life of meaning. The opposite of depression is not happiness; it's *praise.*

> "He was despised and forsaken of men, A man of sorrows and acquainted with grief…" (Isaiah 53:3 NASB)

God knows our pain. When we go through particularly dark times, it's so tempting to believe that He is distant and uncaring. Sometimes it's hard to see the path we are called to walk, and we begin to panic. Our thoughts and feelings can lead us down paths we were never meant to follow, but they can *lie.* God is *incapable* of lying; His Word is always Truth, and He will always provide enough light to see the next step.

Where are your thoughts leading you?

> "How long must I wrestle with my thoughts and day after day have sorrow in my heart?" (Psalm 13:2 NIV)

Post-Traumatic Stress Disorder (PTSD)

You may hear the term bandied about in jest ("Don't talk about that history test, I still have PTSD!") but for those who have been through *actual* trauma, PTSD can be debilitating and disabling. Loud noises, cramped rooms, bright lights, and other triggers can all cause the sufferer to feel as if they are reliving past traumatic events.

In PTSD, a memory has become stuck on replay in the mind, leaving the body on high alert in case similar circumstances appear. Just like the overactive response to a perceived bee sting, the mind is constantly scanning the environment for signals that danger is afoot. While the memory of the traumatic event cannot be removed, it can be reframed to bring about peace and healing. Rather than seeing the event as something to be feared and avoided at all costs, the PTSD sufferer can see the event as a *blessing* as it has shaped them into the person they are today: a survivor, an inspiration, a hero.

Dr. Stephen Joseph, aforementioned author of *What Doesn't Kill Us: The New Psychology of Posttraumatic Growth*, has found through his research that many PTSD sufferers are able to move on from their pain and see the benefits of adversity, even using their struggles to help others who have similar stories. Through the use of expressive writing, they could see their immune function boosted, enhanced respiratory function, fewer migraines, and other changes that exceeded the emotional benefits. Writing their feelings on paper, Dr. Joseph says, was easier and less intimidating for patients than having to express themselves out loud. [1] Expressing your feelings doesn't have to be public or dramatic. Journaling can be hugely beneficial in bringing the hidden out into the light where others can see and understand. Journaling can hold you accountable and help you own your own thoughts, and it can also help you see the changes you have made, no matter how small and gradual they may be. Most importantly perhaps, sharing your story encourages others to do the same, so your struggle can serve as a blessing in someone else's life. For these PTSD sufferers, facing their demons rather than hiding from them brought healing. The healing they needed went beyond the pain and discomfort; they needed a resolution and a greater explanation for their sufferings.

Taking medications for PTSD might reduce the pain, but it will also remove your memories and prohibit growth and development that could lead to a more meaningful life as a result of all the lessons learned from your traumatic experiences. Which route would you rather take? Wouldn't you rather your trials have meaning and purpose, and to be able to see the blessings that have resulted from them? [2]

Adversity brings blessing and transformation, not just to people who have gone through intense trauma but to all of us. [3] Hiding from discomfort brings more of the same. How would a renewed understanding of the benefits of adversity impact the psychiatric community? Would pills still be the remedy of choice, or would psychologists recommend a more outward approach: share your sufferings and in so doing, help others? Maybe "bearing one another's burdens" has the added blessing of finding your own load lightened in the process.

If a broken bone is seen to have a definite external cause, why wouldn't a broken heart or a broken mind? Speaking to a solid Christian counselor or pastor, or even a caring friend, can do more good for the sorrowful heart than a dozen vials of antidepressants. We need to feel validated, understood, encouraged, and ministered to by others, and having your feelings labeled "disorders" can have the opposite effect.

Questions to Ask Yourself

1. Do you find your life lacking meaning? What meaning does God attribute to your life?
2. When the Bible commands us to not be anxious, did it ever occur to you that that is *possible*?
3. How can obedience be the solution to depression?
4. How does the meaning you assign to events affect your feelings about those events?
5. How can depression be an opportunity for you to make changes in your life?
6. Who do you think might benefit from hearing about your struggles?
7. How can trauma in your life be used to encourage others?

Chronic Fatigue Syndrome (CFS)

Chronic fatigue has been around for centuries, but under different names. In 1869, it was called "neurasthenia" and in 1955, "myalgic encephalomyelitis." Attempts have been made to attribute chronic fatigue to the Epstein-Barr virus, but no real correlation has been proven. [1]

Fatigue acts in much the same way that pain does. The brain makes a decision based on a set of physical and emotional factors to make you fatigued. If the brain senses you need to conserve your strength because you have been working hard for several hours, it may cause you to feel like sitting down and resting. If you are ill or have a discernible disease, the fatigue will last as long as the illness does. But if you are emotionally fatigued, no amount of physical rest will take it away. [2]

When you're sick, your body makes you sleepy. Once the illness has passed, your energy returns. Depressed individuals attempt to sleep their despair away, only to feel the whole impact of the sorrow return upon awakening. Sleep does nothing for emotional pain, but only delays it until it can best be faced and overcome.

Chronic fatigue works much the same way. It is the mind's attempt to push "pause," distracting both mind and body by an extreme weariness in an almost anesthetic state in order to avoid a breakdown. Chronic fatigue is actually an overload of energy, [3] continually being repressed in an attempt to restrain an imminent emotional outburst. It is one of the most heartbreaking pain disorders, as the sufferer has to use every ounce of strength they possess to hold back the emotional pain.

One could argue that chronic fatigue is the extreme end of the spectrum of emotional pain due to its immobilizing, all-consuming nature. It's as if the body goes into standby mode, unable to cope with the internal turmoil, paralyzed by fear that the emotion will escape. Fatigue is an emotion just like chronic pain, designed to prevent the harm that can result from unwelcome emotional expression. [4]

Imagine trying to push an inflatable ball under water and hold it there. The ball represents your emotions that you so desperately want to suppress. The amount of energy you will need to expend to keep the ball under the surface indefinitely will wear you out rapidly, leaving no strength left for other activities of daily life. Neglecting interests and hobbies and enjoyable activities because of the exhaustion leads to despair, another emotion to add to the pile.

Sufferers have described the sensation as if "all blood had been drained out," or "my limbs were so heavy they felt like bricks." All power is diverted to the mental work of keeping unwanted feelings hidden.

CDC researchers concluded that childhood abuse contributes to a greater chance of developing CFS — up to 800% greater [5] — and that CFS "evolves from early and severe stress." [6]

If you grew up in a home where there was abuse or neglect, you may be dealing with misplaced shame. Victims often blame themselves for the abuse in an attempt to regain some sense of control over the events. There is a fear that others will judge them, recoil in disgust from them, or abandon them if they voice their experiences out loud. These beliefs are deceptions of the evil one, intending to isolate you from a body of believers who are called to help carry your burdens and a God who desires for you to cast *all* your cares on Him.

Your childhood may have appeared to be normal to the outside world. And maybe it was. But what matters is the feelings you carry with you about your childhood. You don't have to have been physically abused to harbor difficult feelings about your early life. Whatever your circumstances, it is important that you address the feelings and beliefs you may have had at such a young age, as they have shaped the person you are today.

What if you can't remember any emotional pain from childhood or otherwise? Emotional memories are stored in a separate part of your brain from other types of memory. The amygdala stores the emotional memories, while the cortex deals with awareness and cognition, storing the memories that are more tangible like your address and your best friend's middle name. Oddly enough, while both are essential for optimal memory, emotional memories that are stored in the amygdala aren't always conferred to the cortex, which can yield some puzzling emotional reactions,[7] as you may react to situations out of an emotional memory that your cortex cannot bring to your conscious' forefront in detail. The emotional memories are there, and your insular cortex uses that data to determine the extent and the meaning of your pain,[8] but you may be left feeling confused and out of the loop, with only your pain and fatigue left behind from the emotional pain you no longer remember. The amygdala is the first stop on the highway for your sense of smell, so if you ever wonder why certain smells evoke odd feelings, it's all because of the ability for smell to access emotional memories otherwise closed off to the conscious mind. We learned about how memories evolve every time they are recalled, so compound an already confusing situation by adding more and more emotional memories, and you have a chaotic mess of emotions with no clear origin or purpose, all of which the mind is attempting to suppress and deny.

The best way to combat chronic fatigue is to address those difficult feelings head-on. This may be difficult, as the emotions have been under wraps for so long that they may be unrecognizable as your own. Sometimes it is of benefit to pursue those activities you enjoyed previously, regardless of how exhausted they may initially make you. If you are waiting for the energy required, it will never come. After all, activity generates energy, not the other way around. [9]

My mother had chronic fatigue for as long as I can remember, and she would often say that she was waiting for some energy to come. Sometimes it would make a brief appearance, but she would always end up "crashing" immediately afterwards. She would sadly list all the things she wanted to do but couldn't because she was simply too tired to do them. Only after she started dealing with the emotions, adding activity to her life gradually, and seeing progress and hope for the future, was she able to be completely healed of chronic fatigue.

We don't become tired through activity as much as we do through inactivity; when we abstain from doing things we love, miss out on life experiences, and avoid responsibilities. [10]

Your emotions are not beyond your control. Your emotions can control you if you let them, but you also can take back the reins through reclaiming your thoughts. Power lies in realizing the emotions you are trying to hide and harnessing them to grow into the person God has created you to be. [11]

Avoiding pain and repressing emotions results in an extreme drain on the body's resources for energy. [12] The body simply cannot remain at a heightened, tense, fearful state for long — pain and exhaustion result. And the pain continues to spread and grow as the fear of pain grows along with it. It's a nasty cycle, and the only remedy to be found is back where it all began: your thoughts.

Questions to Ask Yourself

1. Take some time to be alone with your thoughts. Are there any areas of your past that frighten you? Any thoughts that seem out of place or off limits?
2. What would it take for you to just let go emotionally?
3. What do you really want out of life, and what are you willing to do to get it?

Fibromyalgia

Fibromyalgia is the epitome of chronic pain. Sufferers experience intense pain throughout their body, and it can be debilitating. Interestingly, while the pain appears to be somewhat constant, it can intensify as a result of stress or other triggers.

Fibromyalgia usually goes hand in hand with chronic fatigue, and the principle behind both diseases is the same: trying so desperately to hold back the emotional flood that you are in physical pain and completely exhausted most of the time. The kind of tension required to repress such strong emotion results in both fatigue and physical pain, as every muscle is strained to its limit.

There is no one accepted cause or cure for fibromyalgia. Doctors are stumped at its origin, and this may be a blessing in disguise. If there were a proposed medical solution, it would most certainly be invasive, expensive, and bring with it devastating side effects. If surgery is recommended for mere back pain, what would be the suggested treatment for pain all over the body?

Our mind loves to work in pictures — when someone is feeling agitated, they say, "They are really pushing my buttons." Fibromyalgia is in a sense experiencing pain in multiple "buttons" all over the body. Having so many "buttons" suggests living in a constant state of irritation. This heightened physical sensitivity results from being an overly sensitive person overall. Placing one's own emotions and desires above those of others can create an unsolvable dilemma when they are not met. Pain allows those desires to be tended to compassionately while saving face; instead of being seen as "needy" or "selfish," the individual is accommodated with grace and empathy.

Being a sensitive person is not the same as being a compassionate person. We are called to love one another (John 13:34) and weep with those who mourn (Romans 12:15), but this level of sensitivity is directed outward, never inward. We are not to be sensitive to insults but rather to "turn the other cheek" (Lamentations 3:30 NLT) and forgive others their sins (Matthew 6:15). Nowhere are we told that it is okay to demand justice (Hebrews 10:30) or to hold grudges (Job 5:2).

If we hold others to higher standards than they can possibly meet, we will live in constant disappointment and resentment. We may present a forgiving facade, but those accumulated offenses will end up destroying intimacy with others, leaving us isolated, sorrowful, and in pain.

> "Moreover, all his days he eats in darkness, with much sorrow, sickness, and anger." (Ecclesiastes 5:17 BSB)

> "Get rid of all bitterness, rage and anger, brawling and slander,

along with every form of malice. Be kind and compassionate to one another, forgiving each other, just as in Christ God forgave you." (Ephesians 4:31-32 NIV)

Questions to Ask Yourself

1. How much of your life is spent defending your illness to others? What do you *really* want to hear from your loved ones? What emotional need has been unmet to the point of your body needing to compensate?
2. What standards do you hold for others? For yourself?
3. What "buttons" do you have, ways that people annoy you or offend or provoke you?
4. If you were given a microphone and a stage, what would be the topic you would speak about? Be honest. What insights can you learn from this passion?

Autism (ASD)

Having a child with autism can be lonely and heartbreaking; especially when it seems everyone wants to tell you what to *do*, what foods to eat, how to "cure" autism, which therapies work, etc. I've heard the phrase, "If you've met one child with autism, you've met one child with autism," pointing out that every child is different, and what works for one does not work for another. The uniqueness of the disorder is uncomfortably similar to the uniqueness of chronic pain because it suggests a deeper root than we have up to this point been willing to explore.

How is autism similar to chronic pain? Perhaps not autism itself, but certainly what it has become in our modern culture. Many of the geniuses of years past were most likely at least mildly autistic: Michelangelo, Sir Isaac Newton, and Mozart, among others, would probably have been diagnosed with autism today. The Autism Spectrum Disorder (ASD) diagnosis, however, being a spectrum, includes many individuals that would not be traditionally considered autistic; in fact, we all fall on this spectrum at one time or another in our lives. Such a diagnosis is too broad to be considered helpful, and one should question the implied definition of "normal" human behavior.

The question is: is how we deal with diagnosing autism now actually contributing to hiding behavior?

I would argue that expanding the diagnosis to include much of what would have been considered "normal" only a half century ago is actually a disservice to children, rather than a benefit. Let me explain.

We've all heard of Hans Asperger, the Austrian pediatrician for whom *Asperger's Syndrome* was named. *Asperger's Syndrome* was a diagnosis conferred on children for whom the term autistic seemed too extreme. *"Asperger's,"* as it came to be known, was the term used to describe children that were moderately autistic but still highly functioning. Dr. Asperger's findings on the subject were groundbreaking, as they appeared to explain odd behaviors in children that previously had been misunderstood as juvenile delinquency or mental illness.

However, it's what we don't hear about Dr. Asperger's findings that should concern us. Although he publicly distanced himself from the Nazi regime, he appeared to buy into the belief that fascism (from *fascio*, meaning "group") was a noble goal for a society. Nazism set forth a standard of behavior and social compliance that must be adopted in order for the group to prosper. One element of that social compliance was connectedness. Proper emotions, proper responses, and proper relationships — all in an attempt to elevate and unite the Nazi regime and eliminate individuality. There was a "model kind of personality"[1] Nazism desired to duplicate among the people. Antisocial individuals were seen as a threat or a burden to the nation, and Nazism sought to remove them for the greater good.

It is into this culture of conformity that Dr. Asperger began his work on identifying autistic psychopathy. He would go on to describe autism as a defect of *Gemüt*, meaning "soul" or a lack of "commitment to the national community."[2] Ultimately, a child's responsibility to the state trumped all other commitments, even to family. A child must conform to society or be removed from it altogether.

Just how did he diagnose the condition? Surprisingly, he had little to no criteria other than what he found odd or unappealing: bad posture, flat feet, clumsiness, poor hygiene, or soft voices could all be considered autistic — anything that didn't "fit in."[3] If he didn't like a child, he assumed no one else would, and that their very presence would burden others who might find them annoying or unusual. Whether or not he personally condoned it, these children were often put to death while under his care. He routinely denied their humanity, so he may have seen it as a mercy to terminate their lives. For some, he allowed "special education," which was basically a "collection basin for negatively selected children"[4] in order to quarantine them from the normal, healthy children who were contributing to society. I find it disturbing that the origins of "special education" had its roots in such sinister intentions.

Asperger's description of autism was inconsistent and without set parameters. He applied his diagnosis to either prove a child was worthy or to deem them inhuman, judging a child's very existence via a random and ever-changing list of descriptors. Every aspect of a child's life was subject to judgment. [5]

Seen through the lens of a diagnosis of autism, the children had no "normal" qualities; even talents were seen as autistic anomalies. Behavior was the main criterion for diagnosis, as no physiological precondition was ever identified.

Perhaps we may never have heard of Dr. Asperger, had his work not been introduced to the United States in 1981 by British psychologist Lorna Wing. Armed with a looser definition of autism, rates of diagnoses exploded from 6% a year to 15% a year in the 2000s. By 2016, one out of every 68 children had the diagnosis, now termed "Autistic Spectrum Disorder" (ASD). [6] One description of the disorder in the DSM-V is that it involves "deficits in social communication and social interaction" — not a far cry from Dr. Asperger's original definition of the disorder.

Unfortunately, Lorna Wing regretted bringing the concept of Asperger's into popular view, saying she would prefer to toss all labels aside. According to her, labels are meaningless. [7] We will never know what would have happened had the condition not been introduced to the English-speaking world.

Today, we still don't have a fundamental basis for what appears on the list of criteria for ASD, other than they are behaviors that seem "off" to us. Asperger himself, after the fall of the Third Reich, appeared to distance himself from his previous Nazi-era conclusions that autism was a psychopathy, preferring to call it a "character anomaly" or "character variant" and that *anyone* may act in an autistic manner when depressed or in "a state of great creativity and mental activity." [8]

Just what accounts for the Asperger's explosion in the 1990s? While many point to toxins, nutritional deficits, vaccines, and other environmental factors, it is more likely more subtle a cause.

The 1990s were a time of increased pressure on parents, our healthcare system, and our schools to meet higher standards for our children. With the increased criticism came increased opportunities to fall short, producing a fertile soil in which more and more defects could be identified. [9]

Parents, teachers, and society at large became more critical of behavior in children that up to that point had been considered a normal part of growing up. With the rise of technological advances, parents were freer to pursue interests outside the family, leaving "latchkey kids" to fend for themselves after school. Less and less supervision of children, combined with increased expectations for their behavior, created a pressure cooker of stress for both parent and child. It is no wonder that parents looked to science for a medical explanation for why their kids acted the way they did.

When we feel safe, we are able to engage with the world around us. Feelings of vulnerability and insecurity can immobilize us, both emotionally and physically. We can go from being open and aware to closed and shut down, depending on our perceived level of safety. [10]

Feeling threatened can cause us to see no need for social interaction, can leave us overstimulated, and can cause "digestive problems, restlessness, sleep disruption and visceral pain," [11] all commonly reported symptoms for autistic children.

There are so many factors that go into a diagnosis of autism, and most of them are continually in flux. Legislation, school policy, awareness campaigns, the media, parental involvement, research funding, and social opinion can all influence our approach to autism. Diagnoses serve as an artificial way of constructing and defining humanity, as they end up determining behavior and self-perception in the one diagnosed. As the patient's behavior changes as the result of the diagnosis, the perception of the diagnosis also evolves to include those added behavioral changes. [12] There is simply no objective set of criteria to apply when making a diagnosis for ASD; therefore, we always run the risk of a false diagnosis since all we have to go on is bias and opinion.

Taking what we've learned about how disorders are diagnosed — by consensus rather than by biological evidence — is it surprising to hear how frequently autism is misdiagnosed, how normal childhood behavior is often confused with autism? By calling it the Autistic *Spectrum*, we now label many behaviors as autistic which ordinarily would simply be considered a normal phase of childhood, slow development, high intellect, or a normal reaction to stress.

Dr. Enrico Gnaulati, in his book *Back to Normal*, has some amazing insights into the devastating effects that can occur from a false diagnosis: because we as a culture shy away from identifying certain traits as being male or female, we make inaccurate judgments. "Poor eye contact, long-winded monologues about ones' new favorite topic, being overly serious and businesslike, appearing uninterested in other's facial expressions..." are all *normal aspects of boy behavior.* [13]

Many of our expectations for human interaction are based on female behavior: empathy, verbal proficiency, the ability to sit still for long periods of time, and cooperative play are all traits more common to girls. If a boy does not share these characteristics, he is not deficient; he is merely a *boy*.

We are also beginning to test for autism in younger children, which can prove to be risky. When evaluations are conducted as early as toddlerhood, there is a greater chance for misdiagnosis, as the tests themselves have been known to produce stress in these small children, thus compelling them to mimic autistic behavior. [14]

What Causes Autism?

What is autism really? The concept of autism has been around for centuries; however, it was only in the last forty years that it has become a household term. Autism literally means "self-focused" — a person with true autism cannot interact with the world outside their mind. Most are non-verbal and need assistance with daily activities. Once we include more and more individuals in this category, our ability to find solutions becomes diminished, as the lines between the disorder and normal human-ness become blurred.

There are as many theories as to the cause of autism as there are individuals living on the spectrum. Some have found dietary changes hugely successful, others behavioral therapy, and still others, medication. Again, why are there such discrepancies? Why would one thing work for one person and not for another? Visit any library or bookstore and there is bound to be a massive selection of works on curing autism or coping with autism, along with various programs to follow and menu plans galore. **If even *one* of them worked, the rest would never have been written.** The mere fact that there are so many opinions suggests that autism is not one-dimensional; this makes sense because neither are we!

One of the more modern theories is that autism isn't what we have traditionally thought it to be: it's not neurological, nor is it biological — it's personal.

- *Genes are not the cause:* Genetic defects only occur in a small minority of autistic people, "leaving the vast majority of cases of autism genetically unexplained." [15] Tests that claim to reveal predispositions to ASD have not been proven reliable. The test for ASD produced by CARE Clinic has been deemed a failure in that those identified as having ASD received no clinical benefit from treatment, strongly suggesting they did not have the disorder. [16]
- *Biology is not the cause:* Identical twins don't share an autism diagnosis nearly as often as one would expect, while fraternal twins share the diagnosis more often than predicted, suggesting that nurture trumps nature in the development of autism. [17]
- *Life itself is the cause:* Autism has been linked to multiple stressors present from the time of conception to toddlerhood: toxins, home stress, viruses, infections, and other factors. Children tend to engage in self-protective behaviors when faced with insurmountable or frightening challenges – we see them acting strangely and give them the label "autistic." [18]

(Note: No one is to blame for a child's becoming autistic. [19] No fingers are being pointed here. By avoiding the possibility that stress in the home can contribute to autism, what favors are being done? As we are all less than perfect parents, it does no good to compare experiences, as it only leads to shame or pride. Two children can grow up in the same home and perceive the situation differently; one insists their parents are kind and loving, the other that their parents were cruel and harsh. Much depends on the personality of the child and how they *react* to their environment, not merely the environment itself. I also wonder if the *fear* of a child becoming autistic could contribute to the actual development of autism. I was afraid of my youngest growing up too fast, and her biggest fear to this day is getting older. Could I have imprinted my fears onto my children's DNA? It's worth considering, as the Bible does say that sins of the fathers are visited on the third and fourth generation (Exodus 20:5). Either way, I prefer to look forward in hope rather than backwards in shame and regret.)

Could it really be that simple? Or, shall I say, that complex? Research has shown that autistic individuals all have a brain connectivity issue, causing them to struggle to make connections in their environment. Consider what happened when an anti-anxiety medication was given to autistic subjects to further this research: the medication calmed the chaos in their brains enough to allow them to connect with those around them, suggesting that brain connectivity can be improved solely by reducing stress. [20]

Autism is most likely not a result of some error in a child's genes or some deficiency in their biology, but is more likely a series of behaviors that are designed to help them cope with stress or trauma. When we are stressed, we behave differently than when we are calm and reassured. We all act autistically in certain situations, because autistic behavior is part of our perfectly normal human reaction to feeling at risk or in danger. Autistics just feel this way more often. [21]

Stress and fear can cause us to shut out the world, retreating inwardly, self-soothing, becoming overly sensitive to textures and sounds. Observe any hospital waiting room, and you will see knee-tapping, humming, rocking, covering of ears, drowning out sounds with headphones, and isolation behaviors. People under stress are hyper-vigilant and self-protective. Autism is stress taken to its extreme conclusion: a life that is shut off from others. Changing one's diet can reduce a degree of stress on the immune system, behavioral therapy can provide some routine and predictability, and a quiet and soothing environment can be calming, but none of these provide a complete solution.

This idea that autism is caused by stress is certainly not the mainstream understanding of the condition, and I hope I don't sound too cynical when I say that there is no money in compassion and true understanding. Fitting people into categories and providing means for them to fit the mold of these categories is far more lucrative and far simpler to implement. Could it be that our desire for conformity is at the heart of the autism explosion? There has been a huge increase of ASD diagnoses of late; could we be applying the term "autistic" too broadly? If stress causes autistic-like behaviors, couldn't we *all* fit the label?

What does this have to do with hiding? Children are good at hiding, too. Born in sin, they react to their environment sinfully. When faced with emotional trauma or stress, a child will opt for hiding responses just as easily as adults will. Hiding emotions, antisocial behavior, self-protective actions, and a general feeling of being overwhelmed are all on the table, and these may mimic autism.

The situation is magnified once and if a child can understand that they have been given a diagnosis. Just as we adults long for a legitimate excuse for our actions, children readily pick up on the times a parent explains their behavior away as "they're just tired" or "she must be hungry." If a child's label becomes their identity, they are less likely to take responsibility for their behavior. [22] Children know how to behave in order to acquire their parents' attention, and if given a built-in excuse, they will take advantage of it.

Children are exceedingly skilled in acting in ways that compel or even force their parents to give them attention, both physically and emotionally, when they are in need. [23]

Children know what works and what doesn't. Giving psychological terms to bad behavior allows the child to persist in that behavior without consequence. Wrongly classifying behaviors as legitimate autistic attributes can set children up for failure. For example, not all fidgeting is "stimming" and not all nagging is "fixating;" these terms, when applied incorrectly, remove responsibility from a child who might otherwise benefit from constructive redirection. Allowances made for disobedience, assuming the child "can't help it," only ensures disobedience will continue.

Once a label has been attached to a child, no more meaningful analysis of behavior takes place. No other cause is considered. Not only are the bad behaviors explained away, the child's giftedness is often seen as a mere symptom, not as something to be valued and cultivated. [24] Medications are often given that dull the mind and the emotions in order to regulate the child's behavior, as if normalcy and "fitting in" were good things!

Expanding the definition of autism to include normal childhood behavior trivializes autism as a whole; lumping the common cold in with heart disease decreases the probability that solutions will be found for either.

Too often we parents choose also to hide behind a diagnosis, as we are too proud or fearful to ask for help with a struggling child. Having a diagnosis provides the child with services that would otherwise not be available, gives the parents a team of specialists to back them up and support them, offloads some responsibility to the teachers and counselors, and makes them feel like they are not alone anymore in raising a difficult child.

Judy Rapoport from the NIMH is reported to have said, "I'll call a kid a zebra if it will get him the educational services I think he needs." [25]

Every parent needs support, and every child has "special" needs, as they are all special. We have all been uniquely created with gifts, talents, desires, and needs that God will utilize for His purpose and His glory. Seeing each child as an individual enables us to love them with intention and a fresh perspective. Simple behavior modification never works. All children are created in God's image and are capable of having a relationship with their Creator, even if that looks different to us.

Seeking to define people by narrow characteristics and rigid labels affects the way people are treated, impacting their entire lives. [26] Seeing everyone as being on a spectrum could benefit our entire culture, even eliminating racism and other forms of discrimination based on categorizing people by a single characteristic.

Labels create a ripple effect, and the children we most aim to help are often the ones that suffer the most from those labels.

So, what do you do if your child has been diagnosed with ASD? Just as with any other diagnosis, ask yourself if it makes sense. ASD includes a large majority of behaviors that may be phasic and temporary, and yet the label itself is most often permanent. Is the diagnosis, and all that comes with it, worth it? Also, is a diagnosis absolutely necessary for their success in life? How are you defining success? Considering the works of genius created by autistics in years past, is your current plan of care encouraging greatness or stifling it? Also, considering that the world is not an autism-friendly place, would it be better to remove the child from the world or to prepare him/her for it?

These are all questions you must personally explore, for only you know the answers. But be aware that your child's label could easily become your label, too. Are you hiding behind their diagnosis? Do you fear other parents' judgment if the label were removed? Do you find comfort in knowing that you have something to fall back on should your child act out or do something embarrassing or inappropriate? Have you made the label *your* identity, aligning yourself with the cause, befriending other moms of autistic children and seeking acceptance because of your situation?

Is your child given the chance to grow beyond the label? If all their activities are geared toward some goal or centered on their label (therapies, special classes, and such), how will they see what else is possible?

If the word "autism" were off the table, what words would you use to describe your child? Focused, gifted, creative, loyal, and brave? Have those adjectives become lost in the label's shadow? After all, zeroing in on what makes your own child unique is more meaningful than those general characteristics common to autism as a whole.

How well do you truly know your child? I don't mean just food preferences and favorite clothing; I mean truly *know* them. Emotional discussions can be difficult, but is the door kept open, and your child's heart relentlessly pursued?

Do you allow your child to express their emotions in raw form? Much of the behavioral therapy today is geared toward teaching an autistic child to fit in, to be polite and socially acceptable. However, if autism is caused by intense stress, there is likely a vast reservoir of feelings beneath the surface that needs to be exposed. If there is no freedom to express these emotions, no outlet for them, their stress will only increase.

My Autism Story

If ASD hadn't been relatively unheard of when I was a child, I would have certainly been diagnosed. I displayed many of the common symptoms — social phobia, nervous tics, digestive issues, sleeplessness, aversion to being touched, inability to read people's facial expressions, and rigid thinking. I would listen to the same record over and over for hours without moving from my spot under the buffet table. I would follow strangers home, not realizing they weren't my parents. I was on medication for sleeping and for relaxing my nerves, which seemed to fire constantly at night, leaving me itchy and squirming and sleepless. I was tested for my IQ, which was very high, but none of that intelligence helped me figure out how to navigate relationships with people.

I had been seeing a psychologist who prescribed antidepressants, but the meds always made me feel fuzzy and distant from reality. While home from college, I called my doctor and explained that the meds weren't working, that I was frustrated that I just wasn't feeling normal. He recommended a complete neurological examination to see what the cause could be. I hung up the phone to discuss the option with my dad. My father gave me some of the best advice I have ever received. He said, "Even if they could prove that you had a chemical imbalance in your brain, can they prove that the imbalance caused the depression? Or did the depression cause the imbalance?" I immediately called my doctor back and told him I was going off all medication right away. (I don't recommend that for everyone.)

[The question my dad asked me was ahead of its time, as more and more scientists are realizing that even if it were possible to prove that there are lower levels of serotonin in a depressed brain (which has never *been* proven), that could be a result of depression, not the cause. Brain chemistry and behavior can impact each other in equal measure, and there's no way to determine which came first. [27]]

I struggled off and on with relationships into my adulthood, and began reading books on Asperger's Syndrome, seeing myself in every page. Unfortunately, this discovery was not as helpful to me as it would appear.

On the surface, I was jubilant that I had finally been understood, that there were others like me out there. (Isn't that what we *all* want?) But I fell into the trap of seeing myself as somehow exempt from the normal social conventions, that I was not as privileged as the "neurotypical" ones for whom relationships came easily. I'm embarrassed to admit that I wrote letters to some of my friends explaining all my difficulties and how they could not expect me to know how to relate normally. I found that the more I delved into understanding my disorder, the more disordered I became. I stopped *trying*, convinced that it would be too difficult for me to fit in, to act "normal," to have real friendships. It was only when I released my attachment to the disorder that I could see myself from God's eyes: I may be broken, but I am not *damaged*. I began to see how *all* of us are broken, and yet when we come together as the body of Christ, our brokenness becomes complete as we function together in unity.

Society tends to place people into groups and label them according to their value to the rest of the members of the community. Paul dealt with this same tendency in his letter to the church of Corinth:

> "But now indeed there are many members, yet one body. And the eye cannot say to the hand, 'I have no need of you'; nor again the head to the feet, 'I have no need of you.' No, much rather, those members of the body which seem to be weaker are necessary… And if one member suffers, all the members suffer with it; or if one member is honored, all the members rejoice with it." (I Corinthians 12:20-26 NKJV)

Yet so often, we see this separation happen in our churches today. Often churches will offer support groups such as divorce recovery or chronic pain or "new moms" groups. There is a benefit in sharing with others who have similar experiences, and yet there is more richness to be found in the community at large. New mothers can learn from veteran ones, people going through a divorce can find encouragement in watching healthy marriages and seeing where theirs went wrong, and children with special needs can make friends with "normal" kids who can learn humility and servanthood as a result. The act of forming groups comes so naturally to us; perhaps it's time we rethink why that is. Grouping people can reinforce problems rather than encourage solutions.

I personally benefitted from *not* being grouped with my fellow ASD comrades. I studied my "normal" peers' facial expressions, mimicked their phraseology, immersed myself in books laden with emotion to better access my own, and emerged out of myself a better person for the struggle. Perhaps our current methods of dealing with the ASD community are too focused on management and control, separating them into special education classes, assigning them a label and a stigma, rather than focusing on the *person* within. Just as we hide behind our pain and illness, are we also hiding our children behind these labels? Are we seeking for them to be merely understood, rather than to be fully known?

Perhaps much of what we do stems from our definition of autism: calling it a neurological disorder makes sense to our logical brains. I had nervous tics and sensory issues, so it would resonate that my symptoms came from my nervous system. We also throw around the term "sensory issues" as if to explain the odd aversions autistics have to sound, light, and textures, when there is often an emotional reason behind these responses.

When I was four years old, my family and I went to Iran as missionaries, leaving my beloved grandparents behind in Colorado. I *adored* my grandmother and hated leaving her. I developed a strong fear of ice cubes, wind, and flushing toilets. My hatred of these things was so intense, I filled the entire airplane with my screams and protests when the flight attendant brought my water with ice. When the wind would blow, I would run outside and hold on to the tree in the backyard, as if to keep it from being ripped out of the ground by the roots. My mother was intuitive enough to discern what all these things had in common: they all signified something *leaving* — the ice cubes melt, the wind blew things away, the toilet flushed all the water down the drain. My sensory issues weren't as much related to the sensing of the thing as they were to the emotions attached to what the thing represented. Once my mother could reassure me I would see my grandma again soon, my aversions evaporated. One friend recently told me her hatred of loud noises could have stemmed from hearing her grandparents argue loudly when she was a small child. Dismissing sensory issues as just that, neurological *issues*, misses an opportunity to look into your child's mind and see what is truly going on inside.

God is not limited by autism. I was never an emotional kid and didn't cry easily even when in pain. I don't remember loving anyone other than my parents. One night at the dinner table when I was about 12 or 13, I was expressing my frustration that I could not love people. I said to my mother, "God is love, and He says that if I don't have love, I don't have God, so does that mean I'm going to hell?" I was in a panic, and my mom prayed for me to feel love. Suddenly, I started bawling huge tears — something very foreign to me! And I knew then and there that God had given me a heart of flesh instead of my heart of stone (Ezekiel 36:26). God will accomplish His purpose for and through your child, autistic or not.

Autism may present challenges for a loving parent, but it is no match for a loving God who is more than capable of reaching the autistic child's heart. By evaluating our response to our child's challenges and abandoning hiding behaviors in favor of being known, we can be better conduits of God's grace and redemptive love to hearts that so desperately need it. What better gift can we give *any* child than security in Jesus?

Attention Deficit (Hyperactivity) Disorder (ADD/ADHD)

Much of the same principles for autism can be applied to ADD/ADHD. Forty years ago, the concept of ADD was relatively nonexistent. Kids had access to sunshine and physical education, minimal TV and video games, much more face-to-face interaction with peers, and a higher standard of discipline in the home. Of course, there were children who fidgeted and were noisy during class, kids who needed extra help on their homework, and who challenged the norms. There is a broad spectrum of human behavior, and not all of us can sit still for hours at a time. To label a child or an adult with ADD/ADHD can be just as damaging as any other label; it can create a false sense of incompatibility with society, a defect in one's own nature that requires medication to function properly.

Sadly, ADHD is more likely to be diagnosed in children born towards the end of the year solely because they are younger than their peers in the classroom. [28] A year can make a huge difference in the maturity level of a child, and when you compare the younger kids to the older ones, they seem hyperactive and unable to pay attention. They're simply younger.

Still, many patients consider the increased ability to focus while on ADHD drugs as confirmation of their diagnosis. However, these drugs have been shown to help *anyone* focus, even those without a diagnosis. Doctors who use results as confirmation of their diagnosis are not just putting the cart before the horse; they're putting the horse in the cart itself. Imagine the danger of diagnosing a patient with hypertension solely because medication lowered his blood pressure. [29] Drawing such conclusions is not only bad science; it can also be deadly.

ADD / ADHD has been traced back to anxiety. (Are you noticing a pattern here? Thoughts are at the root of all our dysfunctions!). In fact, the problem with an ADD/ADHD sufferer is not that they are unable to pay attention, but that they interpret anxiety as boredom, which makes it harder for them to pay attention. [30]

As with autism in the 1980s/90s, our children are responding to the increase in pressure to perform. The greater the pressure placed on children to learn faster, perform better, and to be more productive and competitive on a global stage, the greater the opportunity for differences to be seen as defects. [31] Normal human behavior will no longer be considered acceptable, as only those individuals who can exhibit superior self-control and attention skills will be valued and deemed "healthy." The bar has simply been raised too high, and our children are suffering as a result.

I'm not about to glorify the "good old days" (Ecclesiastes 7:10), but there is something to be said for living simply. Not all progress is beneficial. I picture a tower of Babel of sorts that we are building out of knowledge and success and performance, abandoning the needs of the heart: community, intimacy, and grace.

ADD/ADHD has also been linked to other environmental causes, such as parental conflict, illness of a parent, poor diet, lack of discipline in the home, lack of sleep, too much screen time, neglect, and even a normal childhood phase being falsely attributed to something more serious. [32] As more and more studies are proving that "inconsistent, overly harsh, or overly permissive child rearing" can cause inattention and behavioral problems, [33] it is no wonder that many parents would prefer a diagnosis for their children, even one as severe as ADHD, over being potentially held accountable for their child's behavior.

Not surprisingly, the research done on ADD/ADHD has found that symptoms change depending on levels of homework, stress, and whether the child is engaged in something they enjoy or find dull. [34] But of course! When I am faced with a project I don't want to do, I clean my entire house in a whirlwind of activity. I'm not as much distracted as I am determined to avoid that dreaded task.

Again, what does a diagnosis accomplish? As with an autism diagnosis, are you seeking to be understood or to be known? To be understood means to have an answer for any criticism, a plausible explanation for why you behave the way you do. To be known means to be seen as you are — sins and flaws and all — and still be loved and accepted. Which matters more to you, and which will have a deeper impact on your life?

Children with the ADHD diagnosis have been observed to "blame their misbehavior on the disorder and therefore don't learn how to take control of their actions if they're having a particularly bad day or when their medication starts to wear off in the late afternoon." [35] More disturbing, since the ADHD diagnosis has been included in the Disabilities Education Act for over twenty-five years, allowing ADHD kids to avoid being held accountable for actions that would be considered malicious or unacceptable; they are now considered as helpless victims of a disease, not held responsible for even the most violent of behaviors. [36]

Diagnoses have consequences, while working through the real cause of the disorder can bring healing. Although this is certainly unpopular, the solution to most chronic conditions is in tolerating the discomfort, to "lean into the pain." Leaning into the pain is effective because it removes the power the pain has over you. The fear of the pain is greater than the pain itself. Assigning labels to pain, even emotional ones, only makes it more tempting to avoid discomfort, as the individual is not seen as capable of significant improvement. Rather than seeing these diagnoses as mere snapshots of what one's life looks like *now* and *under present circumstances*, we see them as unavoidable destinies.

Disorders like ADHD are fabricated by a committee of psychiatrists who have determined that a set group of behaviors constitutes a mental disorder. With so much at stake, why do we blindly assume their conclusions are correct? [37]

Marilyn Wedge, in her book entitled *A Disease Called Childhood: Why ADHD Became an American Epidemic*, claims that ADHD certainly "exists" in that it is a grouping of symptoms and behaviors that can be witnessed and studied and measured, but that it is falsely interpreted as a medical condition. [38] ADHD behavior is no different from normal childhood behavior, and should never be medicated or classified as a "disorder."

For a diagnosis of ADHD, the child must have six symptoms of inattention, all of which could describe me while watching a tennis match. The symptoms for hyperactivity could also apply to me after downing a jumbo espresso or in any social situation in which I feel awkward.

If the term "ADHD" did not exist, how would you describe your child/yourself? The acronym distracts us from the actual meaning, and should perhaps be relabeled NPA, for "Not Paying Attention." Under what circumstances do you find it nearly impossible to pay attention? For me it's during a football game on television, when I have to listen to the commentators drone on and on about number 52 running the ball when he should have punted or some such drivel. However, when my *son* is on the football field, I could wax eloquent about how he executed certain plays and is the ref blind? No way was that a penalty!

I don't have an attention problem. I have a desire problem. I have no interest in football, and I find it woefully trivial and unimportant. But I have a deep and fundamental desire to see my son succeed, so I find his football career most interesting and engaging. What do you truly desire?

Questions to Ask Yourself

1. Did you become angry while reading this chapter? How invested are you in your child's diagnosis?
2. Knowing that there is an even longer spectrum of *normal* behavior than there is abnormal, how does that help you better evaluate your child?
3. How difficult would it be for you to release the diagnosis of ASD or ADD/ADHD? Why?
4. What is your parenting style, and can you see how it may affect your children's behavior? How does God parent us?

Addictions

A biblical coach friend of mine told me that addictions are less about moving toward pleasure than they are moving away from pain. When she told me this, I was embarrassed that I had not even considered that angle, as I'm the one writing a book on hiding! She counsels patients to get to the root of the pain in their lives and find contentment in the desert space between pain and temporary pleasure in order to find genuine, lasting pleasure and avoid the pain of addiction, a worse pain than that which they are trying to avoid. Her methods contradict the conventional belief that addictive behaviors stem from some kind of mental or physiological illness. Current and common recommendations are to avoid the addictive behaviors, and any situations or people that may trigger them, for the rest of your life. Porn addiction? You need filters on every device you have access to, and you better invest in a blindfold because triggering images are all around you. But is this true healing?

For example, we have been hearing for years how alcoholism is a disease — alcoholics are victims of biology, and the only real cure is complete and utter avoidance of bars, prior drinking buddies, beer commercials, parties, and anything else that could be a temptation. This view negates any hope for an alcoholic to be released from the bondage that drink holds over them; it's a permanent, tragic burden they must bear forever.

The belief "once an alcoholic, always an alcoholic" is so widely held that if you were to announce a cure, you would be scoffed at openly. However, the science behind this belief does not hold water. As with most other psychological disorders, the research is subjective at best, manipulative at worst.

Defining addiction as a disease has benefits for the rehab industry: it is a powerful marketing tool and can also serve as an explanation when treatments don't work as expected. [1] Diseases are often known to be unpredictable, so doctors can't be held accountable for results.

If research is presented, always ask if it makes *sense*, not only from a medical perspective but also from a biblical one. What is addiction but a sinful pattern of desire leading to behaviors that are immoral or in other ways damaging to the individual and to those around them? Yet we love to identify and name diseases, develop targeted and specific treatments, and quantify our results. [2] Western medicine thrives on logic and order. If we can give it a *name* and design a *solution*, then the *cause* becomes less and less important. Research is only valued if it can be published in a scientific journal; emotions can't be quantified to a specific decimal place and don't easily fit into charts and tables.

Always follow the money. In the medical world, if we can itemize it for the insurance industry, we can place limits on how much will be paid out to the patient. The more specific the diagnosis, the more detailed the treatment plan, and the more control the insurance industry has over your recovery. [3]

To confuse matters, research studies can be confusing — images of brains with areas lighting up under various stimuli complete with explanations that make pseudo-sense can persuade us that there is a biological cause.

What came first? Did brains change because of repetitive behavior or is the repetitive behavior the result of a brain change? And with so many other events occurring in the brain at any given time, it's not likely we can ever pinpoint one trigger as being responsible for any one reaction.

Labeling addiction as a disease may make it easier to procure medical treatment or insurance payouts for patients, but that doesn't make it "good science." [4]

The ends do not justify the means. Just because a subset of sufferers finds relief does not mean that the approach is logical or should be applied to the majority. Also, if you are told you have a disease, that your alcoholism has nothing to do with your desires and all to do with your biology, you are more likely to relapse. [5] True victory is only found by discovering something you desire more than drink or drugs. Consider an alcoholic who has been in bondage to drink for decades, yet one night is involved in a car accident in which his daughter is killed. He had been drinking; the accident was his fault. He never drinks again. His desire for absolution replaces his desire for getting drunk. For others, it is the desire for love, for peace, for joy — see a pattern? The desire for God above all creature comforts can change hearts, and in turn, behaviors — even alcoholism.

Alcoholism, along with other compulsive disorders and addictions, are merely thoughts and desires out of control. Fixating on a substance or behavior to find security or comfort is worshipping something other than God. Worship actually can change your brain, as repetitive thoughts and actions cause deeper and deeper connections between neurons. The key is where you are focusing your attention, your worship. Once you begin to long for something more than you long for the next drink, the lure and attraction of the bottle diminishes and vanishes altogether. No amount of behavior modification can replace the inner heart change that results from coming out of hiding.

It is human nature to want what we want NOW. Our brain thrives on rewards: if the rewards are unexpected, our dopamine neurons fire like crazy! If the rewards are expected, the dopamine neurons fire, but less intensely each time the reward is granted. If expected rewards are not received, the dopamine drops off drastically. [6] This cycle is not describing an illness; it is simply the way the brain works. The good news is that if you replace the expectation, you change the dopamine response. It's not enough to just "quit" addictive behaviors; you need to change the reason you developed them in the first place. What void were you trying to fill? What *should* fill that void?

True freedom from addiction involves an ability to be in the presence of your addiction and feel *no compulsion towards it*. If the addictive object or behavior no longer holds power over you, if there are no more triggers in your brain for physiological responses[7], that is true healing. The conditioning must be totally overwritten by new patterns and responses in order for the addiction to be truly broken. Anything less is just replacing one addiction for another, even the addiction to strict regimens, rules, and support groups. It's been said that people who attend frequent Alcoholics Anonymous meetings end up addicted to donuts and coffee!

Consider other compulsive behaviors — compulsive hoarding, compulsive shopping, compulsive gambling, obsessive-compulsive disorder (OCD) to name a few. All are based on the same principle that steers addiction: something else has taken hold of your heart other than God. Removing excess items from a hoarder's house, or tearing up a compulsive shopper's credit cards will not eliminate the problem. Giving into the addiction increases it. I have a touch of OCD; what begins with simply folding laundry ends up in sorting all my clothes by color and refolding them to all be the same size. The more I clean, the more dirt I seem to see. If I don't deal with the root of my addiction, I can so easily believe the lie that perfection is possible this side of eternity.

If your child has an addiction to a video game and you remove his/her phone, you have only masked the true issue. The root of addiction remains and will either reemerge the moment the phone is returned, or he/she will probably find a different diversion to replace the video game. John Calvin has said that our hearts are "idol factories" — one addiction can be easily supplanted by another unless the heart is captured by God Himself.

By identifying the pain that they are running from and understanding the reason for their attraction to the addiction, an addicted person can find comfort in the space between the two. Paul speaks of making his body his slave in order to run the race set before him (1 Corinthians 9:27). If you are a slave to your body, you are a slave indeed, for we are our own worst taskmasters, always seeking more and more satisfaction. Jesus would not ask us to do anything that He would not empower us to accomplish, and He asks us to seek Him first above all things (Matthew 6:33).

Questions to Ask Yourself

1. Do you have any addictions you are struggling with?
2. How can focusing on something bigger help combat the need to please yourself?
3. What pain are you trying to avoid or alleviate?

Food Sensitivities

Perhaps one of the subtlest forms of psychosomatic pain is that of food sensitivities. The gut contains 95% of the serotonin in your body, [1] so it is not surprising that your emotions and your gut are directly related. Fear and stress are most often felt in the gut in the form of "butterflies" or queasiness — it would make perfect sense for the mind to convince you it wasn't your worry making your stomach hurt; it was that bagel you had for lunch.

I've met several individuals who claim to be allergic and/or sensitive to upwards of 178 foods! Allergy testing, like bloodwork, is simply a snapshot of your body's response to a suspected allergen at a specific time. Even extreme allergies can originate from emotional causes; however, I don't recommend starting with those, especially if you have had an anaphylactic reaction. Most "allergies" are really sensitivities producing stomach discomfort, mild rashes, headaches, and other non-life- threatening sensations.

Let's take non-Celiac gluten sensitivity, for example. A quick glance through the aisles of the supermarket, with the countless "gluten-free" items, might lead you to believe that gluten is to be avoided like the plague. Churches are now serving gluten-free communion bread and signing up for potluck dishes means having to navigate all the various dietary restrictions. When did this all start? People have been eating bread since Bible times, so why did it suddenly become so toxic and irritating to the body? You could argue that the wheat crop itself has changed, or that our diets have become overly processed so that our digestive systems simply gave up, or that wheat should never have been eaten in the first place. But is there any truth to these claims? If there were, one would expect a greater number of gluten sensitive individuals. People should be collapsing in the streets and rushed to the hospital in massive numbers if gluten were indeed responsible for inflicting the damage gluten-free advocates claim.

Why do some eat gluten with no issue at all, and others develop symptoms after only a bite?

It all comes down to "mass sociogenic illness," an illness created out of public hysteria, fueled by others' anxieties, negative expectations, and a fear and distrust of authority. [2] Illnesses are defined as "sociogenic" when a society is mistakenly told that something is dangerous or deadly and the people in the society are predisposed to agree with the misinformation. Self-deception is a powerful force, and cases of this kind of illness have been documented as far back as the fifteenth century. [3]

Many of the reactions to consuming gluten appear to be largely the power of suggestion. It's happened before: the media popularized candidiasis in the 1990s, a disorder that has all but disappeared, replaced by the gluten sensitivity epidemic of the twenty-first century. [4]

Simply asking someone if they have a specific symptom as if it were indicative of something serious can cause them to either begin to experience that symptom or remember a recent time when they had. [5]

Think about all the fad diets through history that have since been proven incorrect or even deadly. What did they all have in common?

Religious language. Glorifying the past, when all was "natural" or like your "grandma used to make." Vilifying modern living and innovation, making the past seem purer and more spiritual than our evil, toxic, sinful generation. Overly processed foods become evil as well, and organic, natural foods are seen as wholesome and righteous.

Statistics that impress. All the claims sound legitimate, with high percentages of people recovering from long lists of diseases once they eliminated such-and-such or started eating thus and so. Statistics can be manipulated easily, also, so that the same data can either show something as lethal or contributing to longevity. [6] By convincing people of a danger that may not really exist, doctors and scientists create the very problems they offer to solve, thereby becoming heroes against a villain of their own design. [7]

Ritualized solutions. Books that include strict menus and restrictive regimens lead us to believe that we can control our health by following their instructions to the letter. Socially acceptable diets that involve strict rituals, and expensive food replacement options tend to be more effective in producing the placebo effect. The gluten-free diet would definitely qualify. [8]

What is it about us humans that drives us to create more and more laws for ourselves? Could it be that we long to be in control of our lives, deciding what is good and what is evil, down to the very foods we consume? Was this another effect of eating the fruit of the tree in the Garden? There is a very compelling correlation to our guilt from eating the fruit back then and the pain we attach to the foods we eat today.

Once we become convinced that a food or food group is unhealthy or even toxic, we develop an anxiety about eating the forbidden foods, and that anxiety can produce the same symptoms as a sensitivity, thus solidifying our belief that we are doing right to avoid those foods. Eliminating the foods provides a form of safety net. We become more and more convinced of our choice as we hear testimonials from others and as we see more foods available for our specific diet pop up in mainstream grocery stores. The more convinced we become, the less likely we will question our own "success," our self-diagnosis. But merely being convinced something is true does not make it so. [9] Even if we eventually hear medical research that negates our belief, we become unwilling to reverse course, due to the "sunk cost fallacy": abandoning the diet means acknowledging you may have been wrong, that all the money and time you spent was a waste. Fear of admitting failure can force us to remain faithful to the diet even if evidence is presented that proves it uncalled for or even harmful. [10]

Hearing of fatal reactions to certain foods in the case of extreme allergy only increases our fear, adding to our symptoms and leading us to dig our heels in to our new diet plan. Add to that all the times we mentioned to our friends how well it's worked for us, and how they should try it too, and so on, and we feel invested to the point of no return. The food and the ideology about its being "unclean" can become an idol, and food idols lead to "bodily sacrifice." [11] We would rather punish ourselves physically than surrender our food religion.

The Truth About Gluten Sensitivities

Allergies rarely develop past childhood, [12] so there is a marked difference between an allergy and a sensitivity, although sometimes the symptoms can appear similar. But what about the IgG test? Doesn't that serve as diagnostic proof that there is genuinely a cause for your sensitivity? Typically, if you suffer from symptoms from eating gluten, you would have your IgG antigliadin antibodies measured and, if they are elevated, that should signify a sensitivity. However, there is a high incidence of individuals who have these antibodies and yet experience no discomfort eating gluten, thus calling into question the legitimacy of these tests. [13] Ultimately, determining a sensitivity relies solely on a self-diagnosis, as there is no reliable biological marker for the disorder, [14] and self-diagnoses are the most difficult to reverse due to the personal investment of the sufferer in their diagnosis.

Gluten and ASD

Perhaps the population most influenced by the gluten-free rhetoric is the ASD community. The ASD community has often been advised to take the IgA and the IgG antibody test, as there is a strong belief that these individuals are more biologically inclined to suffer from gluten intolerance.

The IgA and IgG test is based on the fact that these antibodies react to gluten, so it would stand to reason that if they are present, there would be a risk for gluten sensitivity. However, these antibodies are also found in the bloodstream of people with no reaction to gluten. There is no proven way to connect these antigliadin antibodies to gluten sensitivity. [15]

So, having ruled out the IgG tests as a reliable indicator of sensitivity, the only factor that remains is the impact gluten may or may not have on the behavior of these individuals. Research has never been able to show any positive effect of the gluten-free or casein-free diets on the ASD community. Any reports of positive outcomes are likely due to the parent or caregiver's desire for results. [16]

It just makes sense that a parent would want to feel some semblance of control over a difficult situation. If you fervently believe that there is a cause-and-effect relationship between gluten and behavior, you will see a link every time. Furthermore, children pick up on this belief and take it in as fact. How much of a leap would it be for a child to desire to act out, then to sneak gluten in order to subconsciously concoct an excuse for their behavior, the parent then blaming the food rather than identifying the child themselves as culpable for their actions. If this seems implausible to you, you may be underestimating the depth of the sinful nature. Rather than conclude that a child's behavior is because of their sneaking gluten, the better question to ask is why are they sneaking it in the first place? The disobedient behavior began with an act of disobedience, not as a result of a bite of the forbidden food!

Children with ASD tend to be picky eaters, and are already encumbered by restrictions in every other area of their lives, so why add to their burden? Also, a gluten-free diet is lacking fiber and nutrition and can even contain heavy metals which can affect brain development, thus potentially making a bad situation worse. [17]

Some choose a gluten-free diet based on the belief that gluten is essentially unhealthy. When a person believes something is unhealthy, they may experience symptoms after eating that food item. When I was a vegan, my stomach would ache if I accidentally consumed cheese. Was my system simply unaccustomed to the dairy or was it in my head?

Studies have been performed comparing the actual effects of gluten to the perceived effects, and have shown that if someone believes something is bad for them, it becomes so. The opposite is also true; the mind is that powerful. [18]

But *isn't* a gluten-free diet healthier? What's so wrong with wanting to eliminate a potentially harmful food source? Turns out a gluten-free diet isn't healthier after all, and is even quite the opposite – it's low in fiber, iron, and B vitamins, and high in fat and sugar. The more you avoid gluten, the more likely you are to develop an actual sensitivity to it as well. [19] The pain pathway will become more and more established, and eventually will become a self-fulfilling prophecy.

Gluten-free diets are all the rage these days, but how long will it last? Food sensitivities don't just stay in one place; just like other forms of chronic pain, they expand and may go on to include other foods such as dairy and soy. Food sensitivities take over your life and can place limits on your social life as well — perhaps what your subconscious wanted in the first place.

I was a vegan for ten years and am well aware of how there can be pros and cons to any diet. Eating a ton of processed breads is not healthy. But neither is eliminating gluten altogether, especially for reasons that have no biological basis; once you work through the principles behind other forms of chronic pain, you may find yourself able to eat all the foods you like with no negative reaction.

I had to eat crow a bit (no pun intended) when I started reintroducing meat and dairy into our family's diet; people were shocked when they saw me eating a burger! I had to admit that my diet had become my righteousness, and that I had been neglecting other, more important, factors to health. My pride took a hit, but humility felt good after so long of being prideful. I was free to accept grace, and I could now extend it to others — perhaps the lesson I was being taught all along.

Other Sensitivities

There are a host of disorders that involve sensitivities to various fragrances, sounds, chemicals, substances, and the like. Individuals who suffer from these sensitivities often isolate themselves and find their worlds becoming smaller and smaller in an attempt to avoid their long list of environmental triggers. Sensitivities, like pain, demand more and more of you over time.

Consider the words you use to describe your situation: "I can't handle that," "My body doesn't like that," or "I can't tolerate that." Now ask yourself what it is that you *really* can't handle?

Questions to Ask Yourself

1. When did your allergy or food sensitivity begin? What else was going on in your life?
2. If there were no gluten-free options to be found, how would that affect your commitment to a gluten-free diet?

3. If God called you to the mission field in a location where you would be exposed to allergens, would you go?

Cancer

Cancer, while not usually grouped under the category of "chronic pain," bears so much in common with psychosomatic disorders that it must be addressed. It would be near impossible to find a person whose life has not been touched by cancer, whether by personal diagnosis or that of a loved one. For many, the word "cancer" means "death" and "hopelessness." While many do recover from the disease, the way in which the remaining sufferers die is so cruel and painful that we can't help but feel frightened and outmatched.

There is a myriad of possible causes for cancer, from nutrition to environment to genetic predisposition, yet none of these alone can account for the disease. Not every smoker gets lung cancer, yet some individuals who were never exposed long-term to cigarette smoking contract the disease. Some women are diagnosed with breast cancer who have none of the risk factors, not even the cancer gene. Why do some get sick and not others?

We are all walking around with cancer cells in our bodies, and our immune systems are constantly attacking them and eliminating them. That's what the immune system is for. For cancer to develop, it would ultimately mean that the immune system had not been able to do its job. As we learned in the chapter on back pain, diagnostic testing such as MRIs and scans and x-rays can simply see too much. A test for cancer is likely to find *something*, even cells that would never have caused harm if left alone. Instead of focusing on the cells themselves, the greater question should be asked:

The four factors that contribute to the development of cancer are: genes, diet, exposure to radiation, and other harmful substances. All of us have been exposed to radiation and other toxins at some point in our lives, our diets are likely to have been typically stable for several years, and we all have abnormal cells in our bodies at any given time, regardless of what caused them to appear. Our bodies are normally more than capable of protecting from these invaders, so what was the real reason cancer all of a sudden gained the advantage? What caused the chink in the armor that has been so reliable for so long? [1]

Something had to let it in. Something had to let it win.

The answer involves a whole-person biopsy – cancer serves as an indicator of other problems and stresses that began six to eighteen months before the cancer was even detected; it is an illness that involves the entire person, not just the physical body. [2]

Cancer itself is not a violent invader that comes from some external source; it is instead merely "a weak and confused cell." [3] Cancer originates with a cell that doesn't have the information it needs to perform its assigned task, or has been given the wrong information, so it reacts in confusion.

Cancer is not a monster; it is a part of you that needs healing.

As long as we approach the search for the cure from a solely physical perspective, we will be forever confounded; in order for a true cure to be found, cancer's true origins must be fully understood. The mind in need of emotional healing will always find a new and stronger physical disease in order to secure the help it needs. Just like a virus mutates, our minds will invent newer and more bizarre means to express the unspoken needs that must be met.

The conclusion that cancer results from emotional trauma is nothing new; medical literature on the subject can be found tracing back as far as 200 A.D., and it was the pervasive theory from the 1700s until the 1900s. In 1893, Dr. Herbert Snow wrote in his work entitled *Cancers, and the Cancer-Process*: "Idiots and lunatics are remarkably exempt from cancer in every shape." [4] So compelling was the evidence that emotions were linked to cancer, that it was believed that only those who lived their lives apart from emotional stress were immune to the disease.

Specific emotional risk factors were identified, also, that if present would increase the likelihood of an individual developing cancer. At the top of the list was the loss of a critical relationship, such as a parent or a spouse. Other factors included: finding one's identity in something beyond one's control such as a job or a relationship, unresolved conflict or problems, an inability to cope with difficulty, repressed despair, general hopelessness and/or helplessness, and a need to look good in the public eye. [5]

In two separate studies of breast cancer patients, one in 1952 and the other in 1974, researchers discovered a common characteristic among the women: an "extreme suppression of anger" that led to unresolved conflicts and "unrealistic self-sacrificing behaviors." [6] In more recent studies, it has been shown that one of the most common risk factors among female cancer patients is an inability to express anger and frustration, especially in the six months prior to cancer onset – other risk factors include "hopelessness and lack of social support." [7]

In our modern culture of social media and false intimacy, is there any surprise at all that the human spirit would fall prey to this disease? If cancer cells are weak and confused, could it be because we are as well?

Most scientists today avoid asking questions that could only lead to more questions that science can't answer. For example, we know how bodily processes affect each other, but what initiates these processes? In order for cancer to develop, several things need to occur: there needs to be damage done to DNA, a failure to repair the damage, and an interruption in normal cell death. These processes have one key factor in common: emotion. [8] Admitting an emotional cause requires scientists to admit there is a vast expanse of knowledge that lies beyond their expertise.

Perhaps if physicians had remained on this path of emotional causation, things would be different now. But the medical community latched onto something more tangible and concrete: technology. Technology has yielded much success across many medical disciplines, endearing itself to the doctors who use it, and creating a middleman between physician and patient. While before doctors spent time learning about the sick person, now they could spend more time learning about the sickness itself.

However, focusing on the disease alone is like taking medication for salmonella while still eating the infected food. Doctors are in a sense doling out yellow fever medicine while neglecting to drain the ditches teeming with disease-carrying mosquitos. [9] Our water pipes have burst, but doctors are merely strolling in with towels to mop up the water.

In the late nineteenth century, into the early twentieth-century, there was a common acceptance of cancer's emotional causes. However, it was also a time of medical advancements that were beginning to turn the tide towards finding a more tangible physical cause. Radiation therapy had been discovered, and surgeries were more precise and easier to perform with the dawn of general anesthesia. Using these methods yielded great success for their patients, which only solidified the doctors' belief that cancer was indeed a physical disease. With more resources and treatment methods at their disposal, doctors no longer saw any use in identifying emotional factors; especially as there was little to be done about them even if they did contribute to the disease — there were few tools available for dealing with psychiatric illnesses at the time. Sadly, as psychology began to innovate and potentially discover more ways to link emotion to disease, medical science lost interest in the pursuit. [10]

We are now left with two branches of medicine that are fundamentally incomplete because of a lack of collaboration [11] — working together, medicine could explain the HOW, psychology could explain the WHY. Separately, the disease remains a mystery to each.

Although I commend the diligent researchers who are seeking a cure for cancer, I believe that even if a cure is found, another equally frightening disease will rise and take its place. The villain is not the disease itself; it is the puppet master pulling the strings: the sinful thoughts and emotional pain that we are seeking to hide.

The Bible mentions many illnesses such as leprosy, dropsy (edema), blindness, internal bleeding, and paralysis. The one mention of cancer appears in 2 Timothy 2:17 "their message shall spread like cancer." The word *cancer* is actually more accurately translated *gangrene* from the Greek "γάγγραινα," or "gangraina." Other verses that sometimes use the word *cancer* instead of the Hebrew for "rottenness" are Proverbs 12:4 and Proverbs 14:30. I find it odd that such a prevailing illness in our modern culture is barely touched on in the Bible — most likely because of the ever-evolving landscape of disease; as some are eliminated, new diseases form.

Cancer comes with a need for urgent attention, so I do not discourage medical care; however, emotional care is equally important. Cancer can be an impetus for uncovering wrong thoughts and beliefs, reconciling with loved ones, and forgiving those who have hurt you. Many patients discover that after dealing with their emotional pain, the cancer goes away on its own, having accomplished all it set out to do.

Questions to Ask Yourself

1. If you have cancer, what was going on in your life 6-18 months prior to your being diagnosed?
2. Do you have unresolved anger or resentment that you are suppressing?
3. How has your diagnosis affected the way people treat you? What can that tell you about your emotional needs?

Chronic Lyme Disease

One of the other diseases I hear mentioned repeatedly among chronic pain sufferers is Lyme disease. While Lyme disease can produce some nasty symptoms, *chronic* Lyme disease is based on a deception that Lyme bacteria hides from the immune system. Chronic Lyme is a fictional disease invented to create an industry to sell books, supplements, and therapies. There is a myth being perpetuated that there is an "antibiotic resistant Lyme" [1] at its heart. The truth? Lyme bacteria are "easy to detect and kill." [2]

Lyme disease itself is easily treated; however, some patients never seem to shake the disease, showing symptoms such as joint pain, fatigue and confusion for long after the Lyme has been eliminated. This "post-treatment Lyme disease syndrome" is rather controversial, since no blood test can prove there is still an infection in the body. The symptoms appear to be so vague that they could certainly be emotionally caused. The circumstances under which doctors continue to treat these patients is suspect, especially if they insist that the Lyme bacteria is still a direct cause of their pain. The tests they use ensure a greater number of positive results, and even if the test comes back negative, they argue that the bacteria has simply "evaded laboratory detection…" [3]

The pain no longer serves a purpose, so it makes no sense why there would be lingering pain long after the bacteria has been killed. Research has shown that there is no link between Lyme and chronic pain or fatigue. [4]

I find the image of being afraid of hidden bacteria lurking in the body eerily similar to the truth that we are all hiding from others in one form or another.

Overweight / Thyroid/Hormonal Problems

As a Weight Management Specialist, one of the first questions from my clients is, "Could it be my thyroid?" Well, yes, your thyroid could be involved, but the real question is *what came first, your weight gain or your thyroid issue?* Excess weight can affect the thyroid just as the thyroid can encourage weight gain, and both are originally determined by the mind. Yes, your mind can make you fat! Being overweight serves as a perfect hiding strategy if what you are most afraid of is rejection or abuse. Women who have been sexually abused are at high risk for gaining excess weight, as they are literally insulating themselves from further advances. Being afraid of rejection can lead to subconsciously making oneself as unattractive as possible to not have to endure a relationship that might end painfully.

Dr. Vincent Felitti in the mid-1980s concluded that there are three main reasons a person becomes overweight: to protect themselves from sexual abuse, to protect themselves from physical abuse by appearing larger, and to become invisible to reduce others' expectations of them. [5] Even after obese people lose weight via medical means or strict diets, they regain the weight in record numbers. Only after working through the reasons they became overweight in the first place were they able to lose the weight for good.

Do hormones play a role at all? Not in the way you would think. Just as the mind speaks to the nervous system to induce pain, it also communicates with other systems such as the thyroid, the adrenals, and the reproductive organs. [6]

The issue of weight is not one of vanity but of health and quality of life. Not everyone needs to look like Olympic body builders, and there is not one perfect size to attain. If you are out of breath climbing the stairs, limited in your mobility, and experiencing poor health because of your weight, then you need to take your situation seriously. Knowing that your thoughts can influence even your weight, what thoughts are you thinking about your weight? Do you feel hopeless? What have you gained from being overweight? Are you willing to let those gains go and take the risk of losing weight and becoming a different person as a result? What would that look like to you, and what are you willing to do to achieve it?

Asthma

Asthma has been generally accepted as a MindBody phenomenon, even by the mainstream medical community: [7] allergic inflammation is the MindBody's expression of anger. [8]

Some medical professionals posit that asthma is caused by an overproduction of IgE, an antibody our immune system uses to protect us from parasitic invasion. With scientific acceptance of this theory comes new drugs designed to restore chemical balance to the immune system, causing asthma patients to be dependent on inhalers and medications for their very breath. However, it will never be enough to only block the allergic response; the root cause must be identified — otherwise, there will be no lasting relief, and symptoms can even increase if a patient feels helpless and limited by their treatment. Being dependent on an inhaler and the stigma that can sometimes result can cause a patient to become *angrier* and *more* resentful.

God gave us the gift of the breath of life from His very mouth, and we restrict that breath when we harbor resentment and fear. Smothering relationships may be so named because of the connection to developing asthma. One study concluded that maternal stress that began a year before the child's birth and/or continued during infancy is a significant determinant of whether a child will develop asthma by their second birthday. [9]

We use phrases like "now I can breathe," "I just need to catch my breath," "I need some air," or "I have a weight on my chest" when we feel like we are being controlled by others and unable to break free. Exhaling connotes a letting go, a forgiveness and acceptance of others who have "knocked the wind out of us."

Questions to Ask Yourself

1. What phrases do you use to describe your physical condition? Try applying them to your emotional condition as well; what do you learn?
2. Do you have a history of abuse? Are you able to talk about your experience and your feelings with a trusted friend or counselor?

Aging

It's no secret that everyone ages, and yet we would all prefer to pretend we will live forever. Instead of envisioning a peaceful time of reaping all the benefits of a life well-lived, we often see aging as a downward descent into deterioration and humiliation. Aging appears to have become synonymous with disease with countless advertisements suggesting that if you are above 65, you must suffer from arthritis, dementia, ED, memory loss, and chronic pain.

A terrifying threat looming over our elderly population is that of Alzheimer's Disease. I can't think of anything more frightening than to lose yourself, your memories, your sense of history and your hope for the future.

Just as we have seen with other psychiatric disorders, the science is not reliable. Alzheimer's Disease (AD) cannot be diagnosed definitively, as there is no biological marker for the disease. Also, there has never been shown to be a difference between healthy, normally-aged brains and those diagnosed with AD, even in postmortem studies. [1]

Could the diagnosis itself be a factor in the development of symptoms?

An Alzheimer's diagnosis is never certain, and it never can be. There is simply no way to prove its existence. However, the effects of the diagnosis can be devastating and change the course of a patient's life, as it can play on their fears and cause them to become reality. [2]

Old age can be a time of reaping rewards of a long well-lived life. Inhibitions are lessened, expectations are lowered, and your labors are coming to their end. There should be freedom and joy in just *being*. However, the drive for success and accomplishment that we developed in our youth is hard to abandon. Too often, the elderly lament their lack of ability to achieve the same level of *doing* as in their youth, and a depression sets in. We have already seen how depression can affect health, and this is only augmented in old age. We can become confused and detach from the present in favor of the past, when hope abounded and the sky was the limit.

There is also the desire to regain childlike freedom from responsibility and social expectations. Seniors with dementia are more playful, returning to their childhoods and releasing the burden of adulthood that has consumed them for so long. I wonder if we all took more time to play and rest from our heavy workloads during our middle-aged years would we eliminate the emotional need for dementia altogether?

My father, when he turned seventy-two, started making comments about how old he had become. My mother, now a firm believer in the power of beliefs, scolded him gently that his referring to himself as elderly would speed up the aging process! When you address yourself as sick or old, you adopt certain "old and sick" behaviors. For example, stooping or shuffling or giving "organ recitals" when people ask how you're doing — running off the list of all the aches and pains you have! My grandmother lived until her late 90s, and that was one thing I always admired about her: she never complained about her health. She would express interest in others and keep up to date on the latest news so she would have more to talk about than her physical well-being. I firmly believe that is one reason she lived so long!

Being surrounded by people complaining about illness can make you sick, just as being around people discussing wellness and health can encourage healing. You don't need to be constantly told how sick you are; you need to hear how amazing the body's healing abilities are, as positive messages promote health! [3]

Many of our old age ailments arise from the belief that they are inevitable. Other cultures don't experience aging the same way we Americans do; they have different beliefs about old age; gray hair is an honor and a status symbol in many cultures, while in America we see it as a stigma and something to fend off as long as possible. When the elderly are revered and allowed to take part in family activities, not just observe them, they remain the more active and alert. The old phrase "if you don't use it, you lose it" applies to our minds and our bodies — muscles that are not used atrophy, minds that are not used become demented.

Menopause is a normal stage of a woman's adult life, but it has been termed "estrogen deficiency" — suddenly, it is a medical condition that needs to be treated. ⁴ There seems to be no such thing as aging naturally anymore — even wrinkles and hair loss are considered symptoms demanding a treatment. Massive amounts of medications are marketed to the elderly, as they are told that anything less than a youthful appearance is dangerous and a sign of illness.

The elderly are all too often considered to be hopeless cases. For example, any mental confusion is considered senility or dementia, and possible vitamin deficiencies are not typically pursued. The aged are often simply seen as being "on their way out," so creative and aggressive efforts to remedy and treat illness are not as actively taken. My grandmother fell into a coma for many months, and my grandfather, a distinguished surgeon, continued to search for solutions. He determined that she had a sodium deficiency, something the hospital staff had neglected to test. Had she been fifty years younger, I'm sure they would have been more proactive and attentive to her. She simply didn't fit their criteria for drastic measures.

When we carry in our minds this view of aging, it isn't surprising that aging should be rife with disability and pain. The Bible does not adhere to this negative view of aging:

- "They will still bear fruit in old age, healthy and green..." (Psalm 92:14 HCSB)
- "Even to your old age and gray hairs I am he, I am he who will sustain you. I have made you and I will carry you; I will sustain you and I will rescue you." (Isaiah 46:4 NIV)
- "The silver-haired head is a crown of glory, if it is found in the way of righteousness." (Proverbs 16:31 NKJV)
- "Wisdom is with aged men, and with length of days, understanding." (Job 12:12 NKJV)
- Caleb was 85 years old when he asked the Lord to let him take the mountain!

"As yet I am as strong this day as on the day that Moses sent me; just as my strength was then, so now is my strength for war, both for going out and coming in. Now therefore, give me this mountain..." (Joshua 14:11-12b NKJV)

You are still you, no matter how many years you have lived. Age can soften emotional pain, forgetting can be a blessing, slowing down can be conducive to intimacy with loved ones. Age can also reveal hidden bitterness and anger, as inhibitions are lowered. How you age is up to you.

As long as you harbor negative emotions, you cannot expect to enjoy physical health, as it is impossible not to suffer the consequences of "sowing the seeds of disease in your mind." [5]

Auto-Immune Disorders

Auto-immune disorders, as we have seen, are not just the body attacking the body; rather, self attacking self. There are several reasons self would attack self:

Not knowing who you are. I don't mean amnesia. I am referring to a lack of self-awareness that can sometimes be due to the loss of a loved one at an early age, childhood abuse, any scenario that has rendered the individual to be unable to forge their own opinions, personality, and preferences.

Trying to be someone you know you aren't. Perhaps your parents always wanted you to be a doctor, so you became one, but you secretly wanted to be a ballerina. Or there is societal pressure to act in a way that you despise in order to fit in with the crowd. Even pretending that you are a kind person when you would rather tell everyone to leave you alone. When the lines are blurred between who you *are* and who you pretend to be.

Hating who you have become. You may have had expectations of yourself that you have long since resigned. Or you may have had dreams and goals that you could never meet. Blaming others is one thing, blaming yourself can cause a tear in the very fabric of your own self-identity.

Terminal Illnesses

Our emotions transmit messages to our immune system, telling it to activate or to shut down. If we feel despair in our lives, if we desire escape from monotony or heartache, if we don't see meaning in our current situation, we will communicate to our immune system that we fundamentally desire to die. [6] I'm sure most of you reading this are thinking that simply cannot be true! Who in their right mind would make such a claim?

I am definitely not saying that cancer sufferers consciously choose their disease. Very few people would intentionally decide to catch a cold, let alone suffer a potentially fatal disease. There is, however, a subconscious thought process that has been shown to predispose individuals to terminal illnesses.

Dr. Bernie Siegel, MD has identified several risk factors for disease in his book *Love, Medicine, and Miracles*: [7]

Patients desire not to outlive their usefulness. If they associate a long life with frailty and helplessness, then they may prefer a cancer diagnosis — there's the sense that they can control when and how they go, even if that way is excruciatingly painful. For some, knowing when they will die is far more valuable than a long life of uncertainty.

Patients have experienced loss or grief one to two years before the onset of disease. If they had recently been divorced, filed for bankruptcy, lost a loved one, or experienced a traumatic event, then a diagnosis may come as a blessed relief. Illness is the body's way of expressing despair on a molecular level. [8] Often, when there is a situation in a patient's life that seems hopeless, and the work involved to remedy the situation seems insurmountable, the easier way out is to become a victim. [9]

Patients have assigned a new meaning to their disease. As most of us have associated being sick with being cared for, tended to, and accommodated, [10] illnesses can mean a reprieve from responsibility, a much-needed rest, a way to hear loving messages from family members that had never been expressed in times of health. Illness identity becomes a factor as well. Listening to a patient's description of their disease is enlightening, and may offer clues to ministering to their true needs: those of the heart.

Patients need their illness to achieve a specific purpose. Along with the meaning assigned to the illness, there is a deep need for whatever the illness provides. For a person who has been overloaded with responsibility in their life, an illness is a desperate attempt to be appreciated. For a person who has suffered abandonment and heartbreak, an illness can mean an end to the suffering is in sight.

Our bodies respond to our innermost desires and seeks to grant them regardless of the cost; if we want to die, our bodies will attempt to make that happen. [11]

Of all illness sufferers, it has been shown that the majority would rather remain under a doctor's care than cooperate with their healing by bearing any degree of responsibility, a small percentage actually desire to die, and only a very few refuse to remain victims. [12]   For those in the last group who are ready to face their emotional scars, real hope exists.

Ecclesiastes 7:3-4 says, "Sorrow is better than laughter, for by a sad countenance the heart is made better. The heart of the wise is in the house of mourning, But the heart of fools is in the house of mirth" (NKJV).

Getting to the painful root of the issue, even through sorrow and sadness, can produce healing.   Patients who surrendered their depression and rage experienced their tumors shrinking almost simultaneously. [13]

In the church, there is a strong desire to present a holy facade.   If a Christian suffers great loss and hardship, he is praised as being faithful and strong if he can maintain a positive attitude.   If deep feelings of fear and anger are not acceptable among his fellow congregants, there can exist a scenario where the Christian would rather die than express them.   Thus, a terminal disease provides a way out of the suffering while still maintaining a stainless reputation in the church.

Many nutritional books have been written on the subject of "cancer proofing" your health by eliminating processed foods and eating plenty of fruits and vegetables. While that advice is wise to some extent — we should all eat healthier foods — there may be a larger role played by one's attitude toward cancer itself.   If your parent died of cancer, you are more likely to suffer from the same cancer around the same age as your parent, not because of genes, but because you believed you would.   Your thoughts influence your immune system, as do your fears.

In cancer patients, being positive and hopeful about their treatments yielded better results, regardless of how severe their disease had become. [14] Even false hope is better than no hope at all. Hopelessness is fundamentally the cause of the disease.   No life is beyond hope.   Believing life is hopeless may promise to protect you from being disappointed, but it can actually bring about disappointment in the process by cultivating a pessimistic attitude toward life. [15]

Your immune system is listening to your every thought. If you believe that you are vulnerable to disease, you will be.   If you tell yourself you are healthy and strong, your immune system will respond accordingly.   I tried out this concept in my own life. My kids had all come down with horrible colds, and I did NOT want to catch what they had. I have always caught whatever my kids had the moment I heard, "Mommy, I don't feel well." This time, however, instead of compulsively washing my hands and avoiding my children like I would normally have done, I simply told my body that I "don't need this cold." I continued to drink out of their cups and hug them and let them sneeze on me. I never caught the cold. I tried this experiment throughout three of their colds and my dad's bronchitis, never catching even a teeny bit of the viruses. It had never occurred to me how fearful I had been of catching colds! My body was putting so much energy into being afraid that my immune system had nothing left with which to fight. Being freed from the fear freed me from the illness as well.

These are only a select few of the diseases and illnesses I researched. If you would like to know more about your particular disorder or disease, the best way is to spend time with other people who share the same condition; what do all of them appear to have in common? There is a personality behind every disease; here are just a few:

Irritable Bowel Syndrome (IBS) is a functional disorder, meaning there is no definitive cause for the condition. Most female IBS sufferers have been victims of abuse, yet most doctors never ask questions about possible emotional triggers. [16] It is a common occurrence for IBS symptoms to vanish once the patient addresses deep-seated fears, either by removing themselves from the abuse or by finding support for working through the emotions left behind.

Alzheimer's symptoms are linked to "early life experience, emotional repression and lifelong stress." [17]

Rheumatoid arthritis has been seen to afflict people of a specific personality type: "… a stoicism carried to an extreme degree, a deeply ingrained reticence about seeking help" also described as being perfectionists, strong independence, a denial of their own anger, and a fear of experiencing their own intense emotions. [18] Research has shown that flare-ups often accompany a decrease in stress several days later, thus proving a protective function of the disease – their pain had allowed them to avoid stressful activities. [19]

Multiple Sclerosis (MS) has been traced to an exposure to chronic stress in childhood, while the ability to "engage in the necessary flight-or -fight behavior was impaired." [20] Other factors include codependency on a parent, a strong need for approval and love, and the "inability to feel or express anger." [21] These descriptions were seen across cultures; many Iranian women suffer from MS after a lifetime of having to serve their families without complaint, all the while being seen as second-class citizens, even property. They are not given societal permission to refuse an intolerable situation, so their body does the refusing for them.

Amyotrophic lateral sclerosis (ALS) has been traced to an unwillingness to ask for help, a denial of physical or emotional pain, and a strong inner drive to succeed or perform, [22] all of which "predate the onset of illness."[23]

Parkinson's Disease bears much in common with both ALS and MS, and sufferers of all three share similar personality traits.

This list is not exhaustive. Headaches, sinus infections, hay fever, seasonal allergies, and more could all be attributed to the MindBody phenomenon — many of which we dismiss as almost amusing: procrastination, laziness, antisocial tendencies, being "high-maintenance," and more.

One helpful tool in determining your own disorder's personality is to pay attention to the words you use to describe your pain or illness. We tend to use words like "aching," "burning," "feels like sharp knives stabbing me," "heavy," among others. Try then using those same adjectives to describe your emotions. The body takes over for the mind in trying to communicate troublesome emotions, so often those words will describe how you feel in your mind almost perfectly.

Is there a cure for chronic pain? Yes, and no. Since our physical bodies manifest our inner emotions, we will most likely always struggle with pain of one sort or another. But I believe that when we apply the principles found in the Word, we can experience victory more often. It all goes back to the verse in John chapter 5 where Jesus asks the sick man by the Bethesda Pool, "Do you want to be made well?" Why wouldn't a person want to be made well? The answer is simple: when the cure is perceived to be more painful than the pain itself. And what was the cure for the sick man by the pool? He had to surrender what was most dear to him: his desire for pity, his excuses, his hopelessness. For some of us, that's not an acceptable alternative to the pain we are suffering. All disease and chronic pain serve a purpose — it is a sinful mind's means to meet emotional needs, sacrificing even the body's physical health to do so.

We dealt with this a little when we talked about secondary gain from our pain. It helps to get out a sheet of paper and write all the benefits you receive because of your pain. It may sound absurd to think of pain having benefits, but here are a few you may not have considered:

1. I'm not expected to do certain household chores.
2. If I don't want to go somewhere, I have a built-in excuse.
3. People ask me how I'm doing and seem genuinely to care.
4. I know my husband would never leave me alone in this condition.
5. I've met wonderful people who share my condition and really understand me.
6. I don't have to try things and risk failure; I'm given freedom to stay where I am in life.
7. I have something to talk about; I'm seen as an expert on my condition.

Do any of these resonate? My favorite is #2. I really don't enjoy going places or spending time with people outside my immediate family. I'm outgoing when I need to be, but most of the time I prefer solitude and studying. Even cleaning the house is more enjoyable than being out with others. Yet deep down I know this is not how I am called to behave. I am called to unity in the body of Christ, and I can't be unified with others if I am avoiding them. I don't *want* to be social. But I *need* to. How can I reconcile those two truths?

So, I develop a headache. No, I really do. I'm not making it up or pretending. I actually get a headache and a stomachache and I feel exhausted. So tired I can't keep my eyes open. And I develop a weird nervous tic where I jerk my shoulder and it gives me neck pain. I'm a complete mess. But when people ask me if I want to go out, I can honestly tell them I'm exhausted and I have a headache, and they don't pry further. It gets me out of being social but it doesn't address the problem at its root — that I am sinful and selfish and hoarding my gifts, not sharing them with the Body of Christ. This ruse can only go so far, and I will end up suffering the consequences, as the headaches come more frequently and become chronic.

In the last year, I have yielded my desire for solitude to the Lord and opened up my calendar for others. Fully expecting God to bring me annoying friends and people who drive me crazy, He surprised me (it shouldn't surprise me He is *good*, however) with a group of friends who have blessed me and who truly understand me. I can tell them I don't want to go out sometimes, and they get me. The more they understand me, the more I want to go out with them! Turns out people aren't so bad after all!

There is freedom in yielding, freedom in coming out of hiding and being known by a loving God.

Ask yourself: do you *want* to be made well? Do you want all that comes with healing, the increased responsibility, the greater risk for being emotionally hurt or rejected, the possibility that God may ask you to do something you don't want to do? This is not a rhetorical question; if you answer in the negative, there is no need to keep reading this book. You must desire wellness more than you desire to escape. The sad truth is that by running from your fears, they become eventual reality. The woman who shops to numb the pain ends up wasting her retirement and losing her home. The man who works himself weary to prove he is not a failure ends up with a debilitating chronic pain condition, forcing him to live on disability. The child who works himself into sickness to avoid a test he fears he may fail ends up failing the entire class due to his prolonged absence.

Satan has our number. He knows exactly how to defeat us — by making us view victory as defeat and defeat as victory. He doesn't need to push us towards failure; we run right to it! And when we realize the error of our judgment, he convinces us it's too late to turn around.

Jesus tells us the truth about our condition if we have ears to hear. We are all sinners, not one is righteous, NO NOT ONE. We cannot make ourselves holy or pure by sheer willpower, nor can we outrun the grace of the Cross. He has already won the battle we are fighting. We need only surrender and embrace the victory He has already assured us. That is *true* wellness. Now, do you want to be made well?

Questions to Ask Yourself

1. What are your expectations for your old age? Do you want to live to be one-hundred?
2. In what way can knowing when you will die bring peace? How has having a terminal illness changed the way you treat those around you? How would you live differently if you didn't know when the end would come?
3. Do you want to be made well?

CHAPTER SEVEN:
IMPLICATIONS –
THE FUTURE OF MINDBODY MEDICINE

If a lot of this is sounding absurd to you, it's only because we have been conditioned to see the body as a machine we inhabit. We have a mind, but it's simply driving this body just like you would drive your minivan. Need an oil change, head to the garage. Flat tire, call a tow truck. There's really nothing else you can do about engine trouble than to either call a mechanic or pick up a wrench yourself. It's not like you can communicate with your car on a deeper level, let alone fix it with the power of your mind.

By viewing the body as a separate entity to the mind, we are at a disadvantage. Once the body breaks down, we are fully reliant on medical intervention for healing. And if there is no healing available, we are out of luck.

Why do we continue to study the human body as if we only exist outside of it? [1] We are more than just physical bodies; we are also mind and spirit (I Thessalonians 5:23). The three are beautifully and intricately intertwined in an elaborate dance. Science is just starting to scratch the surface of the complex interactions between our minds and our bodies, and the results so far are enough to challenge our entire medical belief system.

Research is slowly showing that our emotions are not abstract constructs that have no bearing on reality, but that they are directly wired to our immune system. Emotions that are not expressed become a kink in the works and can block the body's healing capabilities. Psychological becomes physiological, as blurred emotional boundaries lead to an immune system that is "too confused to know self from other or too disabled to defend against danger." [2]

The link between emotion and immunity has immense implications. Potentially, all disease and illness could be affected by how we think and feel. Research into cancer, autoimmune diseases, autism, mental illness, asthma, and allergies has been conducted with amazing results. The mind can heal the body. We are not just victims of bacteria and viruses and genetic predispositions.

The medical community has no clear answer to why most chronic pain and illnesses even exist. Sure, they have guesses, but none fully explain why some people suffer and others don't, why some have tremendous pain and some have none, and why some survive and others die. Ask any two doctors and you are likely to be given two different explanations or two different methods of treatment. When surgery or medication doesn't work, the explanation can be confusing and unhelpful.

Science has had its chance to explain pain and disease, but it falls short in that it cannot prove a definite cause, effect, or solution. It must be concluded that either the answer lies outside of science or that science is leaving key bits of data out of their equation. I argue for the latter. We cannot set aside the fact that we are made in the image of God and all that entails. Leaving that aspect of our humanity out in the cold means we are not getting the whole story.

Where is the line drawn between what we can influence with our mind and what is our genetic or biological destiny? The medical evidence is highly suggestive, if not overwhelmingly convincing, that we can control our physical health with our thoughts and emotions. We have seen that negative thoughts can lead to physical illness and pain. On the converse, the mind can *heal* the body just as easily. Potentially *all* illness and disease and chronic pain could be reversed using these principles, just as it is possible to lower your heart rate, change your skin temperature and reduce muscle tension, among other physical states normally considered only involuntary by the use of biofeedback. [3] The more we learn about the MindBody connection, the more we see we are only limited by our beliefs. God did not create machines, and yet we continue to view our bodies as such.

New developments in brain scanning has revealed that thoughts can become agents of biological change throughout the body, affecting cells, organs, and tissues. Our health and emotions are not as dependent on our experiences as they are on our beliefs and thoughts. [4]

Any disorder that is considered "functional" — a term for any "condition in which the symptoms are not explainable by any anatomical, pathological, or biochemical abnormality or by infection" [5] — should be suspect. Does the disorder itself make *sense*? Why *this* disorder, why *now*, why *me*? Doctors tend to fear uncertainty, thus making diagnoses based more on tests and biopsies than on the patient's own experiences and interpretations. [6] Be sure to educate your doctor on anything that you deem relevant — your emotional state, struggles you are facing, any trauma you have experienced — if they don't seem interested or imply that those occurrences are irrelevant, you may need to find another doctor.

Alternative Medicine

It is this frustration with the medical model that has caused many to pursue more natural, alternative methods for healing. Some turn to natural medicine out of a realization that the medical community has failed, some fear that Big Pharma is untrustworthy and doesn't have their best interests at heart.

There's nothing wrong with wanting a more natural way of doing things.[7] Our foods are full of chemicals and our landfills are overflowing and everyone seems to be taking some sort of drug. How is a Christian to be a good steward of a world that appears to be growing more and more toxic?

God declared His creation "good," no doubt about it (Genesis 1:31); but sin has had its effects on this world. I was one of those who believed that if only we could return to the Garden, we could somehow recapture that "good"-ness and be restored to perfect health. I became certified as a nutritionist, and had focused on a plant-based lifestyle, natural remedies, natural cleaning products, you name it. I was a serious food label snob, and it became a source of real pride for me. I saw the natural lifestyle as the cure for all illness and disease, and yet it couldn't cure the sickest part of me: my heart. I was hardened and rigid and judgmental.

Alternative medicines are not holier or even more effective than standard medicines: if an alternative medicine really worked, it would *be* medicine. [8] Not everything manmade is evil, and not everything natural is wholesome and healthy. There are plenty of natural foods that can kill you in mere moments, and many manmade inventions that have saved thousands of lives. In truth, everything on this planet is natural! Man cannot take credit for a single molecule!

The issue with both the medical and the alternative medicine approaches to chronic illness and pain is that they focus solely on the *physical*. Since no two people respond the same way to interventions, either traditional or alternative, we are left wondering if there is more to the story.

The human race has developed many medical advancements, and it can appear confounding how we ever managed without them; obviously we survived long enough to discover them, so they must not have been critical to our survival. [9] This can also be applied to herbs and supplements, and even much of our produce, seeing as we never would have even heard of some of the fruits and vegetables we see as nutritionally necessary had it not been for modern transportation, genetic manipulation, and refrigeration advancements.

Although many of the alternative remedies that you may have in your medicine cabinet have been debunked and discredited over the years, why do they still seem to work? I swore by homeopathic treatments for over a decade until I learned how they are really made; oddly enough, they quickly stopped working for me once I had that information.

Here is just a short list of facts about alternative medicines and remedies:

Antioxidants can be dangerous. The common belief is that your body is full of free radicals that cause aging and disease; therefore, you must combat these evil entities with antioxidants in large doses. The truth? Free radicals are beneficial: they attack bacteria and fight cancer cells. [10] So before you gulp down a fizzy vitamin C drink, keep in mind that you get plenty of the antioxidants you need from consuming fruits and vegetables. Supplements are unnecessary, and in fact dangerous in high doses, as they have been linked to cancer and other ailments.

Acupuncture is useless. Countless placebo studies have been conducted that have found that there is no difference between real acupuncture and when retractable needles have been used instead. [11] The healing that results from acupuncture is completely the placebo effect.

Chelation doesn't reverse symptoms. If you have been diagnosed with a heavy metal toxicity, or if you are trying chelation to combat chronic disease, you may be surprised to learn that chelation can only prevent further harm; it cannot reverse the harm done already. [12] Many people have experienced healing after chelation; however, this is merely a result of the placebo effect.

Homeopathics are basically water. Sure, it makes sense that homeopathics would work similarly to vaccines: expose the body to a tiny amount of something and let it react by sending out an immune response. However, the amount of dilution in homeopathy renders the substance completely useless.

Homeopathics are made by diluting a substance in a 100:1 ratio of water, then repeating two-hundred times. By the time it's ready, there is not even a single molecule of the substance in the solution. It is in fact so dilute, that if the water volume were as great as the entire universe, there would still be not one molecule of the substance present. One manufacturer uses the heart and liver of a duck to make their popular flu remedy. However, there is not even one bit of duck remaining in the final product. [13] The belief is that, through the diluting process, the water would "remember" the duck; but it is a reassuring fact indeed that our earth's water doesn't "remember" everything that has passed through it, considering what all that would mean! [14]

Herbs and oils are drugs that have not yet been approved. Herbs and some oils are nature's pharmaceuticals, and therefore should never be taken or used topically or internally on a daily basis. Anything taken in excess or without being mindful of interactions can be deadly; for example, certain oils are not to be used on young children, and certain herbs can render other drugs or foods poisonous or ineffective. Just because a fellow mom told you she swears by a certain remedy does not mean that it is safe to use.

It's so tempting to believe that Big Pharma is the bad guy, intentionally keeping us sick and diseased, so we need to take matters into our own hands. Just because I'm sure that there is corruption in some levels of the pharmaceutical industry doesn't mean that other industries are spotless and well-intentioned! Always follow the money, and there is big money to be made in the alternative medicine industries. I wish I had known the truth about some of these remedies; I spent a small fortune on homeopathic medicines when my children were young — how many sleepless nights did they spend with runny noses when some over-the-counter medicine would have better addressed their symptoms and allowed them (and me!) to sleep through the night, healing their bodies sooner.

No Longer Victims

If we are not carefully attending to our thoughts, our brain will continue to engage in the same patterns. When the brain doesn't get its desired results, it only knows to try harder the next time – it doesn't know to try a new pattern. [15]

Often, these same patterns involve avoiding or self-soothing behaviors. How many office workers get through their day wired on coffee and office gossip? How many moms indulge in a daily glass of wine and a few hours on social media in order to avoid a nervous breakdown? Emotional intelligence is simply to confess our emotions as they truly are: fear of failure, resentment of authority, jealousy of others. Confession releases those deadly emotions and allows them to be replaced with the fruits of the spirit. Concealing rage and pride, thereby nurturing them, causes them to grow and inflict harm in our hearts and in our bodies.

We are not victims. We are not robots. We can "do all things through Christ who strengthens" us (Philippians 4:13 NKJV). If God calls us to be holy, we CAN be holy with the power He provides.

We can **choose** our emotions. [16] We can **choose** our thoughts. And in doing so, we can **choose** to heal.

CHAPTER EIGHT:
THE BIBLICAL RESPONSE

The Church, to be fair, has tried to take a biblical approach to chronic pain and illness. It organizes small groups for the sufferers, prays for them in the service, and discusses Christ's suffering as a model for ours. But just what does the Bible say about pain?

If you're looking for a single verse to connect all the dots, you won't find it. One mistake we make in reading the Bible is viewing it as a Magic 8-Ball, searching for pithy truths we can hang on our wall or use as our social media profile picture. The Bible deals more with larger truths that we can then apply to our lives; we can't get away with just skimming the pages; we must dive deep.

First, the Bible is *always* right. If there is a troubling passage, one that seems to defy science, it is science that is mistaken, not the Word of God. We are making new scientific discoveries every day, and some of them contradict previous ones or negate them altogether. We used to believe the earth was the center of the universe!

Second, God's response to disease and illness has not changed throughout the Bible. He has always provided remedies and healing, albeit in different ways. In the Old Testament, He gave His people commands that ensured they would remain healthy:

"He said, 'If you listen carefully to the Lord your God and do what is right in his eyes, if you pay attention to his commands and keep all his decrees, I will not bring on you any of the diseases I brought on the Egyptians, for I am the Lord, who heals you.'" (Exodus 15:26 NIV)

In the New Testament, Jesus's healing miracles were a huge part of His ministry. And beginning with the early church, He came to dwell within us as the Holy Spirit to "guide [us] into all truth" (John 16:13 NKJV). From prevention and protection, to intervention, to innovation and conviction, you can trace His ultimate plan for our healing throughout scripture. God has drawn closer and closer to us, even dwelling *within* us to heal us from the inside out.

Third, passages relative to healing must be taken in light of Scripture as a whole. Context is critical, and many verses have been falsely applied and misused.

When Christians talk about pain, there are three main passages of Scripture that they usually bring up. The most quoted examples from Scripture of people with physical afflictions are:

Job

Job, as you may recall, was a righteous man who God chose to afflict with great loss to prove to Satan that Job loved God for Himself, not for the blessings He gives. Job was accused by his friends of having done something to "deserve" this punishment, and God spoke from heaven to prove them wrong.

The example of Job is used as a warning to anyone who would suggest that pain and suffering result from divine punishment. And that would be correct. As believers, Jesus has borne our punishment on the cross and we are forgiven and blameless in His sight. Chronic pain is *not* a punishment.

However, it would be equally a mistake to assume that chronic pain is *always* God trying to show others how righteous we are when we have loss. Yes, God does use evil for good, and there are trials He lets us endure for His glory. So, ask, "Is my suffering giving glory to God right now?" Are you becoming a more patient, more peaceful, more loving person because of your pain? Better yet, ask those around you.

What we can learn from Job's example:

Job was a sinner just like us.

We may like to picture Job as being sinless and view his story of pain as indicative that sometimes, bad things happen to good people through no fault of their own. While this is true in a manner of speaking, as we are often sinned against unjustly, we can never claim that we are sinless. Not one person who God could have chosen for this "divine presentation" could fall into the category of "innocent."

Job remained blameless throughout his trials:

While Job remained a sinner, his response to his sin was holy and righteous. He did not sin in his sin, you could say. He patiently endured the cruelty of his friends when they made assumptions that only unrepentant wicked people experienced pain. They neglected to acknowledge God's sovereignty in all things because they enjoyed feeling superior to Job — maybe they had been envious of his success prior to his testing. (If anyone is likely to experience chronic pain, it's those men!). If you are reading Job's story and feeling justified in your attitude toward your own chronic pain, that is pride rearing its ugly head. Job's story should lead us to worship and humility before the Creator of the Universe.

Job never hid his sins before God:

> "Have I covered my transgressions like Adam, by hiding my iniquity in my bosom, Because I feared the great multitude, And the contempt of families terrified me, and kept silent and did not go out of doors?" (Job 31:33-34 NKJV)

Because chronic pain is caused by hiding sin and the emotions it causes, open and honest confession before God is the first step to preventing it before it starts.

Paul

Paul was given a "thorn in the flesh" after he was given a vision of the third heaven, lest he become conceited and arrogant. He pleaded three times for it to be removed, and God told him no, that His grace is sufficient for him (2 Corinthians 12:7-10).

One big mistake believers make is assuming that *any* trial can fall into the category of "thorn in the flesh." Let's be clear. A thorn in the flesh is not to be equated with suffering a consequence of sinful behavior. If the Bible tells us to "be anxious for nothing" (Philippians 4:6 NKJV) then anxiety cannot be considered such a thorn. Many scholars have even argued that Paul's thorn was not medical in nature, but for the sake of argument, I will accept that it may have been a physical ailment of some kind.

The example of Paul is also used frequently regarding chronic pain — we claim that we are also given "thorns in the flesh" in the form of arthritis or knee pain, but we must not make this mistake, as we are *not Paul*. Paul was told expressly by God the reason for his thorn, and given a promise for grace in its midst. Paul was actively seeking God in all his ways, a humble servant of the gospel, and his thorn was given to him so he would not sin, not as a response to sin. I don't know about you, but I sin plenty. A thorn would do me little to no good if I'm already entrenched in bad behaviors.

If you haven't received such a message from God, you cannot assume that your situation is the same as that of Paul. Most of us do not have the ministry that Paul had -- neither were we allowed a vision of heaven, so there would be little need for such a "thorn" in our lives.

What we can learn from Paul's example:

He prayed for healing. Just because we know that our pain is caused by our own thoughts doesn't mean we can't pray for healing. Especially when the pain has grown so great, and our hearts are discouraged and full of despair. We need God's grace to surround us and his strength to uphold us; we cannot change our hearts on our own!

He accepted the answer to his prayers. While many have overcome chronic pain within a short time, it can be a lifelong journey for others. Accepting that God is still good, that He is still in control, and that you are not alone is critical to eliminating chronic pain.

It's interesting to note that nowhere in the Bible does it say that Jesus refused to heal someone during His earthly ministry, saying, "your illness is from God." If Paul's thorn was indeed physical, then it was definitely the exception to how Jesus typically responded to requests for healing. More importantly, if you have been claiming that your illness is directly from God to teach you humility, then why would you seek medical relief? [1]

Every trial will eventually bring glory to God. So, don't despair! Even if our thoughts led to our condition, that doesn't mean that it was all a waste! God never lets our experiences go to waste, whether they be good or bad ones.

The Man Born Blind

Jesus healed a man who had been born blind after being asked, "Rabbi, who sinned, this man or his parents, that he was born blind?" (John 9:2 NKJV) Jesus replied that neither had sinned, but he was born blind so that "the works of God should be revealed in him" (John 9:3 NKJV).

We live in a broken world. Babies are born with genetic disorders, we break bones, we get the flu. It would be wrong to assume that every illness and pain results from an instance of sin; rather, it results from sin in general. But it also would be wrong to assume that pain just "happens" to us, and we bear no role in it. That would mean we could run into traffic and blame our broken bones on a fallen world rather than on our poor decision. We must know when to take responsibility, asking the Holy Spirit for guidance and wisdom.

Even as we learn that some childhood disorders are caused by stress in the parents or genes that they carry, do not lose heart! We all carry the sin nature in our blood, not one of us is guiltier than the other. Christ has paid your debt in full; you are no longer condemned! (Romans 8:1) Sin is a part of this world, but Christ will redeem it and restore it once and for all.

What we can learn from the man born blind:

He wasn't the one who was blind. The Pharisees were the ones claiming to have no sin; therefore, they were the ones who were blind. Hiding your sin makes you blind to it over time.

His suffering led him to worship. (John 9:38) Your worship should not cease, even amid suffering. Worship is a critical step in conquering chronic pain.

Looking for a cause diverts attention from looking for a purpose. [2] No matter what the physical or emotional cause for a particular disease or pain, there is always a divine purpose behind it. God always uses our sin and our trials for good.

It is interesting to note the way physical infirmities are discussed in the New Testament:

1. Other instances in the New Testament of illness/disease mainly involve the healing that the sufferers receive upon encountering Christ. Everywhere Jesus went, he healed people. But more

important that healing their physical bodies, He healed them spiritually.

> "Then Jesus went about all the cities and villages, teaching in their synagogues, preaching the gospel of the kingdom, and **healing every sickness and disease among the people.**" (Matthew 9:35 NKJV, *emphasis mine*)

2. Healing was a direct result of faith in many instances:

> The woman with a hemorrhage who was healed by touching Jesus' robe was told, "Your faith has made you well" (Matthew 9:22 NKJV). The two blind men Jesus healed in Matthew 9 were asked first, "Do you believe that I am able to do this?" and when they said yes, Jesus answered, "According to your faith let it be to you" (Matthew 9:29 NKJV).

3. Illness was also often directly linked to demonic possession:

> "And behold, there was a woman who had a **spirit of infirmity** eighteen years, and was bent over and could in no way raise herself up. But when Jesus saw her, He called her to Him and said to her, 'Woman, you are loosed from your infirmity.' And He laid His hands on her, and immediately she was made straight, and glorified God." (Luke 13: 11-13 NKJV, *emphasis mine*)

> "Now He arose from the synagogue and entered Simon's house. But Simon's wife's mother was sick with a high fever, and they made request of Him concerning her. So He stood over her and **rebuked** the fever, and it left her. And immediately she arose and served them." (Luke 4: 38-39 NKJV, *emphasis mine*)

4. Forgiveness was referred to as "healing." In I Peter 2:24, we see the phrase: "by whose stripes you were healed." Sin is the real disease from which we need healing. After Jesus healed the man at the Pool of Bethesda he made a curious remark:

> "Afterward Jesus found him in the temple and said to him, 'Behold, you have become well; do not sin anymore, so that nothing worse happens to you.'" (John 5:14 NASV)

Jesus Himself acknowledged the connection between spirit and body and how one affects the other:

- The Church is called the Body of Christ (I Corinthians 12:27) and we are unified in the Holy Spirit (Ephesians 4:2).

- The Armor of God blends bodily imagery with spiritual weapons:
    1. Gird your waist with truth.
    2. Put on the breastplate of righteousness.
    3. Shod your feet with the preparation of the gospel of peace.
    4. Hold in your hand the shield of faith and the sword of the Spirit.
    5. Put the helmet of salvation on your head.
       (Ephesians 6:14-17 NKJV)

- The book of Proverbs is full of warnings of how emotions can cause physical pain:
    1. "Hope deferred makes the heart sick." (Proverbs 13:12 NKJV)
    2. "Envy is rottenness to the bones." (Proverbs 14:30 NKJV)
    3. "A good report makes the bones healthy." (Proverbs 15:30 NKJV)
    4. "A merry heart does good, like medicine." (Proverbs 17:22 NKJV)

The book of Proverbs is not meant to be taken as a book of promises, more as a general guideline and a description of what *usually* happens in certain scenarios. Surely not everyone who envies has arthritis! Regardless, the connection is compelling and should give us pause.

God alone understands the way our bodies and minds work together. We couldn't understand, even if He were to explain it to us. The world has offered us one explanation for health and disease, and we cannot accept it, for it is based on our human understanding. We are eternal beings, created in the image of God, and it makes no sense whatsoever that man could provide the answer to a God-sized problem: sin (John 14:6).

Seeing the connection between faith and healing, we may ask if that means that if you have perfect faith, you will be healed of every illness and disease? Because none of us have perfect faith, we will never know! And not all illness is demonic possession, but don't be deceived — Satan loves to use illness and disease to defeat us. The overall message is that we are more than just physical bodies; our emotions and our relationships with others, our choices and our desires all merge into who we are. At the root of it all is sin, and consequently, a barrier between us and God. If we had no sin, we would have no disease. Since we are sinners, we have chronic pain and illness. The question is, "What can we do about it?" How *do* we come out of hiding?

PART FOUR:
A BETTER RESPONSE TO PAIN

CHAPTER NINE:
COMING OUT OF HIDING

Hiding requires darkness and shadow; coming out of hiding requires light and truth. We may have a decent grasp on the truth, but deep-down harbor false beliefs that end up contradicting the truth we claim we know. Since the subconscious is responsible for most our decisions and bodily processes, we must address those false beliefs before they take root.

1.   Know What You Believe

Our beliefs are immensely powerful; they are capable of creating entirely new realities for ourselves and affecting our bodies in ways beyond our understanding. [1]

The Bible has a lot to say about the importance of belief and having the right focus:

- "I will **meditate** on your precepts and **fix my eyes** on your ways." (Psalm 119:15 ESV)
- Peter could walk on water just like Jesus as long as he **kept his eyes** on the Lord. (Matthew 14: 29-31)
- **Believing** in Jesus is the foundation for salvation. (Acts 16:31)
- The Bible warns us not to **believe** every spirit, but to test to see if they are from God. (I John 4:1)
- "For to **set the mind** on the flesh is death, but to **set the mind** on

the Spirit is life and peace." (Romans 8:6, ESV)

- "... **fixing our eyes** on Jesus, the author and perfecter of faith, who for the joy set before Him endured the cross, despising the shame, and has sat down at the right hand of the throne of God. For consider Him who has endured such hostility by sinners against Himself, so that you may not grow weary and lose heart." (Hebrews 12:2-3 NASB)

- "But one thing I do: forgetting what lies behind and straining forward to what lies ahead, I **press on** toward the goal for the prize of the upward call of God in Christ Jesus." (Philippians 3:13-14, ESV)

Beliefs matter, and they direct the course of your life.

Beliefs are not material objects, so what exactly are they? They exist in the realm of quantum physics; they are like little orbs of possibility, holding within their little beings the energy to enact good or evil, health or illness. Fixing your mind on a certain belief involves placing all your energy there, [2] therefore making your beliefs the true driving force behind every action you take. Our bodies can cause our thoughts to become reality; [3] so what we think matters.

False beliefs, by definition, deny the Truth. As believers, we would claim that we are sinners saved by grace. But do we really believe that deep down?

Sometimes, we are allowed a sneak peek into what we truly believe. Being placed in a new environment can cause hidden emotions to bubble up to the surface. Have you ever found vacations to bring out the best *and* the worst in your family? My father, a pastor, always advised engaged couples to hold off on marriage until they had known each other through all four seasons of the year; people behave differently in the summer than they do in the winter! Over all, we take every precaution to keep our thoughts and emotions hidden, perhaps out of fear of what they will expose about us. Yet we are learning how critical it is to our health for us to express those emotions, no matter where they will lead us.

We may not even realize that we are suppressing anything — years of therapy may only scratch the surface for an individual not wanting to be exposed. To admit our feelings, we have to admit the faulty beliefs behind them. For example, we believe we are responsible for not only everything in our lives, but for everything in general. We believe that good people don't get angry or express intense emotions. We believe that to be lovable, we must be strong, capable, and composed. We believe that our actions must justify our existence, and the only way we can deserve love and compassion is if we are *really* sick. [4] It's this last belief that fuels the subconscious creation of chronic illness and disease, as we *all* need the love and care that illness usually awards us.

Not one of us is exempt from believing at least one of these statements at one time or another. These beliefs are contrary to the gospel and belong to our sin nature, our "default setting." If we are not careful, we will fall into one or more of these traps.

At the root of all of them is self. It's all about me. I must do right, I must be right, I must be treated right. Our culture stresses the importance and value of independence, strength, and positive thinking. No one likes a needy, complaining person, and we assume that any expression of need would fit into this category and be rejected by society at large.

Of course, at face value, these beliefs seem ridiculous. No one wants to admit that they believe they aren't lovable! Yet all of these bad beliefs boil down to pride. We hold ourselves to higher standards than we do those around us, and therefore we must never express negative emotions or any kind of *need* whatsoever. Our pride causes us to see no other way out than to create physical pain as an alternate way out.

Psychosomatic disorders are created in order to justify our actions, help us avoid uncomfortable situations, and get us what we truly desire without causing us to lose face or incur blame. The pain that results is actually a "wise investment." [5]

Even very low self-image stems from pride. It is a preoccupation with oneself rather than a focus on one's Creator. It is placing ourselves on the throne of our lives and striving to obey and serve oneself rather than the Almighty God.

So how can we really know what we believe? We may be able to identify our beliefs based on how we act, but actions are not always helpful clues — we can temporarily alter our behavior to appear more generous or happier or less angry. We may try to trace back our thoughts to our beliefs, but this can sometimes prove difficult. Thoughts that are habitual tend to fly under our conscious radars. *Our physical health becomes the only reliable window into knowing what we believe.*

To break the cycle and turn things around for the better, your beliefs have to align with reality. When there is a disconnect between the truth and what you believe, your body and your mind both suffer.

Look at some triggers for MindBody pain and see if you can identify the disconnects:

1. Being forced to make a decision where either option available to you is unacceptable.
2. Being abused by someone in a position of authority.
3. Having unconfessed sin.
4. Not being honest about your emotions such as anger, fear, and inadequacy.
5. Damaged relationships where you are at a standstill.
6. Living a life inconsistent with your beliefs — for example, you may say, "I hate phoniness" and yet you are acting phony, thus essentially you are saying, "I hate myself." A self-hatred in the mind can lead to a body physically destroying itself on a cellular level.
7. Being asked to do something you do NOT want to do, but feel there is no way to decline gracefully.
8. Wanting something that you should not or cannot have.
9. Wanting to be seen as someone you are not — for example, wanting to be praised for your mothering skills, yet not wanting to do the work that motherhood entails.

Notice how all the scenarios on this list involve a truth and a lie trying to coexist. These triggers put you in a position where there appears to be no acceptable way to express the truth about your emotions. Since telling the truth appears to be impossible, the truth becomes shoved deeper and deeper down into the psyche. Emotions become buried and manifest themselves as chronic pain.

Jesus is the way, the truth, and the life (John 14:6). I don't think the grouping of those three words is a coincidence. Truth brings life, lies bring death. There is only one way to healing, and that is through Truth Himself. Only He can reveal to you the truth about your situation.

Truth, and through it, awareness is the primary cure for MindBody pain, and it is a critical part in overcoming virtually all chronic pain. Once you have brought the emotional source of your pain to the forefront, your mind can no longer do its work in secret. Altering your beliefs transforms your emotions which, in turn, communicates new patterns to your body.

Changing your focus to the Truth sends new messages to your cells, rewriting prior pain pathways. Your brain secretes different neuropeptides, which send new chemical messages to every cell in your body, meaning that your body *listens* to what you are thinking. [6] By realizing prior negative emotions and substituting them with God-honoring ones, you can change your body for the better at a cellular level, using the cycle for good rather than evil. Now, instead of bad beliefs setting off chain reactions in your body, gratitude and peace will flood every cell, causing new patterns to develop: patterns of healing.

It's not enough to focus on the lie and try to change it somehow into the truth. It's like having tinnitus — the cure for tinnitus is to not listen to the ringing in your ears. How is that possible? By listening to something *else*. Placing all your attention on the truth will cause the lie to shrivel up and disappear.

The truth will set you free. Living a life of truth will set you free from chronic pain. Releasing your own desire for approval, relinquishing your expectation of comfort, confessing your sins and completely trusting your life to God will put your whole body in a right state of "mind" in which chronic pain is simply no longer needed.

The Bible is full of truths — try choosing a few verses to memorize and call them to mind repeatedly throughout the day. Fill your mind with music that points to Jesus, keep an open line between you and God throughout the day, read His Word and study His truth, and those lies will soon retreat.

Temptation always begins in your thoughts. While ideas can pop into your head through no fault of your own, you don't need to pull out the sofa bed. Once you allow a thought to make its home in your mind, you are allowing it to "make its case" to you, thus leaving you vulnerable to acting on the temptation. [7]

What temptations are being allowed free rein in your mind? What do you *believe*?

What are your beliefs about the world you inhabit? Do you believe the world is basically good and good things happen to good people? Do you believe that you are a good person and therefore deserve good things? How do these beliefs contradict the Bible? I wonder if the reason these beliefs are so commonly held is that they were *true* at the time of Creation: we *were* good, we *had* good things, and the world was a *good* place. But not anymore. After the Fall, the contrast of good was introduced: evil. We no longer deserved good, but *death*. The world is not a just or fair place; however, we serve a just God who promises to set all things right when He comes again. We do have good things in Christ Jesus, but *only* in Him, not in ourselves. Once we accept those truths, we can better understand why people can hurt us, why we can hurt others, how our sin hurts both ourselves and those we love, and how pain is not only possible, but *inevitable*.

What do you believe about your pain and your illness? Do you believe they are linked to your emotions? Are you willing to address those emotions and make necessary changes? What stresses and emotions are you addicted to? Do you find yourself falling into the same traps over and over again? You may need to try something completely different, something out of your comfort zone, just to break the addiction. My 15-year-old daughter was telling me how she eats when she's sad and then gets sad when she eats. I told her, "Keep thinking that way, and you'll be as round as your vicious cycle." Of course, we both laughed, but it's true! More of the same will leave you with more of the same. What are you willing to do to break out of the loop? You need to want freedom more than you want familiar.

What do you believe about yourself? Just who do you think you are? Do you see yourself as a victim? Do you believe you are above reproach and that people dare not contradict or confront you? Do you believe you need to be right? In control? Accepted and admired? Do you expect allowances to be made for your mistakes, for others to understand and have compassion on you? Are your beliefs biblical?

2. Take Your Thoughts Captive

Once you have identified your beliefs, you can then see your thoughts more clearly. If a thought arises that appears to contradict what we claim to believe, either we need to go back to square one and relearn the Truth, or we may be under spiritual attack. We take it for granted that we own our own thoughts. Many times, Satan sneaks a few of his own in there, and we need to know the difference!

Whatever has control of our mind controls our lives and our very bodies. Maybe I should say **who**ever has control, because the real war for our minds only has two players: Satan and Jesus. You can tell who authored the thought by who wins if the thought is true. If you think that you are worthless and you will never amount to anything, who benefits from that thought? Satan would give anything to sideline you and take away your power, so he definitely will use self-destructive thinking to achieve that purpose.

What power does a thought have? Significantly more than most of us realize. Every thought you think creates a domino effect in the body, triggering neural networks, controlling the issuing of neuropeptides, sending signals to hormonal centers and cell receptor sites, selecting and regulating DNA, expressing proteins; [8] every cell in your body is listening to what you are thinking.

Dieting apps help users succeed by requiring them to enter every calorie they eat during the day. Calories are then analyzed as being beneficial or detrimental to the user's weight loss goals. If we were to spend the same effort on our thoughts, how much better off we'd be!

Thoughts lead to emotions (pain is an emotion, remember) which lead to behavior, which lead back to thoughts. And around and around we go. We must be mindful to trace every pain back to the emotion connected with it, and then trace that emotion back to the thought that inspired it.

If nothing changes, nothing will. Your brain will continue to anticipate the same thoughts, and in turn, expect the same results. Your body becomes equal to the mind; they are experiencing the same things at the same time so you are no longer able to distinguish between the two. You will be stuck in a tragic loop, feeling hopeless, that you will never change, that your pain will never go away. [9] The only way to beat this cycle is to make a change at the outset: change your thoughts. Thoughts create new connections in the brain which then activate genetic, chemical, and neurological changes. Merely by thinking, "you can personally activate new genes right away... mind over matter." [10]

Positive thinking alone is not enough — you have to believe what you are thinking, not just mask false beliefs with spiritual-sounding thoughts — that's why we looked at beliefs first. Positive thinking also neglects to deal fully with the lies that have taken root in your mind; they must be replaced with the truth. Positive thinking that does not account for the truth is actually more of the same hiding behavior that got us into this predicament in the first place. Allowing yourself to think about the unpleasant and the negative, while applying the truth of God's Word to those thoughts, will have a greater impact on your health than trying to force emotions that perhaps should not even be there. If you have lost a loved one, there is no purpose in feigning happiness. If you have been wronged, pretending it doesn't bother you will not take the anger away. If you are afraid, acting like you are brave can only go so far. The truth must be the guiding factor behind all our thoughts, not public expectation.

We must take our thoughts captive, one by one, never allowing even one straggler across our threshold, because they are not innocent or harmless!

They have the power to create and destroy:

Thoughts create chemicals that produce emotional and physical reactions in the body. We then become accustomed to the chemical result of these thoughts, and we will go out of our way to recreate those chemical levels in our bloodstream. We humans crave balance, even in our body chemistry. [11]

Repetitive thoughts create a chemical reaction that becomes *addictive*. We become so accustomed to the physical sensations linked to the thought we attempt to recreate them at any cost. We seek experiences that will reinforce those thoughts and avoid experiences that will challenge them. The ensuing emotions are "chemical recipes" [12] that we develop a real taste for, and our brains build "highly developed neural net and hard-wired pathway[s] for" [13] anger, shame, fear, and lust. When you see a person stuck in a bad relationship or at a dead-end job, even though you know they *could* leave, the truth of the matter is that they aren't *physically* stuck, they are *neurologically* stuck.

Most interpersonal conflict is derived from this need to fuel our chemical addictions, as it becomes more about reaching a biochemical homeostasis then about reaching a consensus or finding a solution to a disagreement. [14] The more we indulge in this chemical addiction, the more physical health problems we face, as genes actually can wear out over time just as gears in a car can wear down from overuse. [15.] Not only that, our entire neurological destiny hinges on the kinds of thoughts we think, as they turn on and off brain circuitry, fire neural networks, and activate mental patterns on a continual basis. [16]

The only way to break this cycle is to do what your mother probably always told you: change your attitude. New thoughts become new signals to the cells, and new chemical recipes are formed. Renew your mind to renew your life.

Admittedly, altering thoughts is like aiming at a moving target. If you don't know what you're thinking, how do you change your thoughts? The easiest way is to replace them with gratitude and praise. Simply trying hard to *not* think about something is next to impossible. Focusing instead on God's Word and His glory will overwrite all those sinful thoughts with thoughts that bring Him — and you — joy. Praise and bitterness cannot coexist; neither can pride and worship.

"For what partnership has righteousness with lawlessness? Or

214

what fellowship has light with darkness?" (2 Corinthians 6:14
ESV)

The other night, my 10-year-old daughter was playing with a mini-figure
and noticed that the figure's plastic hair had fallen off. She immediately
teared up and ran for the heating vent in the kitchen, sure that it had fallen
down there and was burning to ashes in the furnace. I knelt down and asked
why she had gone directly to the absolute worst-case scenario. She was in
such a panic; she didn't seem to hear me, and went to sit down on the couch
to bawl pitifully. Again, I knelt down and told her, "You are believing two
lies right now. One, you think your doll's hair is gone forever and you'll never
find it. Two, you think no one cares or will help you. Neither is true. If you
look at me, you see that I am here. And if you get up and start looking, you
will find what you're looking for." She slowly and reluctantly got up off the
couch, looked down, and there the plastic hair was on the floor right where
she had been playing. Too often we fall into deeply grooved patterns of
hopelessness and despair when there is no justification for it simply because
we have been here before. "Here I go again." These kinds of thoughts are
directly from the evil one and must be rejected outright.

Spontaneous healings often occur as a result of a reversal of negative
thinking; once the thoughts that had contributed to the disease are no longer
entertained, the body can muster up enough energy to begin the healing
process. [17]

In order to best accomplish changes in your physical state, the primary
focus needs always be on your mind. Physical-oriented goals usually fail —
New Year's resolutions tend to fade away within 4-6 weeks — but spiritual
goals will always succeed because the Holy Spirit partners with us to grant us
the victory.

Changes in the mind create changes in the body. [18]

It is a challenge indeed to elevate your thoughts above your emotions. [19]
Oh, but we must! We cannot sit around, high on our addictive chemical
soups, while there is victory to be had! Just knowing that you are in complete
control of your thoughts should open up an entire world of possibilities to
you; use that control and don't let your thoughts wander to become negative
and defeatist.

A well-known hymn says it better than I could:

"Turn Your Eyes Upon Jesus"

O soul, are you weary and troubled?
No light in the darkness you see?
There's light for a look at the Savior,
And life more abundant and free!

Turn your eyes upon Jesus,
Look full in His wonderful face,
And the things of earth will grow strangely dim,
In the light of His glory and grace.

Through death into life everlasting
He passed, and we follow Him there;
O'er us sin no more hath dominion—
For more than conqu'rors we are!

His Word shall not fail you—He promised;
Believe Him, and all will be well:
Then go to a world that is dying,
His perfect salvation to tell!
-Helen H. Lemmel, 1922 [20]

3. Know and Be Known

"Now a woman, having a flow of blood for twelve years, who had spent all her livelihood on physicians and could not be healed by any, came from behind and touched the border of His garment. And immediately her flow of blood stopped. And Jesus said, 'Who touched Me?' When all denied it, Peter and those with him said, 'Master, the multitudes throng and press You, and You say, *Who touched Me?*' But Jesus said, 'Somebody touched Me, for I perceived power going out from Me.' Now when the woman saw that **she was not hidden**, she came trembling; and falling down before Him, she declared to Him in the presence of all the people the reason she had touched Him and how she was healed immediately. And He said to her, 'Daughter, be of good cheer; your faith has made you well. Go in peace.'" (Luke 8:43-48 NKJV, *emphasis mine*)

This dear woman had suffered for over a decade when she saw Jesus passing by. She had heard the rumors about Him, maybe even witnessed some of the healing miracles He had performed. *If only I could just touch His garment, then I wouldn't even have to bother Him,* she thought. Many of us approach our illness and pain in this same way. We want the physical healing, but we don't want Him to look too closely beyond it, to see us, to *know* us.

If Jesus hadn't questioned who touched Him, she still would have received her healing. She would have gone on to live a more productive and fulfilling life, able to go about her days without the shadow of illness hanging over her head. But she never would have been called Daughter, nor would she have received the peace that only a relationship with Jesus can offer. I wonder, too, if the faith He ascribed to her was in touching Him, or owning up to it? After all, which act takes more faith: touching a robe or confessing to the crowd that she was sick and desperate?

Which do you want more: physical healing or an encounter with the Healer Himself?

Do you *know* God? Or do you just know a lot about Him, enough to get by in a Sunday school class or a small group Bible study? I'm not asking how many Bible verses you have memorized in your head, but how much truth you have hidden in your heart. How is your relationship with Him? Do you see Him like a customer service desk, just file your complaint and take a number, we'll get to you as soon as we can? Or do you see Him like an angry father who is never pleased with what you've done and only sees your failures? Or maybe He's like a jolly old grandpa who brings you gifts and lets you do whatever you want because you're just so adorable? He is *none* of those things.

Moses asked God: "Suppose I go to the Israelites and say to them, 'The God of your fathers has sent me to you,' and they ask me, 'What is his name?' Then what shall I tell them?" (Exodus 3:13 NIV) God could have used any number of adjectives to describe Himself, but He chose to answer: "**I AM WHO I AM**" (Exodus 3:14 NIV). He is not to be defined by words, He is to be *known* for *who He is.* We don't have the right to tell Him who He is, even though it may be tempting to want to ascribe qualities to God that we personally admire, like God would *never* send anyone to Hell or He would *totally* understand if we never spoke to so-and-so ever again. God will not be mocked (Galatians 6:7), and He will not be defined by you or anyone else.

Do you know who *you* are? The only real way to answer this question is to go back to where *you* started: do you know Who made you? It ultimately stems from a choice between two belief systems: either you are a mass of goo that evolved from more goo zillions of years ago, stumbling around to find a purpose in a meaningless universe that is destined for destruction anyway so you might as well just enjoy yourself OR you are a child of the Living God, created for a purpose, sustained by His mighty right hand, covered by the blood of Jesus, redeemed and adopted and befriended by the Creator of the Worlds. Which do you believe?

Once we accept that we *can* know ourselves, that we are more than just matter, we can begin to be truly self-aware. But we must not stop there. No, that's not the goal here, mere self-awareness. You can be self-aware and see nothing but your flaws and sinfulness or your talents and successes. You must instead see yourself as God Himself sees you.

- I am His child. (John 1:12)
- I am His friend. (John 15:15)
- I am an heir with Christ. (Romans 8:17)
- I am a saint. (1 Corinthians 1:2)
- I am a temple of the Holy Spirit. (1 Corinthians 6:19)
- I am a new creation. (2 Corinthians 5:17)

None of these definitions allow for boasting! All were bought and paid for by His sacrifice, so we can claim none of these on merit (Ephesians 2:8-9); yet we *must* claim them if we are truly to know who we are.

Having an incomplete or incorrect view of yourself creates an inner turmoil, as you become dependent on how others define you, demanding that you bend to their will and strive to meet their expectations rather than come to terms with your own needs and desires.

How would you define yourself? Would you consider yourself a good and decent person? Does your inner thought life match your outward behavior? Are you living as if you fully know yourself?

In order to fully discover who you are, consider how you act when no one else is around. If you wish others to see you as devout and humble, yet you do not confess your sins regularly to God, then does your outside match your inside? If you talk at length about your relationship with God, and yet you haven't prayed in some time, nor are you truly joyful or at peace in your heart, then you are living a lie. [21] If you want others to know you, you must first be honest in knowing yourself, even if the truth is painful or uncomfortable.

Do others *know* you? How are your relationships with others? Are they superficial and meaningless or are they rich and deep and vulnerable? It would appear to be much easier to just stay hidden, in the darkness of our own making. But we can't let the darkness prevail any longer, as we are called to walk in the light (I John 1:7). Being known by God means coming into the light of His presence, and being seen, scars and all. Yes, others will also see our scars, but that's all part of the "bearing one another's burdens" (Galatians 6:2) that the Bible talks about. Those burdens typically end up taking the form of a physical condition, but the true burdens we need help with are those we hide. Walking in the light reveals those true burdens so we can share the load with other brothers and sisters in Christ.

Walking in the light also necessarily means surrendering the darkness. And what lurks in the darkness but self-pity, a licking of the wounds, a harboring of bitterness and grudges, a false protection from others, and a prideful denial of the need for spiritual healing. We dine on the delicacies of deception, not realizing they are but our own vomit that we return to day after day (Proverbs 26:11). Why are we so afraid? Why do we choose foul-smelling putrescence over the aromatic fruits of surrender?

> "For where there are envy, strife, and divisions among you, are you not carnal and behaving like mere men?" (I Corinthians 3:3 NKJV)

I don't think there is any coincidence that living in sin is referred to as being "carnal" or "walk[ing] according to the flesh" (Romans 8:1) when there is such a huge connection between sinful attitudes and our physical circumstances.

Being known is essential to fully knowing yourself and your own heart. [22] In marriage, allowing your spouse to know you fully leads to genuine unity. Keeping thoughts and feelings hidden from your spouse lead to increased conflict, as much of the arguments in marriage come from these hidden places — things that happened in the past that are now echoed in the present. The majority of emotional conflicts in marriage have their roots in feelings about events that occurred before the couple even met, that could not be blamed in any way on the other person [23] — showing how deeply suppressed emotions can wreak havoc if not identified and addressed.

Hiding from others eventually results in hiding from yourself, sending you right back to square one. It becomes so habitual to conceal the truth that you forget what it was you were concealing. Not knowing yourself leads to autoimmune diseases, as well as mental disorders. Mental illness is believed to be caused by a person's not having a defined personality and not fully knowing who they are. [24]

Allowing others to grow closer to us guarantees that we will become hurt.

Often. If we don't know how to forgive and release resentment and bitterness, these hurts will build up and fester inside us. Forgiveness is essential to healthy relationships; if you only have friends who have never hurt you, while leaving a trail of ex-friends behind you, it's safe to say you have no friends at all. True friends will sharpen you as iron on iron. They will say the hard things and sometimes make you feel *awful*; however, all truth can be used for your benefit, even the painful words of a friend. Removing yourself from others to protect yourself actually can lead to disease:

If you are isolating yourself, harboring rage, or are disconnected from others for a lengthy period of time, you can actually set off the process of apoptosis, the process that is responsible for programmed cell death. [25]

Self-protection leads to self-destruction. We are not made to be alone, but to be *known*.

Have You Allowed God to Know You Fully?

Even if we have decided we want the healing Jesus offers us, and have accepted His sacrifice as the atonement for our sins, we still erect our own barriers in the place of the one He has broken down. Hiding still becomes our go-to response to fear and anger. Torn relationships, career setbacks, financial failures can still evoke a hiding response in us no matter how hard we try otherwise.

Just like the man by the Bethesda pool, we've begun to walk! But we are still holding on to our mat just in case we need it later. Hiding necessarily denies that we can ever be fully known. We sincerely believe that we *can* hide from an all-knowing God. Knowing God and being known by God go hand in hand, for the more we understand His omniscient nature and the love He has for us regardless, the less we fear being known by Him.

There is quite a distinction between His knowing us and our allowing ourselves to be known. God is omniscient; He knows us already. You could liken it to the difference between a social media friend and a best friend. Your social media friend may know just as much about you, but your best friend is who you turn to when you feel despair and need a listening ear. God knows you, that's no secret. But do you let Him have *all* of you? Are you making your heart His home or just "liking" Him?

How well we are known by God will be reflected in how well we are known by others. If you desire closer relationships with others, you must first pursue greater intimacy with God. [26]

The very opposite of hiding is being fully known. It is an awesome thing to bow before the Lord and feel His eyes on your very soul, and to feel His love and approval. He has covered you with the blood of Jesus, and when He looks at you, He sees His Son. He isn't ignorant to your sin; He just doesn't hold it against you.

Unfortunately, when we hide our true emotions behind physical pain, we sabotage ourselves. We miss the opportunity to be known, to be loved, to find the real help we need. We settle for superficial concern instead of soul-mending compassion. I found myself viewing my clients and others as challenging problems to solve rather than as people because I was distracted by the external symptoms. Only when I realized that the issues were deeper than their physical health was I able to care more genuinely about them; after all, what would you rather hear: "How's your back today?" or "You look burdened and lonely, may I pray with you?"

Despite our desire to be known, we equally desire to be seen as worthy, and our definition of worthiness too often involves works-based salvation. All other religions of the world have a system of earning your way into the fold of righteous believers. Only Christianity reveals that any attempts on our part to become righteous on our own are futile; Christ has paid the way for us to enter His family as *children*, dispelling all misconceptions that we need to be mature and wise first.

Allowing God to know us sets us free from being our own god, along with all the responsibilities and expectations involved with being on our own throne. One of my all-time favorite books is *The Christian's Secret of a Happy Life* by Hannah Whitall Smith. To illustrate the bondage of self-sufficiency, she uses the story of a man carrying a heavy load, walking along the side of the road. A kind wagon driver offers him a ride, so he gets into the back of the wagon, but keeps his load on his shoulders. The driver asks him why he doesn't set the load down, to which the man answers, "You are so kind to carry me in your wagon; how could I impose upon you to carry my load as well?" [27] How ridiculous!

Let God know you. Let Him carry you. Lay down your load.

Put down your mat.

> "But now that you know God—or rather are known by God—how is it that you are turning back to those weak and miserable forces? Do you wish to be enslaved by them all over again?" (Galatians 4:9 NIV)

CHAPTER TEN:
NEXT STEPS

Illness and pain have served a purpose in your life until now. They have insulated you from uncomfortable realities, they have provided you with a means to secure love and affection, and they have allowed you to indulge in the sinful pursuit of trying to earn your own salvation. Perhaps the greatest benefit of illness and pain is to reveal the truest need [1] of your heart: a Savior.

None of us can truly face our own emotions alone; those feelings we suppress hold the power to devour us alive if we aren't armed with the truth and the grace that only Jesus offers. On our own, we reach for fig leaves time and time again, never learning a better way, as we become trapped in a cycle of pain and memories and anger that seems endless and hopeless.

1. Make an Assessment

Many articles and books on chronic pain deal with the problem of people just not understanding the pain sufferer, or how hurtful it is to have their pain not acknowledged as true pain. I imagine it is! These books only encourage hiding: the pain you most want acknowledged is not physical.

To begin the healing process, you will need to assess your connection with your pain. Has it become your identity? How have you been feeling while reading this book — angry, defensive, offended? How quickly did you mentally write me a letter to defend your particular situation? The degree to which you "own" your pain will determine how long your recovery will be. How you *feel* about your pain increases your pain as well. [2]

How do you feel about your pain? What story have you attached to your pain? [3] What would your life look like without your pain? Allow the Holy Spirit to guide you as you begin to ask yourself difficult questions such as these and allow Him to illuminate your life with His truth.

2. Make a Timeline

In order to best understand the origins of your pain, it is helpful to create a "Pain Timeline." On a blank sheet of paper, I suggest that you draw four columns:

1. Type of Pain

2. When Pain Began (try to be as specific as possible, down to the day)

3. What else was going on in your life at the time of the pain's onset (Were you in college? Were your parents fighting? Were you expecting a child? Even if it seems insignificant, write it down.)

4. How were you feeling emotionally at that time in your life? This might be the most difficult part of the exercise, as emotional feelings often become replaced by the physical ones. Do your best to remember how you were *really* feeling.

You may notice some interesting connections between not only events and pain but between pains themselves. Sometimes pain comes in a cluster, as the mind determines a headache is not enough to distract you, and moves on to your back, your shoulders, your knees, etc. This exercise is perhaps the most critical tool in your journey to becoming pain free. Allow yourself time to thoughtfully make this timeline, as those things you are hiding from will not be the first to pop into your head. I was speaking to one woman who had chronic pain, and she swore that nothing else was going on in her life at the time of the pain's onset. Only months later did she mention a bad relationship in her past, and when I asked her when that relationship took place, she casually mentioned the time frame. I asked, "Isn't that about the time your pain began?" She looked genuinely surprised. "Oh, yes, I do believe you're right! How interesting!" You would have thought that would have stood out in her memory, but then that's exactly how hiding works.

3. Make a Plan

Pain and hardship are parts of life, and more are bound to be around the corner. How will you cope with the next obstacle you encounter?

People cope with difficulties in different ways: some prepare in advance and hope to prevent problems from occurring, others deal with the problems head on to find solutions, some try to discover a greater meaning behind the problem, some try to control the problem or adjust to it, and some reframe the problem and seek support in the midst of it. But perhaps the worst response to problems is avoidance. If disengagement is your response of choice, you will find that your pain will only continue to increase. [4]

Enlist a friend or family member to hold you accountable, someone who understands the MindBody connection. Tell them to ask you how you're *feeling* next time you mention you are in pain. Just a note: this is super annoying at first, but give it a chance — over time, you will come to see it as a blessing! It's become a bit of a joke in our home that even if we get a paper cut, we ask, "But how are you *feeling*?" Hey, laughter is supposed to be good medicine!

4. Make a Change

> "See, I am doing a new thing! Now it springs up; do you not perceive it? I am making a way in the wilderness and streams in the wasteland." (Isaiah 43:19 NIV)

Doing the same thing over and over in the same environment creates conditioned responses. Something needs to change in your environment in order for your responses to change. What are you willing to change *in* your life to *change* your life?

Real change on the outside requires that kind of inner change that comes from bringing all those hidden thoughts and emotions into the light. What do we do when we become aware of emotions that have been hidden so long? Do we just let them spill out in a flood of ugliness?

Is venting a proper form of expression? Short answer: No. "A fool vents all his feelings, but a wise man holds them back" (Proverbs 29:11 NKJV).

God's Word gives us the tools and the language we need to express our emotions healthily and respectfully:

- "Let no unwholesome word proceed from your mouth, but only such a word as is good for edification according to the need of the moment, so that it will give grace to those who hear." (Ephesians 4:29 NASB)

- "Let your speech always be with grace, as though seasoned with salt, so that you will know how you should respond to each person." (Colossians 4:6 NASB)

- "This you know, my beloved brethren. But everyone must be quick to hear, slow to speak and slow to anger." (James 1:19 NASB)

His Word should guide *our* words: "Your Word have I hidden in my heart, that I might not sin against You" (Psalm 119:11 NKJV).

Remember that others are dealing with their own fig leaves and may not respond ideally to your new vulnerability. Remember to show others the same "grace upon grace" (John 1:16) that you have been shown.

Expressing your emotions will lead to change, freeing you to experience a deeper relationship with God. It may not be comfortable at first, but the more you confess and the more you yield to God's discipline, the closer you will become to Him:

> "In your struggle against sin, you have not yet resisted to the point of shedding your blood. And have you completely forgotten this word of encouragement that addresses you as a father addresses his son? It says, 'My son, do not make light of the Lord's discipline, and do not lose heart when he rebukes you, because the Lord disciplines the one he loves, and he chastens everyone he accepts as his son.' Endure hardship as discipline; God is treating you as his children. For what children are not disciplined by their father? If you are not disciplined—and everyone undergoes discipline—then you are not legitimate, not true sons and daughters at all. Moreover, we have all had human fathers who disciplined us and we respected them for it. How much more should we submit to the Father of spirits and live! They disciplined us for a little while as they thought best; but God disciplines us for our good, in order that we may share in his holiness. No discipline seems pleasant at the time, but painful. Later on, however, it produces a harvest of righteousness and peace for those who have been trained by it. Therefore, strengthen your feeble arms and weak knees. 'Make level paths for your feet,' **so that the lame may not be disabled, but rather healed."** (Hebrews 12:4-13 NIV, *emphasis mine*)

You are fit to serve in any way God calls, so be ready! You may not be called to heavy labor, but in whatever area God places you, you are to work to the best of your abilities:

> "But we urge you, brethren, to excel still more, and to make it your ambition to lead a quiet life and attend to your own business and work with your hands, just as we commanded you, so that you will behave properly toward outsiders and not be in any need." (1 Thessalonians 4:10b-12 NASB)

Healing may take time. While we are called to bear one another's burdens, we are not meant to *be* one another's burdens! Whining and complaining and relying too extensively on others is a disservice to the body of Christ.

> "Not that I speak from want, for I have learned to be content in whatever circumstances I am. I know how to get along with humble means, and I also know how to live in prosperity; in any and every circumstance I have learned the secret of being filled and going hungry, both of having abundance and suffering need. I can do all things through Him who strengthens me." (Philippians 4:11-13 NASB)

Will there be moments of relapse? Of course. While I have come a long way in my own odyssey of MindBody awareness, I still have residual ailments that I can't seem to shake, especially when I find myself tasked with things I don't enjoy. We will always battle our flesh, sometimes almost literally!

> "Keep watching and praying that you may not come into temptation; the spirit is willing, but the flesh is weak." (Mark 14:39 NASB)

> "Therefore let him who thinks he stands take heed that he does not fall." (1 Corinthians 10:12 NASB)

The battle belongs to the Lord, and He is faithful to complete the good work He has begun in us (Philippians 1:6). Obedience and perseverance bring blessing.

> "Dear friends, if our hearts do not condemn us, we have confidence before God and receive from him anything we ask, because we keep his commands and do what pleases him." 1 John 3:21-22 NIV)

You may find that once the emotional scars have been brought to light and dealt with, the healing you experience is far deeper than mere relief from illness or pain; the work involved in dealing with the true source of your pain will result in your healing emotionally as well, a far better and truer healing. [5]

My hope for you is that you will feel the freedom that accompanies coming out of hiding. It may be a lifelong process for you, as I'm sure it will be for me, too. Imagine a world where believers can spend more time in prayer for revival and the salvation of the lost than for hip replacements and back surgeries! Imagine being free to minister to and serve one another without pain. Our physical bodies are part of the Body of Christ (I Corinthians 6:15), not just our spiritual bodies. What happens in our bodies affects the rest of the body of believers. We are called to glorify God with our bodies (I Corinthians 6:20b); God *cares* about our physical bodies!

I have included some questions at the end of several of the chapters for your further study. There is also a recommended book list if you need more information on a particular topic mentioned. I pray for healing for every one of you — the healing that encompasses your entire being: heart, soul, mind, and body.

> "May God himself, the God of peace, sanctify you through and through. May your whole spirit, soul and body be kept blameless at the coming of our Lord Jesus Christ." (1 Thessalonians 5:23 NIV)

Questions for Further Reflection

1. **What responsibilities are you avoiding?** Is there someone in your life that you steer clear of because of unfinished business? Are there tasks you put off because you feel incompetent? Are there decisions you aren't ready to make? Are there relationships that are suffering because you aren't fulfilling your God-given responsibilities?

2. **Have you been blaming your lack of responsibility on your illness or your pain?** Blaming health issues for your behavior becomes a self-fulfilling affair — soon health will imprison you and take over every area of your life. What may be a convenient scapegoat at first will become the very thing that controls you.

3. **In what ways are you saying, "if only"** — if only I felt better, if only I had more energy, if only I didn't have this pain? Those who

are faithful in little are faithful in much — remember the widow's mite — if you aren't generous in poverty, you will not be generous in wealth.

4. **What types of activities give you stress?** Under which conditions? How does your attitude affect your stress level? What steps will you take to change the way you take part in maintaining your stress? [6]

5. **Is there something I want, but do not have?** A smaller waist? A fuller bank account? A better relationship with a loved one? Nothing worthy of desire is easily attained. All good things require work. Is it possible you want these things but are not taking steps toward acquiring them?

6. **Is there something I want to do, but can't?** Play the piano? Cook a gourmet meal? Run a marathon? Talents need to be nurtured over a long period of time. Even the slowest progress is still progress, so don't give up. If there is a legitimate reason you cannot do something, perhaps there is a greater purpose at play.

7. **Is there something I have to do, but do not want to do?** Keep your house clean? Get up early? Help at church? Be honest with yourself about your attitude and accept the natural consequences.

8. **Is there someone I am jealous of?** If you are envious of another person, wishing to be that person perhaps, it is a sure sign you are viewing others as objects and not human beings. Only by entering that person's life will be see their unique challenges and needs, and you will have a greater perspective on your own blessings!

CHAPTER ELEVEN:
COMMON OBJECTIONS

1. "You're telling me that my pain is all my fault!"

I really hope that's not the main message you're getting from this book, but I can see how many people would hear that in my words. When someone is in pain, the first thing they want to hear is that they are loved and validated. And you are. If that is all you need to hear, then perhaps this book isn't for you. But I'm guessing that there is a pain inside you that goes beyond the physical, a pain that is desperately in need of healing. I'm not writing this book to be popular; I'm after your *heart*.

All pain comes from sin. That doesn't mean that pain is a punishment for sin, nor does it mean that pain can be used as a gauge for how sinful a person is compared to others. Pain is just a reality in a world where we have let sin rule over our minds, and in turn, our bodies.

It is tempting to adhere to one of two extremes: one, that we can heal all pain and disease with the power of our minds, and two, that pain is something that just happens to us and we bear no responsibility. Neither are the case. We are fully responsible, yet God is fully sovereign. There will always be a tension between the two, especially in understanding the role we play in our health. It is simply not helpful to play the part of God and point fingers at those who suffer, nor is there to be shame if you are the one suffering. **The purpose of this new frontier of understanding is to show *more* grace,**

not less — to see beyond the external pain to address the pain buried deep, tucked away behind years of self-protection and hiding.

Pain may have served you well for many years and giving it up may seem threatening and even impossible. Pain may not even be your favored method of hiding, and you may now view other behaviors differently — once you embrace the concept of hiding, you will see hiding behaviors everywhere. While we don't want to "glory in [our] shame" (Philippians 3:19 ESV), it is just as sinful to hide from our sin and pretend it doesn't exist. We should neither treat pain like a badge of honor nor like a scarlet letter.

To avoid further disappointments and pain, we abandon our dreams, avoid praise and prayer, numb our hearts, indulge in worry and fear and resentment, and lower our expectations; all of which lead to an incapacity to experience God's presence. [1] What frees us from this cycle of self-protection is the blessing of hope and trust that can only come through experiencing suffering and seeing God's love in the heart of it. [2]

I hope not only that you can see health in an entirely new way after reading this book, but that you will also see yourself and others in a more compassionate light. We have been opting to bear the easiest of burdens — health issues — while overlooking the deeper, more difficult ones: the burdens of our hearts. In our attempt to minister to physical needs, we have overlooked the needs of the soul. We not only have hidden from our own emotional pain, but from that of others as well.

This new paradigm will challenge you. It requires going deeper than providing meals or asking for help with household chores. It requires a vulnerability that goes beyond asking for prayer for surgery outcomes or raising money for cancer awareness. You will need to see past the ailing flesh and discover the ailing heart within.

The world has plenty of wisdom for worldly problems, but we are not of the world; therefore, our solutions must be spiritual ones. Science may one day discover the cure for every physical pain and ailment on earth. But only Jesus has the cure for what is truly ailing us: our sin nature. We may rein in the body biologically someday, but there will always be an outward sign of our inner rebellion against God.

Your pain has run its course. As you become more aware of the areas of your life in which you have been hiding, you will see what chronic pain really is: a distraction, a disguise, and a deception. Join with me in shedding our fig leaf disguises and accepting the grace and love of our Savior, who desires to clothe us with His righteousness, and with it, healing.

2. "But animals get diseases, too!"

That is certainly true! Animals are not capable of sin themselves, but they do share in the consequences of our sin. In the Old Testament, this was certainly made evident. From being offered as sacrifices, to perishing in the flood (Genesis 7:21), to being put on the menu for Noah and his descendants (Genesis 9:3), animals shared in man's punishment. On the converse, they also shared man's blessings: they thrived when the people were obedient (Deuteronomy 28:4; 30:9). If you wanted to know if a people honored God, you could just look at their livestock and their children; anything in their care.

Consequences trickle down to those for whom we are responsible. If the same rule applied today, what would an honest look at our children and animals tell other nations about the condition of our hearts before God?

3. "Are you saying that *all* pain is MindBody pain?"

As I've stated before, there *is* acute pain, and it serves a very needful purpose. So how can you tell if your pain is legitimately something to be concerned about, or simply due to hiding behaviors?

When a pain first arises, it's important to determine whether it is due to a genuine cause, such as an injury, or if it is simply psychosomatic.

Has an injury occurred? Have you just fallen down the stairs or slammed your hand in a drawer? Pain that spontaneously arrives out of nowhere, not directly resulting from injury, is most likely psychosomatic pain.

Can you pinpoint the source? The brain rarely hones in on a specific location at first; if your pain is vague and without focus, it's more likely to be psychosomatic. That's not to say that the brain won't eventually settle on a location the more you focus on it, as usually is the case when leaving a doctor's office with a diagnosis. True injury has a focal point, with pain emanating from it.

Is the pain constant? If the pain ebbs and flows depending on your activity or emotions, then it's not likely to be genuine pain.

Does the pain move around? If your leg pain moves from side to side or even switches legs, then it's most likely not a result of real pain.

What is the timing of the pain? Did the pain appear right before plans with the in-laws? Or soon after your kids asked you to take them to the mall? Are you under stress, dealing with a bad relationship, feeling isolated or angry? Just as we scan our bodies physically whenever something appears "off," we also need to scan our emotional state to get the complete picture of what could be wrong.

My pain of "choice" was a headache. Headaches were my nemesis; they made my stomach hurt and they affected my vision and my mood. When I got one, I would slow down and try to figure out what I was feeling. Once I'd ruled out the three common physical reasons for headaches — vision changes, hunger, and dehydration — I knew for certain that there was an emotional cause. Usually I'd be running from some task I don't enjoy or I'd be avoiding a conflict with someone. Now that I have identified headaches as MindBody pain for me, I no longer get them.

What about diseases? Where is the line drawn between mind and body in genes and biological causes? Is there a line at all? The answer is as complex as we are: imagine a rainbow-colored pinwheel. When it's still, you can make out the individual "spokes," each with its own unique color. But spin the pinwheel, and all the colors run together. Our bodies and our minds affect each other in such complicated ways that it can be impossible to determine which causes which. Ultimately, our mind makes all the decisions in the body, however, even affecting our very DNA.

We used to believe that DNA was the driver of our destiny, when in fact *we* are behind the wheel. Our thoughts have influence over our very cells, and the relationship between ourselves and our "inner and outer worlds" is what determines our direction. 3

Health is like an eighteen-wheeler speeding down the road. If your semi is heading for a collision with an oncoming car, by all means turn the wheel by seeking medical intervention! But in the end, *you need to address the driver.* Otherwise, you will have a lot of close calls on this highway called life.

Addressing a disease as merely a physical occurrence would tie one hand behind your back. Medical intervention is sometimes required, as emotional growth can take longer than the body can endure, but always make sure not to neglect the discovery of emotional causes!

Maybe someday science will identify the microscopic element that accounts for the MindBody connection. Quantum physics is nowhere near that level of discovery to date. But even if they could point to a specific entity, I have no doubt that it would not be removable. We are not meant to be healed merely by a surgeon's knife piercing our flesh, but by our Great Physician who was pierced *for* us.

Secular science, even as it denies our creation at the hands of an omnipotent loving God, has now determined that the most effective method of treating sick patients lies in the balancing of medical advancements with the patient's own perception of their illness and how willing they are to consider their own contributions to its development and to their healing. [4] In the search for determining the source of your pain, the emotional can never be outright dismissed. Medical science must always be seen in the light of how we were created: mind *and* body, in the image of our Creator.

True health is more than just repairing damage; it is "more than freedom from symptoms of disease. It means being whole. While *curing* may remove physical symptoms, it provides only superficial relief, leaving the roots of disease untouched. But *healing* goes much deeper. It involves the integration of mind and body… turns you toward the illness and encourages listening nonjudgmentally to what it may be telling you." [5] The goal of healing should never be a mere absence of illness or pain. If that were the case, then placing people in medically induced comas would be sufficient to meet that goal.

Medicine can cure the body, but it cannot heal the mind. Should we abandon medical research? Of course not! We are called to be good stewards of God's creation, and there is a definite place for medicine and healthcare. But if our beliefs wander from a faith in Him to a faith in ourselves, the consequences will be devastatingly unsatisfying. God is the Great Physician, so keep that in mind as we look at our human approaches to medicine and why it has for so long fallen short of true healing.

CHAPTER TWELVE:
HOW TO HELP A LOVED ONE

If you are reading this book for a relative or friend who is suffering from chronic pain or disease, first let me encourage you that you are showing true love to them in not just wanting to ease their physical burdens, but to meet their needs on a heart level.

People in pain are not always pleasant to be around. I know I'm super grouchy when I don't feel one hundred percent, and I can read it in the faces of my family members that yes, they love me, and yes, I'm being annoying. It's really the elephant in the room here — it's not considered kind to be frustrated with an ill loved one, but hiding those feelings will put you right in the sickbed next to them!

Often caretakers go through a cycle:

1. **Compassion.** We feel empathy for the person in pain and would give anything to take their pain away, so we spend energy and hours and money investing in their wellness, which leads to...
2. **Weariness.** We become tired and worn down, perhaps even succumbing to illness ourselves, but still we keep on until we collapse, and then we feel...
3. **Guilt.** How can we feel so tired when it's they that are carrying the heavier burden? How dare we complain when they are going through so much? So, we go right back to feeling the compassion,

but this time, we are a little bitter, as we stuff down our feelings of "when is it my turn?"

This cycle is exhausting. My husband had horrible back pain for years, and I was slowly building up resentment as he would retreat to the bedroom to rest his back while I was stuck with the housework and taking care of the kids. He didn't want to go places with us, even play games as a family, all because of his back. I *knew* he wasn't faking it, I knew the pain was real; I was just mad because I felt I had lost him as a partner! His back pain would make him irritable and fussy, whereas I had fallen in love with a fun-loving, spontaneous hero of a man! Where had he gone?

I was so tempted to ignore him and pull away from him altogether, leaving him to his own misery so I didn't have to suffer with him. I wanted to have fun and pretend the pain didn't exist. Unfortunately, when I would withdraw from him, it only perpetuated his pain, as he then needed to up the ante to get the love and affection he was so desperately craving.

So, then I would try to accommodate his every need, thinking that my love would heal all wounds. What I thought was empathy quickly became enabling. Sadly, this approach made it worse, as his pain had now become "successful" and was more firmly established in his mind.

The only approach that made any difference was when I showed him love without enabling him, when I showed him new ways to deal with his emotions, and when I encouraged him to grow and learn and venture out of his comfort zone. I would distract him away from the pain and "change the subject" — ultimately proving to be not only better for his state of mind, but better for our marriage as well. Talking about pain can wear both parties down, and it can easily become *all* you talk about.

My first two responses were not only unsuccessful; they are unbiblical. We are commanded to speak the truth in love (Ephesians 4:15) and to confront and expose sin (Ephesians 5:11). I was abandoning my mandate to do so when I was allowing his emotions to take over and cause him pain. He didn't *know* what was happening in his subconscious, and my ignoring it or enabling it was *harming* him.

Doesn't this sound awfully close to judging? Absolutely! Several oft-quoted verses on judging have been taken out of context:

- Romans 2:1 "Therefore you have no excuse, every one of you who passes judgment, for in that which you judge another, you condemn

238

yourself; for you who judge practice the same things." (NASB) The previous chapter had just discussed God's wrath on the unrighteous and those outside the Church, and chapter two is a warning that we are not to judge those who have not yet accepted the gospel. We were once dead in our sins also, and if not for the grace of God would be in the same boat as they are!

- Matthew 7:1-2 "Judge not, that you be not judged. For with what judgment you judge, you will be judged; and with the measure you use, it will be measured back to you" (NKJV). We are to treat others the way in which we want to be treated, and this includes the manner in which we judge them. We would not have wanted to be judged by the Church before we even had a chance to know Jesus, but we also hopefully would want to be informed by our brothers when we are falling into sin.

We simply cannot be quoting the above verses as if they were the final word on judging without considering the other passages that would appear to tell a different story:

- "What business is it of mine to judge those outside the church? Are you not to judge those inside?" (1 Corinthians 5:12 NIV) God will be the Judge of those outside the Church, and we need to let Him do His job; but for those inside the Church, God allows judgment to come from fellow believers. In the previous paragraphs, Paul had mentioned an individual guilty of a heinous sexual sin, and was astonished that this person had not been removed from the Church body. Immorality must be dealt with and expunged, even to the point of handing the unrepentant sinner over to the "destruction of the flesh" (1 Corinthians 5:5 NKJV) by Satan himself!

We are to judge righteously, in humility and love, without assigning motives or attacking other's character:

- "Stop judging by mere appearances, but instead judge correctly." (John 7:24 NIV)

- "Brothers and sisters, if someone is caught in a sin, you who live by the Spirit should restore that person gently." (Galatians 6:1 NIV)

Matthew 18 outlines the steps we are to take when dealing with a sinning brother:

1. Approach him directly and go alone. If he doesn't listen, then...
2. Bring one or two fellow believers with you and approach him again. If he doesn't listen, then...
3. Tell the Church to get involved. If he doesn't listen, then...
4. "Let him be to you like a heathen and a tax collector" (v.17 NKJV). But remember, if he is considered outside the Church, then the commandment not to judge further applies! Rather, he is to be prayed for, sought after, and treated like one who needs the gospel. If he repents, he is to be welcomed back into the body of believers, forgiven, comforted, and loved (2 Corinthians 2:7-8).

Paul rejoiced that his words brought repentance to the Corinthian Church, even though they had to endure sorrow at first. Godly sorrow brings about repentance, but worldly sorrow — self-pity and defensiveness — brings about death (2 Corinthians 7:10).

The overarching message is to be that of love — it simply is not loving to allow a brother or sister to remain in their sin without first alerting them to the danger, then exhorting them to repentance and restoration. If you've ever looked in the mirror after returning home from a dinner out with friends, only to see broccoli sticking out of your front teeth, and if you've gotten upset at those friends for not telling you it was there, then why aren't you more upset that a friend has not mentioned a sin sticking out of your heart for all to see? Why then do you instead get upset with them when they bring it to your attention?

Your loved one deserves the truth. When my husband began putting on weight, I did everything I could to avoid mentioning it, out of a concern that I not hurt his feelings. His sister, who is also a fitness trainer, came right out and told him he was overweight and needed to start a fitness plan. To my surprise, he agreed, and started working out the following week. He's so much happier and has more energy now. I don't know why I thought it would be more loving to let him remain miserable! The truth sets us free! (John 8:32)

ENDNOTES

Endnotes
Preface
[1]Sarno, John E. *The Divided Mind: The Epidemic of Mindbody Disorders.* New York: Harper Collins, 2007. http://public.eblib.com/choice/

Part One: Pain
(What is Pain?, Where Does Pain Come From?, Many Types of Pain, Chronic Pain)
[1]Lombard, Jay, and Patrick J. Kennedy. *The Mind of God: Neuroscience, Faith, and a Search for the Soul.* New York: Harmony Books, 2017, p.96.
[2]Ananthaswamy, Anil. *The Man Who Wasn't There: Investigations into the Strange New Science of the Self.* New York, New York: Dutton, 2015, pp. 149-150.
[3]Tatta, Joe. *Heal Your Pain Now: The Revolutionary Program to Reset Your Brain and Body for a Pain-Free Life.* First Da Capo Press edition. Boston, MA: Da Capo Lifelong Books, 2017, p. 28.
[4]Ibid.
[5]Ibid, p.31.
[6]Ibid, p.28.
[7]"What Is a Pain Neurotag?" *Dr. Joe Tatta, DPT, CNS-*, 16 Feb. 2018, www.drjoetatta.com/pain-neurotag.
[8]Amthor, Frank. *Neuroscience for Dummies.* 2nd edition. For Dummies. Hoboken, NJ: John Wiley & Sons, Inc, 2016, p. 85.
[9]Kuttner, Jonathan, and Naomi Kuttner. *You Pain Free: The 6 Keys to Break Free of Chronic Pain and Get Your Life Back*, 2016, p. 94.

[10]Simonton, O. Carl, Stephanie Simonton, and James L Creighton. *Getting Well Again: A Step-by-Step, Self-Help Guide to Overcoming Cancer for Patients and Their Families.* Place of publication not identified: Random House Publishing Group, 2009, p.214..

[11]Thompson, Curt. *Anatomy of the Soul: Surprising Connections between Neuroscience and Spiritual Practices That Can Transform Your Life and Relationships.* Carol Stream, IL: SaltRiver, 2010, p. 76.

Part Two: Our Traditional Response to Pain
How Diagnoses Are Made

[1]Davies, James. *Cracked: The Unhappy Truth about Psychiatry*, 2013, p.16.

[2]Ibid, p.15.

[3]Ibid, p.27.

[4]Ibid, p.22.

[5]Martinez, Mario E. *The Mindbody Self: How Longevity Is Culturally Learned and the Causes of Health Are Inherited.* Carlsbad, California: Hay House, Inc, 2017, p.38.

[6]Davies, James. *Cracked: The Unhappy Truth about Psychiatry*, 2013, p.41.

[7]Hari, Johann. *Lost Connections: Uncovering the Real Causes of Depression-- and the Unexpected Solutions.* New York: Bloomsbury, 2018, p.40-43.

[8]Davies, James. *Cracked: The Unhappy Truth about Psychiatry*, 2013, p.53.

[9]Ibid, pp.106-107.

[10]Lambert, Kelly. *Lifting Depression: A Neuroscientist's Hands-on Approach to Activating Your Brain's Healing Power.* New York: Basic Books, 2008, p.17.

[11]Davies, James. *Cracked: The Unhappy Truth about Psychiatry*, 2013, p.105.

[12]Lambert, Kelly. *Lifting Depression: A Neuroscientist's Hands-on Approach to Activating Your Brain's Healing Power.* New York: Basic Books, 2008, p.18.

[13]Davies, James. *Cracked: The Unhappy Truth about Psychiatry*, 2013, pp.103-104.

[14]Ibid, p.246.

[15]Pert, Candace B. *Molecules of Emotion: Why You Feel the Way You Feel.* New York, NY: Scribner, 2003, p.267.

[16]Lambert, Kelly. *Lifting Depression: A Neuroscientist's Hands-on Approach to Activating Your Brain's Healing Power.* New York: Basic Books, 2008, p.20.

[17]Hari, Johann. *Lost Connections: Uncovering the Real Causes of Depression-- and the Unexpected Solutions.* New York: Bloomsbury, 2018, p.59-64.

[18]Davies, James. *Cracked: The Unhappy Truth about Psychiatry*, 2013, p.33.

[19]Ibid, p.197.

[20]Ibid, pp.194-195.

[21]Ibid, pp.30-31.

[22]Wedge, Marilyn. *A Disease Called Childhood: Why ADHD Became an American Epidemic.* New York: AVERY, a member of Penguin Group (USA), 2015, p.93.

[23]Davies, James. *Cracked: The Unhappy Truth about Psychiatry*, 2013, p.183.

[24]Hari, Johann. *Lost Connections: Uncovering the Real Causes of Depression-- and the Unexpected Solutions.* New York: Bloomsbury, 2018, p.146.

[25]Davies, James. *Cracked: The Unhappy Truth about Psychiatry,* 2013, p.178.

[26]Arterburn, Stephen. *Healing Is a Choice: Ten Decisions That Will Transform Your Life & Ten Lies That Can Prevent You from Making Them,* 2011, p.194.

[27]Joseph, Stephen. *What Doesn't Kill Us: The New Psychology of Posttraumatic Growth.* New York: Basic Books, 2011, p.10.

[28]Ibid, pp.10-11.

[29] Delle Fave, Antonella & Massimini, Fausto & Bassi, Marta. (2011). *Hedonism and Eudaimonism in Positive Psychology.* 2. 10.1007/978-90-481-9876-4_1.

[30] Joseph, Stephen. *What Doesn't Kill Us: The New Psychology of Posttraumatic Growth.* New York: Basic Books, 2011, p.18.

[31]Martinez, Mario E. *The Mindbody Self: How Longevity Is Culturally Learned and the Causes of Health Are Inherited.* Carlsbad, California: Hay House, Inc, 2017, p.48.

[32]Kirsch, Irving. *The Emperor's New Drugs: Exploding the Antidepressant Myth.* New York, NY: Basic Books, 2010, pp.169-173.

[33]Joseph, Stephen. *What Doesn't Kill Us: The New Psychology of Posttraumatic Growth.* New York: Basic Books, 2011, p.167.

[34]Ibid, pp.166-167.

Tests and Scans

[1]Tatta, Joe. *Heal Your Pain Now: The Revolutionary Program to Reset Your Brain and Body for a Pain-Free Life.* First Da Capo Press edition. Boston, MA: Da Capo Lifelong Books, 2017, p.18.

[2]Kuttner, Jonathan, and Naomi Kuttner. *You Pain Free: The 6 Keys to Break Free of Chronic Pain and Get Your Life Back,* 2016, p.187.

[3]Yass, Mitchell T. *The Pain Cure Rx: The Yass Method for Diagnosing and Resolving Chronic Pain.* Carlsbad, California: Hay House, Inc, 2015, p.20.

[4]Tatta, Joe. *Heal Your Pain Now: The Revolutionary Program to Reset Your Brain and Body for a Pain-Free Life.* First Da Capo Press edition. Boston, MA: Da Capo Lifelong Books, 2017, p.18.

[5]Yass, Mitchell T. *The Pain Cure Rx: The Yass Method for Diagnosing and Resolving Chronic Pain.* Carlsbad, California: Hay House, Inc, 2015, p.60.

[6]Hanscom, David. *Back in Control: A Surgeon's Roadmap out of Chronic Pain,* 2017, p.37.

[7]Yass, Mitchell T. *The Pain Cure Rx: The Yass Method for Diagnosing and Resolving Chronic Pain.* Carlsbad, California: Hay House, Inc, 2015, p.149.

[8]Ibid, p.88.

[9]Ibid, pp.79-80.

[10]Ibid, p.93.

[11]Rabinowitz, Elana. "I Almost Got Knee Surgery But These Things

Worked Instead." *Tonic,* Tonic, 27 Sept. 2018,
tonic.vice.com/en_us/article/pa8ay7/i-tried-to-fix-my-knee-pain-when-
my-doctor-proposed-surgery.
[12]"Opioid Crisis Fast Facts." CNN, Cable News Network, 17 Jan. 2019,
www.cnn.com/2017/09/18/health/opioid-crisis-fast-facts/index.html.
[13]Przekop, Peter. *Conquer Chronic Pain: An Innovative Mind-Body Approach.*
Center City, Minnesota: Hazelden Publishing, 2015, p.32.

Patient History
[1]Kaplan, Robert M. *More than Medicine: The Broken Promise of American Health.*
Cambridge, Massachusetts: Harvard University Press, 2019, p.43.
[2]Moalem, Sharon, and Matthew D. LaPlante. *Inheritance: How Our Genes Change
Our Lives, and Our Lives Change Our Genes.* First edition. New York: Grand
Central Publishing, 2014, p.x-xi.
[3]Dispenza, Joe. *You Are the Placebo: Making Your Mind Matter.* Carlsbad,
California: Hay House, Inc, 2014, p.85.
[4]Hamilton, David R. *How Your Mind Can Heal Your Body.* Carlsbad, Calif: Hay
House, 2010, pp.45-46.
[5]Moalem, Sharon, and Matthew D. LaPlante. *Inheritance: How Our Genes Change
Our Lives, and Our Lives Change Our Genes.* First edition. New York: Grand
Central Publishing, 2014, p.52.
[6]Dispenza, Joe. *You Are the Placebo: Making Your Mind Matter.* Carlsbad,
California: Hay House, Inc, 2014, p.96.
[7]Ibid, p.86.
[8]Ibid, p.95.
[9]Ibid, p.101.
[10]Dispenza, Joe. *You Are the Placebo: Making Your Mind Matter.* Carlsbad,
California: Hay House, Inc, 2014, p.92.
[11]Kaplan, Robert M. *More than Medicine: The Broken Promise of American Health.*
Cambridge, Massachusetts: Harvard University Press, 2019, p.34.

What if We Have it Wrong?
[1]Harrington, Anne. *The Cure within: A History of Mind-Body Medicine.* 1st ed.
New York: W.W. Norton, 2008, pp.68-69.
[2]Ibid.
[3]Shorter, Edward. *From Paralysis to Fatigue: A History of Psychosomatic Illness in
the Modern Era.* Place of publication not identified: Free Press, 2014.
http://rbdigital.oneclickdigital.com, location 97.
[4]Davies, James. *Cracked: The Unhappy Truth about Psychiatry,* 2013, p.197.
[5]Ibid, p.198.
[6]Ibid, p.199.
[7]Shorter, Edward. *From Paralysis to Fatigue: A History of Psychosomatic Illness in
the Modern Era.* Place of publication not identified: Free Press, 2014.

http://rbdigital.oneclickdigital.com, location 87.

[8]Davies, James. *Cracked: The Unhappy Truth about Psychiatry*, 2013, p.198.

[9]Ibid.

[10]Martinez, Mario E. *The Mindbody Self: How Longevity Is Culturally Learned and the Causes of Health Are Inherited*. Carlsbad, California: Hay House, Inc, 2017, pp.183-184.

[11]Davies, James. *Cracked: The Unhappy Truth about Psychiatry*, 2013, p.182.

[12]Martinez, Mario E. *The Mindbody Self: How Longevity Is Culturally Learned and the Causes of Health Are Inherited*. Carlsbad, California: Hay House, Inc, 2017, p.185.

[13]Davies, James. *Cracked: The Unhappy Truth about Psychiatry*, 2013, p.202.

[14]Martinez, Mario E. *The Mindbody Self: How Longevity Is Culturally Learned and the Causes of Health Are Inherited*. Carlsbad, California: Hay House, Inc, 2017, p.40.

[15]Platoni, Kara. *We Have the Technology: How Biohackers, Foodies, Physicians, and Scientists Are Transforming Human Perception, One Sense at a Time*. New York: Basic Books, a member of the Perseus Books Group, 2015, p.171.

TMS, TMS and the Symptom Imperative

[1]Sarno, John E. *The Divided Mind: The Epidemic of Mindbody Disorders*. New York: Harper Collins, 2007.

[2]Ibid, p.148.

[3]Sarno, John E. *Healing Back Pain: The Mind-Body Connection*, 2018, p.57.

[4]Simonton, O. Carl, Stephanie Simonton, and James L Creighton. *Getting Well Again: A Step-by-Step, Self-Help Guide to Overcoming Cancer for Patients and Their Families*. Place of publication not identified: Random House Publishing Group, 2009, p.212.

[5]Ozanich, Steven Ray. *The Great Pain Deception: Faulty Medical Advice Is Making Us Worse*, 2014, pp.80-89.

[6]Sarno, John E. *The Divided Mind: The Epidemic of Mindbody Disorders*. New York: Harper Collins, 2007, pp.353-354.

[7]Ozanich, Steven Ray. *The Great Pain Deception: Faulty Medical Advice Is Making Us Worse*, 2014, p.119.

[8]Shapiro, Debbie. *Your Body Speaks Your Mind: Decoding the Emotional, Psychological, and Spiritual Messages That Underlie Illness*. Boulder, CO: Sounds True, 2006, p.19.

[9]Pert, Candace B. *Molecules of Emotion: Why You Feel the Way You Feel*. New York, NY: Scribner, 2003, p.141.

[10]Simonton, O. Carl, Stephanie Simonton, and James L Creighton. *Getting Well Again: A Step-by-Step, Self-Help Guide to Overcoming Cancer for Patients and Their Families*. Place of publication not identified: Random House Publishing Group, 2009, pp.124-126.

[11]Sarno, John E. *The Divided Mind: The Epidemic of Mindbody Disorders*. New

York: Harper Collins, 2007, p.13.

Buried Emotional Trauma

[1]Based on the five stages of grief outlined in: Kübler-Ross, Elisabeth. *On Death and Dying.* New York, NY: Macmillan Pub. Co., 1993.

[2]Levine, Peter A. *Waking the Tiger: Healing Trauma: The Innate Capacity to Transform Overwhelming Experiences.* Berkeley, Calif: North Atlantic Books, 1997, pp.147-149.

[3]Jawer, Michael A., and Marc S. Micozzi. *Your Emotional Type: Key to the Therapies That Will Work for You.* Rochester, Vt: Healing Arts Press, 2011, p.58.

[4]Davies, Kyle, and Gabor Maté. *The Intelligent Body: Reversing Chronic Fatigue and Pain from the inside Out.* First edition. New York: W.W. Norton & Company, 2017, p.49.

[5]Pert, Candace B. *Molecules of Emotion: Why You Feel the Way You Feel.* New York, NY: Scribner, 2003, p.141.

[6]Schubiner, Howard, and Michael Betzold. *Unlearn Your Pain: A 28-Day Process to Reprogram Your Brain.* Pleasant Ridge, MI: Mind Body Publishing, 2012, p.36.

[7]Levine, Peter A. *Waking the Tiger: Healing Trauma: The Innate Capacity to Transform Overwhelming Experiences.* Berkeley, Calif: North Atlantic Books, 1997, p.183.

[8]Ray, Marie Beynon. *How Never to Be Tired.* Bobbs-Merrill, 1945, p.124.

[9]Lipton, Bruce H. *The Biology of Belief: Unleashing the Power of Consciousness, Matter & Miracles.* First edition. Carlsbad, California: Hay House, Inc, 2015, p.122.

[10]"Job Switching." *I Love Lucy.* Writ. Jess Oppenheimer, Bob Carroll Jr., and Madelyn David. Dir. William Asher. Season 2, Episode 1. CBS. 15 September 1952. Television.

[11]Kuttner, Jonathan, and Naomi Kuttner. *You Pain Free: The 6 Keys to Break Free of Chronic Pain and Get Your Life Back,* 2016, pp.211-213.

[12]Ibid, p.218.

[13]Simonton, O. Carl, Stephanie Simonton, and James L Creighton. *Getting Well Again: A Step-by-Step, Self-Help Guide to Overcoming Cancer for Patients and Their Families.* Place of publication not identified: Random House Publishing Group, 2009, p.213.

The Story of Pain

[1]Pert, Candace B. *Molecules of Emotion: Why You Feel the Way You Feel.* New York, NY: Scribner, 2003, p.143.

[2]Wimberger, Lisa. *Neurosculpting: A Whole-Brain Approach to Heal Trauma, Rewrite Limiting Beliefs, and Find Wholeness.* Boulder, Colorado: Sounds True, 2014, p.58.

[3]Hanscom, David. *Back in Control: A Surgeon's Roadmap out of Chronic Pain,* 2017, p.53.

⁴Ibid, p.151.

⁵Sarno, John E. *The Divided Mind: The Epidemic of Mindbody Disorders*. New York: Harper Collins, 2007, pp.307-318.

⁶Ozanich, Steven Ray. *The Great Pain Deception: Faulty Medical Advice Is Making Us Worse*, 2014, Chapter 9.

⁷Colbert, Don. *Deadly Emotions: Understand the Mind-Body-Spirit Connection That Can Heal or Destroy You*. Nashville, Tenn.: T. Nelson, 2006, p.21.

⁸Beauregard, Mario. *Brain Wars: The Scientific Battle over the Existence of the Mind and the Proof That Will Change the Way We Live Our Lives*. 1st ed. New York: HarperOne, 2012, pp.105-106.

⁹Siegel, Bernie S. *Love, Medicine & Miracles: Lessons Learned about Self-Healing from a Surgeon's Experience with Exceptional Patients*. New York: HarperPerennial, 1990, p.124.

The Placebo Effect

¹Hamilton, David R. *How Your Mind Can Heal Your Body*. Carlsbad, Calif: Hay House, 2010, p.20.

²Dispenza, Joe. *You Are the Placebo: Making Your Mind Matter*. Carlsbad, California: Hay House, Inc, 2014, p.31.

³Ibid, p.30.

⁴Ibid, p.50.

⁵Hamilton, David R. *How Your Mind Can Heal Your Body*. Carlsbad, Calif: Hay House, 2010, p.18.

⁶Dispenza, Joe. *You Are the Placebo: Making Your Mind Matter*. Carlsbad, California: Hay House, Inc, 2014, p.50.

⁷Siegel, Bernie S. *Love, Medicine & Miracles: Lessons Learned about Self-Healing from a Surgeon's Experience with Exceptional Patients*. New York: HarperPerennial, 1990, p.129.

⁸Kirsch, Irving. *The Emperor's New Drugs: Exploding the Antidepressant Myth*. New York, NY: Basic Books, 2010, pp.111-114.

⁹Beauregard, Mario. *Brain Wars: The Scientific Battle over the Existence of the Mind and the Proof That Will Change the Way We Live Our Lives*. 1st ed. New York: HarperOne, 2012, p.23.

¹⁰Ibid, pp.36-37.

¹¹Martinez, Mario E. *The Mindbody Self: How Longevity Is Culturally Learned and the Causes of Health Are Inherited*. Carlsbad, California: Hay House, Inc, 2017, p.183.

¹²Simonton, O. Carl, Stephanie Simonton, and James L Creighton. *Getting Well Again: A Step-by-Step, Self-Help Guide to Overcoming Cancer for Patients and Their Families*. Place of publication not identified: Random House Publishing Group, 2009, pp.26-27.

Visualizations

[1]Dispenza, Joe. *You Are the Placebo: Making Your Mind Matter*. Carlsbad, California: Hay House, Inc, 2014, p.32.

[2]Hamilton, David R. *How Your Mind Can Heal Your Body*. Carlsbad, Calif: Hay House, 2010, p.62.

[3]Dispenza, Joe. *You Are the Placebo: Making Your Mind Matter*. Carlsbad, California: Hay House, Inc, 2014, p.46.

[4]Hamilton, David R. *How Your Mind Can Heal Your Body*. Carlsbad, Calif: Hay House, 2010, p.47.

[5]Offit, Paul A. *Do You Believe in Magic? The Sense and Nonsense of Alternative Medicine*. First edition. New York: Harper, 2013, p.235.

[6]Dispenza, Joe. *You Are the Placebo: Making Your Mind Matter*. Carlsbad, California: Hay House, Inc, 2014, p.15.

[7]Hamilton, David R. *How Your Mind Can Heal Your Body*. Carlsbad, Calif: Hay House, 2010, p.50.

[8]Ibid, p.46.

[9]Ibid, p.56.

[10]Dispenza, Joe. *You Are the Placebo: Making Your Mind Matter*. Carlsbad, California: Hay House, Inc, 2014, p.133.

[11]Ibid, p.xiv.

[12]Siegel, Bernie S. *Love, Medicine & Miracles: Lessons Learned about Self-Healing from a Surgeon's Experience with Exceptional Patients*. New York: HarperPerennial, 1990, p.65.

Children and the MindBody Syndrome

[1]Dispenza, Joe. *You Are the Placebo: Making Your Mind Matter*. Carlsbad, California: Hay House, Inc, 2014, pp.199-213.

[2]Maté, Gabor. *When the Body Says No: Understanding the Stress-Disease Connection*. Hoboken, N.J: J. Wiley, 2003, p.172.

[3]Ibid, p.188.

[4]Colbert, Don. *Deadly Emotions: Understand the Mind-Body-Spirit Connection That Can Heal or Destroy You*. Nashville, Tenn.: T. Nelson, 2006, p.13.

[5]Rankin, Lissa. *The Fear Cure: Cultivating Courage as Medicine for the Body, Mind, and Soul*. Carlsbad, California: Hay House, Inc, 2015, pp.63-65.

The Danger of a Diagnosis

[1]Thompson, Curt. *Anatomy of the Soul: Surprising Connections between Neuroscience and Spiritual Practices That Can Transform Your Life and Relationships*. Carol Stream, IL: SaltRiver, 2010, p.166.

[2]O'Sullivan, Suzanne. *Is It All in Your Head?: True Stories of Imaginary Illness*, 2016, p.138.

[3]Another term for psychosomatic illnesses is "conversion disorder" — you can remember it by picturing emotions converting into physical symptoms.

[4]Kuttner, Jonathan, and Naomi Kuttner. *You Pain Free: The 6 Keys to Break Free*

of Chronic Pain and Get Your Life Back, 2016, p.93.

[5]Dispenza, Joe. *You Are the Placebo: Making Your Mind Matter*. Carlsbad, California: Hay House, Inc, 2014, pp.3-5.

[6]Levinovitz, Alan. *The Gluten Lie and Other Myths about What You Eat*, 2015, p.51.

[7]Ozanich, Steven Ray. *The Great Pain Deception: Faulty Medical Advice Is Making Us Worse*, 2014, p.210.

[8]Thernstrom, Melanie. *The Pain Chronicles: Cures, Myths, Mysteries, Prayers, Diaries, Brain Scan, Healing, and the Science of Suffering*. 1st ed. New York: Farrar, Straus and Giroux, 2010, p.295.

[9]Doidge, Norman. *The Brain's Way of Healing: Remarkable Discoveries and Recoveries from the Frontiers of Neuroplasticity*. New York, New York: Viking, 2015, p.9.

[10]Dispenza, Joe. *You Are the Placebo: Making Your Mind Matter*. Carlsbad, California: Hay House, Inc, 2014, pp.15-16.

[11]Ibid, p.160.

[12]Davies, Kyle, and Gabor Maté. *The Intelligent Body: Reversing Chronic Fatigue and Pain from the inside Out*. First edition. New York: W.W. Norton & Company, 2017, pp.107-108.

[13]Colbert, Don. *Deadly Emotions: Understand the Mind-Body-Spirit Connection That Can Heal or Destroy You*. Nashville, Tenn.: T. Nelson, 2006, p.152.

[14]Ibid, p.153.

[15]Martinez, Mario E. *The Mindbody Self: How Longevity Is Culturally Learned and the Causes of Health Are Inherited*. Carlsbad, California: Hay House, Inc, 2017, p.127.

[16]Shapiro, Debbie. *Your Body Speaks Your Mind: Decoding the Emotional, Psychological, and Spiritual Messages That Underlie Illness*. Boulder, CO: Sounds True, 2006, pp.39-42.

[17]Harrington, Anne. *The Cure within: A History of Mind-Body Medicine*. 1st ed. New York: W.W. Norton, 2008, p.85.

[18]Ray, Marie Beynon. *How Never to Be Tired*. Bobbs-Merrill, 1945, p.128.

[19]Simonton, O. Carl, Stephanie Simonton, and James L Creighton. *Getting Well Again: A Step-by-Step, Self-Help Guide to Overcoming Cancer for Patients and Their Families*. Place of publication not identified: Random House Publishing Group, 2009, p.128.

[20]Ibid, p.130.

[21]Shorter, Edward. *From Paralysis to Fatigue: A History of Psychosomatic Illness in the Modern Era*. Place of publication not identified: Free Press, 2014. **http://rbdigital.oneclickdigital.com**, location 106.

[22]Ibid, location 94.

[23]Simonton, O. Carl, Stephanie Simonton, and James L Creighton. *Getting Well Again: A Step-by-Step, Self-Help Guide to Overcoming Cancer for Patients and Their Families*. Place of publication not identified: Random House Publishing

Group, 2009, p.105.
The Catalogue of Psychosomatic Disorders
[1]Shorter, Edward. *From Paralysis to Fatigue: A History of Psychosomatic Illness in the Modern Era.* Place of publication not identified: Free Press, 2014. **http://rbdigital.oneclickdigital.com,** location 115.
[2]Kuttner, Jonathan, and Naomi Kuttner. *You Pain Free: The 6 Keys to Break Free of Chronic Pain and Get Your Life Back*, 2016, p.92.
[3]Ibid, p.96.
[4]Tatta, Joe. *Heal Your Pain Now: The Revolutionary Program to Reset Your Brain and Body for a Pain-Free Life.* First Da Capo Press edition. Boston, MA: Da Capo Lifelong Books, 2017, p.17.
[5]Kaplan, Gary, and Donna Beech. *Total Recovery: Solving the Mystery of Chronic Pain and Depression : How We Get Sick, Why We Stay Sick, How We Can Recover,* 2015, p.142.
[6]Hatch, Steven. *Snowball in a Blizzard: A Physician's Notes on Uncertainty in Medicine.* New York: Basic Books, a member of the Perseus Books Group, 2016, p.41.
[7]Welch, H. Gilbert, Lisa Schwartz, and Steve Woloshin. *Overdiagnosed: Making People Sick in the Pursuit of Health.* Boston, Mass: Beacon Press, 2011, p.179.
[8]Maslow, Abraham. *The Psychology of Science: A Reconnaissance.* Chapel Hill, NC: Maurice Bassett Publishing, 2002.
[9]Dillon, Brian, and Brian Dillon. *The Hypochondriacs: Nine Tormented Lives.* 1st American ed. New York: Faber and Faber, Inc, 2010, p.9.

Why Pain Increases
[1]"Actor's Hollywood career spawned 'Six Degrees of Kevin Bacon'". *Telegraph.* 6 June 2011. Retrieved 14 March 2019.
[2]Kessler, David A. *Capture: Unraveling the Mystery of Mental Suffering.* First edition. New York, NY: Harper Wave, an imprint of HarperCollinsPublishers, 2016, p.37.
[3]Dispenza, Joe. *You Are the Placebo: Making Your Mind Matter.* Carlsbad, California: Hay House, Inc, 2014, pp.69-70.
[4]Fehmi, Les, and Jim Robbins. *The Open-Focus Brain: Harnessing the Power of Attention to Heal Mind and Body.* 1st ed. Boston: Trumpeter Books, 2007, p.73.
[5]Hutchinson, Alex. *Endure: Mind, Body, and the Curiously Elastic Limits of Human Performance.* First edition. New York, NY : William Morrow, an imprint of HarperCollinsPublishers, 2018, p.96.

Feel the Pain to Heal the Pain
[1]Fehmi, Les, and Jim Robbins. *The Open-Focus Brain: Harnessing the Power of Attention to Heal Mind and Body.* 1st ed. Boston: Trumpeter Books, 2007, p.75.
[2]Ibid, p.62.
[3]Platoni, Kara. *We Have the Technology: How Biohackers, Foodies, Physicians, and

Scientists Are Transforming Human Perception, One Sense at a Time. New York: Basic Books, a member of the Perseus Books Group, 2015, p.144.
[4]Ibid, p.141.

We DO Have it Wrong About Chronic Pain
[1]Schubiner, Howard, and Michael Betzold. *Unlearn Your Pain: A 28-Day Process to Reprogram Your Brain.* Pleasant Ridge, MI: Mind Body Publishing, 2012, pp.18-19.
[2]Pert, Candace B. *Molecules of Emotion: Why You Feel the Way You Feel.* New York, NY: Scribner, 2003, p.185.

The "Stress" Compromise
[1]Dispenza, Joe. *Evolve Your Brain: The Science of Changing Your Mind.* Dearfield, FL: Health Communications, 2007, p.275.
[2]"stress." Merriam-Webster.com. Merriam-Webster, 2019. Web. 9 Jan 2019.
[3]Siegel, Bernie S. *Love, Medicine & Miracles: Lessons Learned about Self-Healing from a Surgeon's Experience with Exceptional Patients.* New York: HarperPerennial, 1990, p.71.
[4]Dispenza, Joe. *You Are the Placebo: Making Your Mind Matter.* Carlsbad, California: Hay House, Inc, 2014, p.138.
[5]Simonton, O. Carl, Stephanie Simonton, and James L Creighton. *Getting Well Again: A Step-by-Step, Self-Help Guide to Overcoming Cancer for Patients and Their Families.* Place of publication not identified: Random House Publishing Group, 2009, p.75.
[6]Siegel, Bernie S. *Love, Medicine & Miracles: Lessons Learned about Self-Healing from a Surgeon's Experience with Exceptional Patients.* New York: HarperPerennial, 1990, p.29.
[7]Amir, R.E.H.S., Fred. *Rapid Recovery from Back and Neck Pain.* Health Advisory Group, LLC, 2002, p.10.
[8]Ibid, p.94.

Part Three: What Fig Leaves and Chronic Pain Have in Common (Hiding, What is Hiding?, The Unusual Suspects, Where We Went Wrong, The Truth About Fig Leaves, Can We Truly Hide Ourselves From God?)
[1]Handford, Martin. *Where's Waldo?* 1st U.S. ed. Boston: Little, Brown, 1987.
[2]Siegel, Daniel J. *Mindsight: The New Science of Personal Transformation.* 1st ed. New York: Bantam Books, 2010, p.125.
[3]Colbert, Don. *Deadly Emotions: Understand the Mind-Body-Spirit Connection That Can Heal or Destroy You.* Nashville, Tenn.: T. Nelson, 2006, p.59.

How Do You Know You're Hiding, What Are We Hiding From?, How We Hide

[1]Sternberg, Eliezer J. *Neurologic: The Brain's Hidden Rationale behind Our Irrational Behavior.* New York: Pantheon Books, 2015, p.42.

[2]Chole, Alicia Britt. *40 Days of Decrease: A Different Kind of Hunger, a Different Kind of Fast.* Nashville: W Publishing Group, an imprint of Thomas Nelson, 2015, p.7.

[3]Arterburn, Stephen. *Healing Is a Choice: Ten Decisions That Will Transform Your Life & Ten Lies That Can Prevent You from Making Them,* 2011, p.36.

[4]Ibid, p.271.

[5]Hari, Johann. *Lost Connections: Uncovering the Real Causes of Depression-- and the Unexpected Solutions.* New York: Bloomsbury, 2018, p.74.

[6] "abide." Dictionary.com. Dictionary.com, 2019. Web. 13 March 2019.

[7]"abide." Merriam-Webster.com. Merriam-Webster, 2019. Web. 13 March 2019.

[8]Kessler, David A. *Capture: Unraveling the Mystery of Mental Suffering.* First edition. New York, NY: Harper Wave, an imprint of HarperCollinsPublishers, 2016, p.24.

[9](If you are being physically abused, however, please remove yourself from the situation! Submission to your husband is not commanded if he is asking you to do something immoral or sinful or if he is endangering your life or that of your child. Seek wise counsel and support from leaders in your church if you are being threatened or harmed in any way.)

[10]Jawer, Michael A., and Marc S. Micozzi. *Your Emotional Type: Key to the Therapies That Will Work for You.* Rochester, Vt: Healing Arts Press, 2011, p.29.

[11]Maté, Gabor. *When the Body Says No: Understanding the Stress-Disease Connection.* Hoboken, N.J: J. Wiley, 2003, pp.110-111.

[12]Kaplan, Robert M. *More than Medicine: The Broken Promise of American Health.* Cambridge, Massachusetts: Harvard University Press, 2019, p.40.

[13]Maté, Gabor. *When the Body Says No: Understanding the Stress-Disease Connection.* Hoboken, N.J: J. Wiley, 2003, p.176.

[14]Hanscom, David. *Back in Control: A Surgeon's Roadmap out of Chronic Pain,* 2017, pp.81-98.

[15]Keller, Timothy, and Kathy Keller. *God's Wisdom for Navigating Life: A Year of Daily Devotions in the Book of Proverbs.* New York, New York: Viking, 2017, p.239.

Common Diagnoses:
Back Pain

[1]Kuttner, Jonathan, and Naomi Kuttner. *You Pain Free: The 6 Keys to Break Free of Chronic Pain and Get Your Life Back,* 2016, p.63.

[2]Thernstrom, Melanie. *The Pain Chronicles: Cures, Myths, Mysteries, Prayers, Diaries, Brain Scan, Healing, and the Science of Suffering.* 1st ed. New York: Farrar, Straus and Giroux, 2010, p.284.

[3]Ibid.

[4]Tatta, Joe. *Heal Your Pain Now: The Revolutionary Program to Reset Your Brain and Body for a Pain-Free Life.* First Da Capo Press edition. Boston, MA: Da Capo Lifelong Books, 2017, p.26.

[5]Amir, R.E.H.S., Fred. *Rapid Recovery from Back and Neck Pain.* Health Advisory Group, LLC, 2002, p.10.

[6]Howick, Jeremy. *Doctor You: Introducing the Hard Science of Self-Healing.* New York: Quercus, 2018, p.14.

[7]Hatch, Steven. *Snowball in a Blizzard: A Physician's Notes on Uncertainty in Medicine.* New York: Basic Books, a member of the Perseus Books Group, 2016, p.48.

[8]Kaplan, Gary, and Donna Beech. *Total Recovery: Solving the Mystery of Chronic Pain and Depression: How We Get Sick, Why We Stay Sick, How We Can Recover,* 2015, p.142.

[9]Yass, Mitchell T. *The Pain Cure Rx: The Yass Method for Diagnosing and Resolving Chronic Pain.* Carlsbad, California: Hay House, Inc, 2015, p.18.

[10]Sarno, John E. *Healing Back Pain: The Mind-Body Connection,* 2018, p.120.

[11]Tatta, Joe. *Heal Your Pain Now: The Revolutionary Program to Reset Your Brain and Body for a Pain-Free Life.* First Da Capo Press edition. Boston, MA: Da Capo Lifelong Books, 2017, pp.41-42.

[12]Kuttner, Jonathan, and Naomi Kuttner. *You Pain Free: The 6 Keys to Break Free of Chronic Pain and Get Your Life Back,* 2016, pp.64-65.

Arthritis, Carpal Tunnel Syndrome

[1]Yass, Mitchell T. *The Pain Cure Rx: The Yass Method for Diagnosing and Resolving Chronic Pain.* Carlsbad, California: Hay House, Inc, 2015, p.19.

[2]Ibid, p.45.

[3]Ibid, p.43.

[4]Kuttner, Jonathan, and Naomi Kuttner. *You Pain Free: The 6 Keys to Break Free of Chronic Pain and Get Your Life Back,* 2016.

[5]Snyder, Robert J. Osteophystes: A Fancy Term, but Simply Bone Spurs | OSC News and Events. *Orthopaedic and Spine Center of Newport News,* 5 Apr. 2018, www.osc-ortho.com/blog/osteophytes-a-fancy-term-but-simply-bone-spurs/.

[6]Stecco, C., & Aldegheri, R. (2008, March 01). Historical review of carpal tunnel syndrome. Retrieved from https://link.springer.com/article/10.1007/s12306-008-0033-8

[7]Katz, J., Losina, E., Amick III, B., Fossel, A., Bessette, L. and Keller, R. (2001). Predictors of outcomes of carpal tunnel release. *Arthritis & Rheumatology,* [online] 44(5), p.1184. Available at: https://onlinelibrary.wiley.com/doi/full/10.1002/1529-0131(200105)44:5%3C1184::AID-ANR202%3E3.0.CO;2-A [Accessed 14 Feb. 2019].

[8]Yass, Mitchell T. *The Pain Cure Rx: The Yass Method for Diagnosing and Resolving Chronic Pain.* Carlsbad, California: Hay House, Inc, 2015, pp.68,79.

[9]Tatta, Joe. *Heal Your Pain Now: The Revolutionary Program to Reset Your Brain and Body for a Pain-Free Life.* First Da Capo Press edition. Boston, MA: Da Capo Lifelong Books, 2017, p.48.

Psychiatric Pain

[1]Hari, Johann. *Lost Connections: Uncovering the Real Causes of Depression-- and the Unexpected Solutions.* New York: Bloomsbury, 2018, p.257.

Anxiety

[1]Pittman, Catherine M., and Elizabeth M. Karle. *Rewire Your Anxious Brain: How to Use the Neuroscience of Fear to End Anxiety, Panic, & Worry.* Oakland, CA: New Harbinger Publications, Inc, 2015, pp.2-3,51.

[2]Ray, Marie Beynon. *How Never to Be Tired.* Bobbs-Merrill, 1945, p.170.

[3]Rankin, Lissa. *The Fear Cure: Cultivating Courage as Medicine for the Body, Mind, and Soul.* Carlsbad, California: Hay House, Inc, 2015, p.52.

[4]Colbert, Don. *Deadly Emotions: Understand the Mind-Body-Spirit Connection That Can Heal or Destroy You.* Nashville, Tenn.: T. Nelson, 2006, p.126.

[5]Ozanich, Steven Ray. *The Great Pain Deception: Faulty Medical Advice Is Making Us Worse,* 2014, p.254.

[6]Colbert, Don. *Deadly Emotions: Understand the Mind-Body-Spirit Connection That Can Heal or Destroy You.* Nashville, Tenn.: T. Nelson, 2006, p.155.

[7]Pittman, Catherine M., and Elizabeth M. Karle. *Rewire Your Anxious Brain: How to Use the Neuroscience of Fear to End Anxiety, Panic, & Worry.* Oakland, CA: New Harbinger Publications, Inc, 2015, p.128.

Depression

[1]Colbert, Don. *Deadly Emotions: Understand the Mind-Body-Spirit Connection That Can Heal or Destroy You.* Nashville, Tenn.: T. Nelson, 2006, p.65.

[2]Hari, Johann. *Lost Connections: Uncovering the Real Causes of Depression-- and the Unexpected Solutions.* New York: Bloomsbury, 2018, p.234.

[3]Ibid, p.260.

[4]Lambert, Kelly. *Lifting Depression: A Neuroscientist's Hands-on Approach to Activating Your Brain's Healing Power.* New York: Basic Books, 2008, pp.186-187.

[5]Jawer, Michael A., and Marc S. Micozzi. *Your Emotional Type: Key to the Therapies That Will Work for You.* Rochester, Vt: Healing Arts Press, 2011, p.69.

[6]Ibid.

[7]Siegel, Bernie S. *Love, Medicine & Miracles: Lessons Learned about Self-Healing from a Surgeon's Experience with Exceptional Patients.* New York: HarperPerennial, 1990, p.78.

[8]Martinez, Mario E. *The Mindbody Self: How Longevity Is Culturally Learned and the Causes of Health Are Inherited*. Carlsbad, California: Hay House, Inc, 2017, p.180.
[9]Hari, Johann. *Lost Connections: Uncovering the Real Causes of Depression-- and the Unexpected Solutions*. New York: Bloomsbury, 2018, p.9,11,20.

Post-Traumatic Stress Disorder (PTSD)
[1]Joseph, Stephen. *What Doesn't Kill Us: The New Psychology of Posttraumatic Growth*. New York: Basic Books, 2011, p.159.
[2]Ibid, p.167.
[3]Ibid, Part II.

Chronic Fatigue Syndrome (CFS), Fibromyalgia
[1]O'Sullivan, Suzanne. *Is It All in Your Head?: True Stories of Imaginary Illness*, 2016, p.217.
[2]Ray, Marie Beynon. *How Never to Be Tired*. Bobbs-Merrill, 1945, pp.86-87.
[3]Ozanich, Steven Ray. *The Great Pain Deception: Faulty Medical Advice Is Making Us Worse*, 2014, p.250.
[4]Marchant, Jo. *Cure: A Journey into the Science of Mind over Body*. First edition. New York: Crown Publishers, 2016, p.65.
[5]Jawer, Michael A., and Marc S. Micozzi. *Your Emotional Type: Key to the Therapies That Will Work for You*. Rochester, Vt: Healing Arts Press, 2011, p.44.
[6]Ibid.
[7]Pittman, Catherine M., and Elizabeth M. Karle. *Rewire Your Anxious Brain: How to Use the Neuroscience of Fear to End Anxiety, Panic, & Worry*. Oakland, CA: New Harbinger Publications, Inc, 2015, pp.20-22,32.
[8]Pohl, Mel. *A Day without Pain*. Rev. and updated. Las Vegas, Nev: Central Recovery Press, 2011, p.34.
[9]Ray, Marie Beynon. *How Never to Be Tired*. Bobbs-Merrill, 1945, p.308.
[10]Ibid, p.218.
[11]Thompson, Curt. *Anatomy of the Soul: Surprising Connections between Neuroscience and Spiritual Practices That Can Transform Your Life and Relationships*. Carol Stream, IL: SaltRiver, 2010, p.95.
[12]Fehmi, Les, and Jim Robbins. *The Open-Focus Brain: Harnessing the Power of Attention to Heal Mind and Body*. 1st ed. Boston: Trumpeter Books, 2007, p.78.

Autism (ASD), ADD/ADHD
[1]Sheffer, Edith. *Asperger's Children: The Origins of Autism in Nazi Vienna*. First edition. New York: W.W. Norton & Company, 2018, p.19.
[2]Ibid.
[3]Ibid, p.175.

[4]Ibid, p.120.

[5]Ibid, p.176.

[6]Ibid, p.15.

[7]Ibid, pp.243-244.

[8]Ibid, p.240.

[9]Ibid, p.246.

[10]Bridges, Holly. *Reframe Your Thinking around Autism: How the Polyvagal Theory and Brain Plasticity Help Us Make Sense of Autism*. London; Philadelphia: Jessica Kingsley Publishers, 2015, p.21.

[11]Ibid, p.26.

[12]Sheffer, Edith. *Asperger's Children: The Origins of Autism in Nazi Vienna*. First edition. New York: W.W. Norton & Company, 2018, p.245.

[13]Gnaulati, Enrico. *Back to Normal: Why Ordinary Childhood Behavior Is Mistaken for ADHD, Bipolar Disorder, and Autism Spectrum Disorder*. Boston: Beacon Press, 2013, p.165.

[14]Ibid, p.160.

[15]Herbert, Martha R., and Karen Weintraub. *The Autism Revolution: Whole-Body Strategies for Making Life All It Can Be*. New York: Ballantine Books, 2012, p.6.

[16]Kaplan, Robert M. *More than Medicine: The Broken Promise of American Health*. Cambridge, Massachusetts: Harvard University Press, 2019, p.38.

[17]Herbert, Martha R., and Karen Weintraub. *The Autism Revolution: Whole-Body Strategies for Making Life All It Can Be*. New York: Ballantine Books, 2012, p.32.

[18]Ibid, p.13.

[19]Ibid, p.25.

[20]Ibid., p.11.

[21]Bridges, Holly. *Reframe Your Thinking around Autism: How the Polyvagal Theory and Brain Plasticity Help Us Make Sense of Autism*. London ; Philadelphia: Jessica Kingsley Publishers, 2015, pp.32-33.

[22]Gnaulati, Enrico. *Back to Normal: Why Ordinary Childhood Behavior Is Mistaken for ADHD, Bipolar Disorder, and Autism Spectrum Disorder*. Boston: Beacon Press, 2013, p.55.

[23]Ibid, p.87.

[24]Ibid, p.174.

[25]Mnookin, Seth. *The Panic Virus: A True Story of Medicine, Science, and Fear*. 1st Simon & Schuster hardcover ed. New York: Simon & Schuster, 2011, p.83.

[26]Sheffer, Edith. *Asperger's Children: The Origins of Autism in Nazi Vienna*. First edition. New York: W.W. Norton & Company, 2018, p.248.

[27]Chansky, Tamar Ellsas. *Freeing Your Child from Negative Thinking: Powerful, Practical Strategies to Build a Lifetime of Resilience, Flexibility, and Happiness*. 1st Da Capo Press ed. Cambridge, Mass: Da Capo Press, 2008, p.32.

[28]Davies, James. *Cracked: The Unhappy Truth about Psychiatry*, 2013, pp.32-33.

[29]Wedge, Marilyn. *A Disease Called Childhood: Why ADHD Became an American*

Epidemic. New York: AVERY, a member of Penguin Group (USA), 2015, p.19.

[30]Fehmi, Les, and Jim Robbins. *The Open-Focus Brain: Harnessing the Power of Attention to Heal Mind and Body*. 1st ed. Boston: Trumpeter Books, 2007, p.59.

[31]Hinshaw, Stephen P., and Richard M. Scheffler. *The ADHD Explosion: Myths, Medication, Money, and Today's Push for Performance*. New York, NY: Oxford University Press, 2014, p.31.

[32]Wedge, Marilyn. *A Disease Called Childhood: Why ADHD Became an American Epidemic*. New York: AVERY, a member of Penguin Group (USA), 2015, p.90.

[33]Ibid, pp.34-35.

[34]Hinshaw, Stephen P., and Richard M. Scheffler. *The ADHD Explosion: Myths, Medication, Money, and Today's Push for Performance*. New York, NY: Oxford University Press, 2014, p.20.

[35]Wedge, Marilyn. *A Disease Called Childhood: Why ADHD Became an American Epidemic*. New York: AVERY, a member of Penguin Group (USA), 2015, p.91.

[36]Ibid, p.92.

[37]Davies, James. *Cracked: The Unhappy Truth about Psychiatry*, 2013, p.17.

[38]Wedge, Marilyn. *A Disease Called Childhood: Why ADHD Became an American Epidemic*. New York: AVERY, a member of Penguin Group (USA), 2015, p.xx-xxi.

Addictions

[1]Lewis, Marc D. *The Biology of Desire: Why Addiction Is Not a Disease*. First edition. New York, NY: PublicAffairs, 2015, p.19.

[2]Ibid, p.6.

[3]Ibid, p.19.

[4]Ibid, p.9.

[5]Ibid, p.10.

[6]Begley, Sharon. *Can't Just Stop: An Investigation of Compulsions*. New York: Simon & Schuster, 2017, p.277.

[7]Dispenza, Joe. *You Are the Placebo: Making Your Mind Matter*. Carlsbad, California: Hay House, Inc, 2014, p.174.

Food Sensitivities

[1]Green, Peter H. R., and Rory Jones. *Gluten Exposed: The Science behind the Hype and How to Navigate to a Healthy, Symptom-Free Life*. First edition. New York, NY: William Morrow, an imprint of HarperCollins Publishers, 2016, p.108.

[2]Levinovitz, Alan. *The Gluten Lie and Other Myths about What You Eat*, 2015, pp.6-7,10.

[3]Ibid, p.50.

[4]O'Sullivan, Suzanne. *Is It All in Your Head?: True Stories of Imaginary Illness*,

259

2016, pp.190-191.
[5]Ibid, p.191.
[6]Levinovitz, Alan. *The Gluten Lie and Other Myths about What You Eat*, 2015, p.19.
[7]Ibid, p.47.
[8]Ibid.
[9]Ibid, p.6.
[10]Ibid, p.14.
[11]Arterburn, Stephen. *Healing Is a Choice: Ten Decisions That Will Transform Your Life & Ten Lies That Can Prevent You from Making Them*, 2011, pp.82-83.
[12]O'Sullivan, Suzanne. *Is It All in Your Head?: True Stories of Imaginary Illness*, 2016, p.191.
[13]Green, Peter H. R., and Rory Jones. *Gluten Exposed: The Science behind the Hype and How to Navigate to a Healthy, Symptom-Free Life*. First edition. New York, NY: William Morrow, an imprint of HarperCollins Publishers, 2016, p.7.
[14]Ibid, p.177.
[15]Ibid, p.56.
[16]Ibid, p.246.
[17]Ibid, pp.247-250.
[18]Ibid, p.307.
[19]Ibid, p.33.

Cancer

[1]Simonton, O. Carl, Stephanie Simonton, and James L Creighton. *Getting Well Again: A Step-by-Step, Self-Help Guide to Overcoming Cancer for Patients and Their Families*. Place of publication not identified: Random House Publishing Group, 2009, p.44.
[2]Ibid, p.10.
[3]Ibid, p.33.
[4]Snow, Herbert. *Cancers, and the Cancer-Process*. Royal College of Physicians of Edinburge, 1893.
[5]Simonton, O. Carl, Stephanie Simonton, and James L Creighton. *Getting Well Again: A Step-by-Step, Self-Help Guide to Overcoming Cancer for Patients and Their Families*. Place of publication not identified: Random House Publishing Group, 2009, pp.65-67.
[6]Maté, Gabor. *When the Body Says No: Understanding the Stress-Disease Connection*. Hoboken, N.J: J. Wiley, 2003, pp.64-65.
[7]Ibid, p.99.
[8]Ibid, p.92.
[9]Simonton, O. Carl, Stephanie Simonton, and James L Creighton. *Getting Well Again: A Step-by-Step, Self-Help Guide to Overcoming Cancer for Patients and Their Families*. Place of publication not identified: Random House Publishing

Group, 2009, p.11.
[10]Ibid, pp.59-60.
[11]Ibid, p.60.

Chronic Lyme Disease, Overweight/ Thyroid/Hormonal Problems, Asthma

[1]Hatch, Steven. *Snowball in a Blizzard: A Physician's Notes on Uncertainty in Medicine*. New York: Basic Books, a member of the Perseus Books Group, 2016, p.115.
[2]Offit, Paul A. *Do You Believe in Magic? The Sense and Nonsense of Alternative Medicine*. First edition. New York: Harper, 2013, p.150.
[3]Hatch, Steven. *Snowball in a Blizzard: A Physician's Notes on Uncertainty in Medicine*. New York: Basic Books, a member of the Perseus Books Group, 2016, p.112.
[4]Offit, Paul A. *Do You Believe in Magic? The Sense and Nonsense of Alternative Medicine*. First edition. New York: Harper, 2013, pp.150-151.
[5]Hari, Johann. *Lost Connections: Uncovering the Real Causes of Depression-- and the Unexpected Solutions*. New York: Bloomsbury, 2018, pp.106-112.
[6]Maté, Gabor. *When the Body Says No: Understanding the Stress-Disease Connection*. Hoboken, N.J: J. Wiley, 2003, p.88.
[7]Ibid, p.190.
[8]Shafer, Kathryn, and Fran Greenfield. *Asthma Free in 21 Days: The Breakthrough Mind-Body Healing Program*. San Francisco, Calif.: HarperSan Francisco, 2000, p.183.
[9]Ibid, p.184.

Aging, Auto-Immune Disorders, Terminal Illnesses

[1]Whitehouse, Peter J., and Daniel George. *The Myth of Alzheimer's: What You Aren't Being Told about Today's Most Dreaded Diagnosis*. 1st ed. New York: St. Martin's Press, 2008, p.4.
[2]Ibid, p.77.
[3]Hamilton, David R. *How Your Mind Can Heal Your Body*. Carlsbad, Calif: Hay House, 2010, p.61.
[4]Elgin, Suzette Haden. *Staying Well with the Gentle Art of Verbal Self-Defense*. Englewood Cliffs, N.J: Prentice Hall, 1990, p.175.
[5]Allen, James. *James Allen: The Collection*. The Success and Prosperity Library 1002. Independently Published, 2019, p.44.
[6]Siegel, Bernie S. *Love, Medicine & Miracles: Lessons Learned about Self-Healing from a Surgeon's Experience with Exceptional Patients*. New York: HarperPerennial, 1990, p.3.
[7]Ibid, pp.105-108.
[8]Ibid, p.80.
[9]Ibid., p.176

[10]Ibid, p.110.

[11]Beauregard, Mario. *Brain Wars: The Scientific Battle over the Existence of the Mind and the Proof That Will Change the Way We Live Our Lives.* 1st ed. New York: HarperOne, 2012, p.93.

[12]Siegel, Bernie S. *Love, Medicine & Miracles: Lessons Learned about Self-Healing from a Surgeon's Experience with Exceptional Patients.* New York: HarperPerennial, 1990, pp.22-24.

[13]Ibid, p.202.

[14]Simonton, O. Carl, Stephanie Simonton, and James L Creighton. *Getting Well Again: A Step-by-Step, Self-Help Guide to Overcoming Cancer for Patients and Their Families.* Place of publication not identified: Random House Publishing Group, 2009, p.82.

[15]Ibid, p.88.

[16]Maté, Gabor. *When the Body Says No: Understanding the Stress-Disease Connection.* Hoboken, N.J: J. Wiley, 2003, p.154.

[17]Ibid, p.158.

[18]Ibid, pp.170,172.

[19]Ibid, p.186.

[20]Ibid, p.20.

[21]Ibid, p.16.

[22]Ibid, p.43.

[23]Ibid.

Implications, Alternative Medicine, No Longer Victims

[1]Martinez, Mario E. *The Mindbody Self: How Longevity Is Culturally Learned and the Causes of Health Are Inherited.* Carlsbad, California: Hay House, Inc, 2017, pp.150-151.

[2]Maté, Gabor. *When the Body Says No: Understanding the Stress-Disease Connection.* Hoboken, N.J: J. Wiley, 2003, p.176.

[3]Simonton, O. Carl, Stephanie Simonton, and James L Creighton. *Getting Well Again: A Step-by-Step, Self-Help Guide to Overcoming Cancer for Patients and Their Families.* Place of publication not identified: Random House Publishing Group, 2009, p.6.

[4]Shafer, Kathryn, and Fran Greenfield. *Asthma Free in 21 Days: The Breakthrough Mind-Body Healing Program.* San Francisco, Calif.: HarperSan Francisco, 2000, pp.100-101

[5]Maté, Gabor. *When the Body Says No: Understanding the Stress-Disease Connection.* Hoboken, N.J: J. Wiley, 2003, p.141.

[6]Ibid, p.143.

[7](A side note: As I was researching for this book, I came across many suggestions that didn't sit well with my spirit, such as hypnosis, mantras, meditation other than on God, and other seemingly innocent pursuits that really are just putting your self more firmly on the throne of your life. That's

what got us into trouble in the first place!)

[8]Offit, Paul A. *Do You Believe in Magic? The Sense and Nonsense of Alternative Medicine*. First edition. New York: Harper, 2013, p.6.

[9]Howick, Jeremy. *Doctor You: Introducing the Hard Science of Self-Healing*. New York: Quercus, 2018, Part I.

[10]Offit, Paul A. *Do You Believe in Magic? The Sense and Nonsense of Alternative Medicine*. First edition. New York: Harper, 2013, p.61.

[11]Ibid, pp.223-224.

[12]Ibid, pp.208-209.

[13]Ibid, p.238.

[14]Ibid, p.237.

[15] Dispenza, Joe. *Evolve Your Brain: The Science of Changing Your Mind*. Dearfield, FL: Health Communications, 2007, p.251.

[16]Siegel, Bernie S. *Love, Medicine & Miracles: Lessons Learned about Self-Healing from a Surgeon's Experience with Exceptional Patients*. New York: HarperPerennial, 1990, p.190.

The Biblical Response

[1]Wright, Henry W. *A More Excellent Way: Be In Health*. Thomaston, Ga.: Pleasant Valley Publications, 2005, p.13.

[2]I can thank my former pastor, Mark Oshman, for this quote!

Part Four: A Better Response to Pain
Coming Out of Hiding

[1]Lombard, Jay, and Patrick J. Kennedy. *The Mind of God: Neuroscience, Faith, and a Search for the Soul*. New York: Harmony Books, 2017, p.59.

[2]Dispenza, Joe. *You Are the Placebo: Making Your Mind Matter*. Carlsbad, California: Hay House, Inc, 2014, pp.111-114.

[3]Dispenza, Joe. *Evolve Your Brain: The Science of Changing Your Mind*. Dearfield, FL: Health Communications, 2007, p.315.

[4]Maté, Gabor. *When the Body Says No: Understanding the Stress-Disease Connection*. Hoboken, N.J: J. Wiley, 2003, p.231.

[5]Ray, Marie Beynon. *How Never to Be Tired*. Bobbs-Merrill, 1945, pp.125-126.

[6]Shapiro, Debbie. *Your Body Speaks Your Mind: Decoding the Emotional, Psychological, and Spiritual Messages That Underlie Illness*. Boulder, CO: Sounds True, 2006, p.16.

[7]Keller, Timothy, and Kathy Keller. *God's Wisdom for Navigating Life: A Year of Daily Devotions in the Book of Proverbs*. New York, New York: Viking, 2017, p.103.

[8]Dispenza, Joe. *You Are the Placebo: Making Your Mind Matter*. Carlsbad, California: Hay House, Inc, 2014, pp.56-57,67-68.

[9]Ibid, p.67.

[10]Ibid, pp.57-58.

[11]Dispenza, Joe. *Evolve Your Brain: The Science of Changing Your Mind*. Dearfield, FL: Health Communications, 2007, p.302.

[12]Ibid, p.303.

[13]Ibid, p.307.

[14]Ibid, p.317.

[15]Ibid, p.313.

[16]Ibid, p.49.

[17]Ibid, p.292.

[18]Beauregard, Mario. *Brain Wars: The Scientific Battle over the Existence of the Mind and the Proof That Will Change the Way We Live Our Lives*. 1st ed. New York: HarperOne, 2012, pp.105-106.

[19]Dispenza, Joe. *Evolve Your Brain: The Science of Changing Your Mind*. Dearfield, FL: Health Communications, 2007, p.300

[20]*"Turn Your Eyes Upon Jesus."* Helen H. Lemmel, 1922. Public Domain.

[21]Keller, Timothy. *Prayer: Experiencing Awe and Intimacy with God*. New York: Dutton, Penguin Group USA, 2014, pp.22-23.

[22]Thompson, Curt. *Anatomy of the Soul: Surprising Connections between Neuroscience and Spiritual Practices That Can Transform Your Life and Relationships*. Carol Stream, IL: SaltRiver, 2010, p.14.

[23]Ibid, p.72.

[24]Dispenza, Joe. *Evolve Your Brain: The Science of Changing Your Mind*. Dearfield, FL: Health Communications, 2007, p.246.

[25]Lombard, Jay, and Patrick J. Kennedy. *The Mind of God: Neuroscience, Faith, and a Search for the Soul*. New York: Harmony Books, 2017, p.99.

[26]Thompson, Curt. *Anatomy of the Soul: Surprising Connections between Neuroscience and Spiritual Practices That Can Transform Your Life and Relationships*. Carol Stream, IL: SaltRiver, 2010, p.24.

[27]Smith, Hannah Whitall. *The Christian's Secret of a Happy Life*, 1985, p.34.

Next Steps

[1]Simonton, O. Carl, Stephanie Simonton, and James L Creighton. *Getting Well Again: A Step-by-Step, Self-Help Guide to Overcoming Cancer for Patients and Their Families*. Place of publication not identified: Random House Publishing Group, 2009, p.127.

[2]Przekop, Peter. *Conquer Chronic Pain: An Innovative Mind-Body Approach*. Center City, Minnesota: Hazelden Publishing, 2015, pp.168-171.

[3]Ibid, p.23.

[4]Ibid.

[5]Simonton, O. Carl, Stephanie Simonton, and James L Creighton. *Getting Well Again: A Step-by-Step, Self-Help Guide to Overcoming Cancer for Patients and Their Families*. Place of publication not identified: Random House Publishing Group, 2009, p.109

[6]Ibid, pp.179,215.

Common Objections

[1]Chole, Alicia Britt. *40 Days of Decrease: A Different Kind of Hunger, a Different Kind of Fast.* Nashville: W Publishing Group, an imprint of Thomas Nelson, 2015, p.70.

[2]Ibid, p.71.

[3]Wimberger, Lisa. *Neurosculpting: A Whole-Brain Approach to Heal Trauma, Rewrite Limiting Beliefs, and Find Wholeness.* Boulder, Colorado: Sounds True, 2014, p.70.

[4]Martinez, Mario E. *The Mindbody Self: How Longevity Is Culturally Learned and the Causes of Health Are Inherited.* Carlsbad, California: Hay House, Inc, 2017, p.8.

[5]Shafer, Kathryn, and Fran Greenfield. *Asthma Free in 21 Days: The Breakthrough Mind-Body Healing Program.* San Francisco, Calif.: HarperSan Francisco, 2000, pp.2-3

Copyrights of Translations

Scriptures marked NASB are taken from the NEW AMERICAN STANDARD (NAS): Scripture taken from the NEW AMERICAN STANDARD BIBLE®, copyright© 1960, 1962, 1963, 1968, 1971, 1972, 1973, 1975, 1977, 1995 by The Lockman Foundation. Used by permission.

Scripture quotations marked NIV are taken from The Holy Bible, New International Version® NIV® Copyright © 1973 1978 1984 2011 by Biblica, Inc. ™ Used by permission. All rights reserved worldwide.

Scriptures marked NKJV are taken from the NEW KING JAMES VERSION (NKJV): Scripture taken from the NEW KING JAMES VERSION®. Copyright© 1982 by Thomas Nelson, Inc. Used by permission. All rights reserved.

Scriptures marked ESV are taken from the THE HOLY BIBLE, ENGLISH STANDARD VERSION (ESV): Scriptures taken from THE HOLY BIBLE, ENGLISH STANDARD VERSION ® Copyright© 2001 by Crossway, a publishing ministry of Good News Publishers. Used by permission.

Scriptures marked KJV are taken from the KING JAMES VERSION (KJV): KING JAMES VERSION, public domain.

Scriptures marked NLT are taken from the HOLY BIBLE, NEW LIVING TRANSLATION (NLT): Scriptures taken from the HOLY BIBLE, NEW LIVING TRANSLATION, Copyright© 1996, 2004, 2007 by Tyndale House Foundation. Used by permission of Tyndale House Publishers, Inc., Carol Stream, Illinois 60188. All rights reserved. Used by permission.

Scripture quotations marked BSB are taken from the The Holy Bible, Berean Study Bible, BSB Copyright ©2016, 2018, 2019 by Bible Hub. Used by Permission. All Rights Reserved Worldwide.

Scriptures marked HCSB are taken from the HOLMAN CHRISTIAN STANDARD BIBLE (HCSB): Scripture taken from the HOLMAN CHRISTIAN STANDARD BIBLE, copyright© 1999, 2000, 2002, 2003 by Holman Bible Publishers, Nashville Tennessee. All rights reserved.

RECOMMENDED BOOK LIST

- Colbert, Don. *Deadly Emotions: Understand the Mind-Body-Spirit Connection That Can Heal or Destroy You*
- Davies, James. *Cracked: The Unhappy Truth about Psychiatry*
- Dispenza, Joe. *You Are the Placebo: Making Your Mind Matter*
- Gnaulati, Enrico. *Back to Normal: Why Ordinary Childhood Behavior Is Mistaken for ADHD, Bipolar Disorder, and Autism Spectrum Disorder*
- Green, Peter H. R., and Rory Jones. *Gluten Exposed: The Science behind the Hype and How to Navigate to a Healthy, Symptom-Free Life*
- Hamilton, David R. *How Your Mind Can Heal Your Body*
- Hanscom, David. *Back in Control: A Surgeon's Roadmap out of Chronic Pain*
- Harrington, Anne. *The Cure within: A History of Mind-Body Medicine*
- Hatch, Steven. *Snowball in a Blizzard: A Physician's Notes on Uncertainty in Medicine*
- Hinshaw, Stephen P., and Richard M. Scheffler. *The ADHD Explosion: Myths, Medication, Money, and Today's Push for Performance*
- Joseph, Stephen. *What Doesn't Kill Us: The New Psychology of Posttraumatic Growth*
- Kaplan, Gary, and Donna Beech. *Total Recovery: Solving the Mystery of Chronic Pain and Depression: How We Get Sick, Why We Stay Sick, How We Can Recover*
- Kirsch, Irving. *The Emperor's New Drugs: Exploding the Antidepressant Myth*
- Levinovitz, Alan. *The Gluten Lie and Other Myths about What You Eat*
- Lewis, Marc D. *The Biology of Desire: Why Addiction Is Not a Disease*
- Lipton, Bruce H. *The Biology of Belief: Unleashing the Power of Consciousness, Matter & Miracles*
- Maté, Gabor. *When the Body Says No: Understanding the Stress-Disease Connection*
- Offit, Paul A. *Do You Believe in Magic? The Sense and Nonsense of Alternative Medicine*
- O'Sullivan, Suzanne. *Is It All in Your Head?: True Stories of Imaginary Illness*
- Ozanich, Steven Ray. *The Great Pain Deception: Faulty Medical Advice Is*

Making Us Worse

- Pert, Candace B. *Molecules of Emotion: Why You Feel the Way You Feel*
- Platoni, Kara. *We Have the Technology: How Biohackers, Foodies, Physicians, and Scientists Are Transforming Human Perception, One Sense at a Time*
- Pohl, Mel. *A Day without Pain*
- Przekop, Peter. *Conquer Chronic Pain: An Innovative Mind-Body Approach*
- Ray, Marie Beynon. *How Never to Be Tired*
- Sarno, John E. *Healing Back Pain: The Mind-Body Connection*
- Sarno, John E. *The Divided Mind: The Epidemic of Mindbody Disorders*
- Schubiner, Howard, and Michael Betzold. *Unlearn Your Pain: A 28-Day Process to Reprogram Your Brain*
- Sheffer, Edith. *Asperger's Children: The Origins of Autism in Nazi Vienna*
- Shorter, Edward. *From Paralysis to Fatigue: A History of Psychosomatic Illness in the Modern Era*
- Siegel, Bernie S. *Love, Medicine & Miracles: Lessons Learned About Self-Healing From a Surgeon's Experience With Exceptional Patients*
- Tatta, Joe. *Heal Your Pain Now: The Revolutionary Program to Reset Your Brain and Body for a Pain-Free Life*
- Wedge, Marilyn. *A Disease Called Childhood: Why ADHD Became an American Epidemic*
- Welch, H. Gilbert, Lisa Schwartz, and Steve Woloshin. *Overdiagnosed: Making People Sick in the Pursuit of Health*
- Whitehouse, Peter J., and Daniel George. *The Myth of Alzheimer's: What You Aren't Being Told about Today's Most Dreaded Diagnosis*
- Yass, Mitchell T. *The Pain Cure Rx: The Yass Method for Diagnosing and Resolving Chronic Pain*

ABOUT THE AUTHOR

Emily Stewart Esmaili is a Certified Nutrition Consultant, Personal Trainer, and Health Coach. She and her husband live with their three children in beautiful Parker, Colorado.

ABOUT THE DESIGNER

Carrie Knoles (of CK Design) grew up collecting all kinds of pencils, markers and art supplies. Her love of art, and eventually design, continued on to high school when she decided to pursue a degree in Graphic Design. She's been working as a designer for over 20 years, and loves the challenge brought on by creative projects. Carrie is honored to be able to support her dear friend, Emily, by designing her book cover!

ACKNOWLEDGEMENTS

Immense gratitude goes to my family who stood by me during the whole writing process, taking on my responsibilities and offering support and encouragement at every turn. I am also so very thankful to my faithful friends who aided me so generously in the publication of this book: Carrie Knoles, for designing the cover; Tifany Borgelt, for editing and wise counsel; and Alison Morrow, for editing and moral support. I couldn't have done any of this without you.

Index

A

abide, 50, 104, 118
  abiding, 102, 118
abuse, 55–56, 75, 117, 141, 147–148, 179–181, 184, 187
  abused, 148, 179, 210
  abusive, 55
ache, 12, 19, 40, 48, 56, 85, 93, 173, 182
acupuncture, 194
addiction, 14, 67, 73, 141,166–169, 212, 214
  addicted, 168–169, 212
  addictive, 166, 168, 214–215
ADHD, 20, 54, 57, 87, 163–166
adrenals, 180
aging, 27, 69, 78, 134, 136, 181–183, 194
airways, 49
alcoholism, 166–168
allergy, 34, 49, 69, 87, 170, 172, 174, 188, 192
  allergen, 49, 170, 175
  allergic, 12, 48–49, 99, 170, 180
Alzheimer, 54, 181–182, 187
Amir, Fred, 134
amnesia, 184
amygdala, 148
Amyotrophic Lateral Sclerosis (ALS), 188
anaphylactic, 170
anatomical, 193
anesthesia, 177
ankles, 42
anomaly, 27, 132, 153
anorexia, 23, 34, 68
antibiotic, 131, 179
antibody, 172, 180
antidepressant, 3, 21–22, 141, 146, 160
antigliadin, 172

antioxidants, 194
antisocial, 152, 157, 188
anxiety, 2–5, 24, 56, 66, 72, 92, 115, 139–141, 143, 156, 163, 170–171, 200
  anxious, 97, 104, 139, 141, 146, 200
apoptosis, 10, 220
artery, 12
arthritis, 27, 46–47, 64–65, 93, 136, 181, 187, 200, 203
  arthritic, 69, 136
ASD, 151, 153–154, 156–157, 159–161, 166, 172–173.
Asperger, 152–153, 160
asthma, 49, 180–181, 192
athletes, 53, 74
atrophy, 183
autism, 54, 151–160, 162–164, 192
  autistic, 151–160, 162–163.
autoimmune, 192, 219
autopsy, 62

B

bacteria, 179, 192, 194
benign, 29, 136
biochemical, 193, 214
biochemistry, 143
biofeedback, 192
biopsy, 71, 175, 193
bipolar, 20
bleeding, 2, 178
bloodstream, 29, 61, 70, 172, 214
bloodwork, 69, 170
bochorno, 34
bodybuilders, 134
bone, 12, 35, 45, 53, 55, 69, 76, 78, 93, 132, 134, 136, 146, 201, 203
bony, 136
Bowel, 27–28, 121, 187
brainwaves, 20, 55
breathing, 11, 39, 51, 89
bronchitis, 187

fibromyalgia, 1, 4–6, 121, 149–150
flu, 13, 67, 195, 201
fracture, 55
free radicals, 194
Freud, 25, 32, 35

G

ganglia, 44
gangraina, 178
gangrene, 178
gastrointestinal, 34
gemüt, 152
gene, 29–30, 52–53, 58, 69, 71, 156–157, 175, 186, 201, 213–214, 234
genitals, 34
glucose, 70
gluteal, 28
gluten, 170–174
Gnaulati, Dr. Enrico, 154
grudges, 77, 150, 219
gymnasts, 134

H

headache, 4–5, 12–13, 22, 37, 41–42, 47, 53, 55, 92, 170, 188–189, 224, 234
heartache, 56, 121, 184
heartburn, 72
Hebbian, 72
Hedonism, 25
hemorrhage, 202
herbs, 50, 80, 194–195
herniate, 27
   herniated, 27–28, 132
   herniation, 27, 69
Hippocrates, 33
HMOs, 33
hoarding, 68, 92, 169, 189
hobbies, 87, 144, 147
holistic, 70
homeopathic, 194–195
homeostasis, 30, 214
hormonal, 34, 58, 179, 213
HSAs, 33
hwabyeong, 34

hypertension, 163
hyperventilate, 121
hypochondria, 72
hysteria, 32–33, 35, 69, 77, 170

I

IBS, 187
idiopathic, 62
IgA, 172
IgE, 180
IgG, 172–173
immune, 6, 22, 71, 78, 124, 141, 145, 157, 175–176, 179–180, 184, 186–187, 191–192, 195
infection, 1, 27, 156, 179, 188, 193
infirmity, 201–202
inflammation, 12, 37, 40, 74, 132, 135–136, 180
influenza, 52
insomnia, 5
introvert, 123, 128
Irritable Bowel Syndrome (IBS), 121, 187
isotopes, 2

J

Joseph, Dr. Stephen, 145
journaling, 145

K

Klopfer, Dr. Bruno, 50
koro, 34
Krebiozen, 50–51

L

labels, 21, 23, 26, 123, 127–129, 153, 159, 162, 165
laparoscopic, 31
leprosy, 178
lethargy, 68
lightheadedness, 11
liver, 34, 62, 195
lunatics, 176

Made in the USA
Columbia, SC
22 April 2023

15705870R00153